PHYSIOLOGY OF FARM ANIMALS

LONDON
Cambridge University Press
FETTER LANE

NEW YORK · TORONTO
BOMBAY · CALCUTTA · MADRAS
Macmillan

TOKYO
Maruzen Company Ltd

PHYSIOLOGY OF FARM ANIMALS

BY

F. H. A. MARSHALL, Sc.D. (Camb.),
D.Sc. (Edin.), F.R.S.

AND

E. T. HALNAN, M.A.

CAMBRIDGE
AT THE UNIVERSITY PRESS
1932

CONTENTS

ILLUSTRATIONS

Thanks are due to the publishers as well as to the authors, whose names are given above, for leave to use the respective blocks.

PREFACE

As originally planned, this work was to have appeared in two volumes, the first on the general principles of Physiology as applied especially to farm animals, and the second on animal nutrition. Of these two parts, the first only, by one of the present authors, was issued in 1920, and is now out of print. The preparation of the second volume on animal nutrition was undertaken by the late Professor T. B. Wood, but a series of unforeseen circumstances delayed the writing and the plan was finally abandoned through the death of Professor Wood in 1929, leaving many to deplore his loss. Before he died, however, the late professor had arranged with the junior of the present authors (who had already contributed to the first part) that he should become the joint author of the volume on animal nutrition. Professor Wood himself had only composed one complete chapter and since the subject matter of this had long ago been out of date it was decided that the entire section on nutrition should be written anew and that it should be incorporated along with the general principles in one volume. This new portion was undertaken by the junior of the present authors.

The opportunity has been taken to revise the subject matter of the first part, and in some chapters additions have been made. Chapters have also been added on growth and heredity and the response of the body to injury and disease.

The authors wish to express their indebtedness to all those who have afforded them help; in particular they desire to mention Sir Edward Sharpey Schafer, Mr John Hammond and Dr Arthur Walton. They also wish to thank Messrs Longmans, Green and Co. and Messrs Baillière, Tindall and Cox, and the other publishers and authors who have allowed them to reprint illustrations from the works they have issued. It should be mentioned further, that certain paragraphs in the chapter on Heredity are reprinted with little or no alteration from 'The Physiology of Reproduction' or 'An Introduction to Sexual Physiology', published by Messrs Longmans, Green and Co. A number of new figures have been specially drawn for this work by the junior of the two authors.

The book is specially intended for students of Agriculture who wish to obtain some knowledge of the processes of Physiology as they occur in the domestic animals, as well as to act as a guide to the modern science of animal nutrition. It is hoped also that it will prove of service to veterinarians and others interested in animal physiology.

F. H. A. M.

E. T. H.

CAMBRIDGE
October 1932

CHAPTER I

INTRODUCTION

Physiology is the branch of science which is concerned with the functions performed by living things. It is a department of Biology or the science of life. But just as Biology is divisible into Botany which treats of plants, and Zoology which deals with animals, so there are also a Vegetable Physiology and an Animal Physiology, and it is the latter of these which forms the basis of medical and veterinary knowledge. For Physiology is the science which teaches us the way in which the body is built up, and how each part of it works, and the laws which govern its activities. In so doing it helps us to regulate these activities, and by teaching us about the normal working of the body, it shows us how any of its parts may be adjusted when they are out of order. This statement applies to the bodies of animals as well as to those of ourselves.

The present volume deals especially with the Physiology of the domestic animals. This is a branch of the subject which has been much neglected, for notwithstanding the great industrial importance of stock breeding and rearing, it is a business to which physiological science has only recently begun to be applied.

Like Chemistry and Physics, Physiology is founded on observations and experiments. These can sometimes be carried out upon ourselves, but are more often made upon animals. By means of a clinical thermometer we can perform a series of observations upon our own bodily temperature, establishing the fact that under normal conditions our temperature remains constant and is independent of that of the outside air which is usually considerably cooler. In this way we can learn a little about the fundamental nature of the organism, since we are led to perceive that our bodies, like those of other animals, must be supplied with the sources of that form of energy which we recognise as bodily heat. By extending our observations, and noting the increased blood supply of the skin and the tendency to sweat when we feel warm, we learn something about the heat-regulating mechanism which we possess in common with other warm-blooded animals. Again, by taking advantage of the fact that all the parts of an animal do not die at the same time we can perform a great variety of experiments which teach us much about the functions of the different organs of the body. Thus the excised limb muscle of a frog if kept moist by a saline solution, or the heart of a mammal if perfused with an artificial fluid resembling blood serum and preserved at body temperature, may be induced to survive many hours after the death of the animals from which they were taken, and from experiments upon these it is possible to learn much concerning the mechanisms of muscular contraction and the heart beat. Furthermore, we can carry out experiments upon entire animals, pain being avoided by the administration of anaesthetics during the progress of the operation.

Many of the functions of the body are essentially similar throughout the whole animal kingdom, and among vertebrates there is a still closer likeness. Thus the processes of digestion in a frog, a bird, a rabbit, a horse, and a man are, broadly speaking, similar, though there are of course very marked differences which are generally greater the less closely related the animals are. So also the general laws governing the nature of nerve impulses, the movements of the heart, or the processes of reproduction are identical in every case. Thus by investigating any of these processes in a frog or in a rabbit, for example, we can learn a great deal about the functional activities of a horse, or a sheep, or a cow; and it is desirable that before specialising upon the Physiology of farm animals we should possess a general knowledge of the principles of the science obtained by studying whatever animals are most convenient for this purpose.

Furthermore, Physiology must always be studied in close relation to Anatomy or Morphology (that is, the department of Biology which deals with the form and structure of organisms), since it is impossible to acquire an insight into the functions of the various parts of an organism without possessing some knowledge of the composition and structural relations of those parts; and conversely, an intelligent comprehension of the form and structure of an organ can only be gained by a consideration of the part which that organ plays in the general economy of the individual.

The physical basis of all life, both vegetable and animal, is called protoplasm. The vital substance forming the most highly developed animals differs in degree rather than in kind from the undifferentiated protoplasmic mass composing the most simple form of life known. Protoplasm is a semi-fluid, transparent, viscous substance, which occurs usually in small individual particles, called cells. Sometimes it seems to be quite homogeneous but more often a reticulated structure can be detected. A study of its composition reveals that its most abundant constituent is water, which amounts to 75 per cent. of the whole material. The remaining 25 per cent. is made up of solids which consist chiefly of nitrogenous compounds called proteins, but certain metals (potassium and calcium) as well as phosphorus and sulphur are also present in a combined form together with small quantities of fats and carbohydrates.

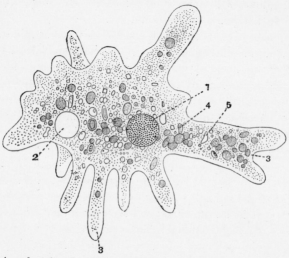

Fig. 1. Amoeba (after Graves, from Shipley and MacBride). 1, nucleus; 2, contractile vacuole through which waste products are excreted; 3, pseudopodia; 4, vacuoles containing food; 5, grains of sand.

An elementary knowledge of the physiology of protoplasm may be gained by studying the vital manifestations of the amoeba. This is a minute organism found in stagnant water, and resembling, when seen under the microscope, a little lump of moving jelly. It can be observed to move about spontaneously, to eat up little particles of food, to excrete or get rid of waste products, to grow in size, and lastly, at a certain stage in its life-history, to reproduce by undergoing a process of simple division into two. In order to perform these functions it is essential that it should receive a supply of food, in just the same way as an engine cannot be made to work unless it is provided with fuel. In the latter case the fuel undergoes combustion which liberates heat. So also in the case of the animal the energy is derived from the complex food material, which undergoes a process of slow oxidation, thereby breaking down into simpler substances and setting free the energy necessary for the discharge of the vital functions. The changes which the food or its constituents undergo in the amoeba or any other organism are classed together under the term 'metabolism': those of them which relate to the building up of the food into the material of the body are referred to as 'anabolic' or 'assimilative'; while the changes which are associated with activity, resulting from a breaking down of complex substances into more simple ones, are known as 'katabolic' or 'dissimilative'.

An amoeba consists of a single cell, that is to say, a minute mass of protoplasm containing within it a certain specialised portion known as the nucleus which can generally be readily identified under the microscope by its more intense staining capacity. The nucleus is essential to the life of the cell. There are many different kinds of unicellular organisms, varying in form but all resembling the amoeba in their general plan. Higher in the scale we find groups of amoeba-like cells, each with their nucleus, aggregated together with little or no division of function. Such an arrangement occurs in the simpler kinds of sponges. But in the majority of multicellular animals whole groups of cells are separated off to subserve particular functions; and these form the various tissues. The body of a higher animal is, however, derived from a single cell essentially similar to that of an amoeba, and this, in the process of individual development, undergoes a long series of divisions in the progress of which the nuclei also divide. The products of division, that is to say, the cells with their contained nuclei, become gradually specialised to form the different tissues—bone, cartilage, muscle, nerve, connective tissue, etc. Thus the outer layer of cells becomes adapted for protection and for receiving the impressions produced by changes in the surroundings; the inner layer lining the gut becomes adapted for the digestion and assimilation of food; while between these are developed the skeleton and general framework of the body, and all the other tissues which assist in performing the vital functions.

These functions may now be considered more closely. The parts concerned with each function are usually called systems, and the subsidiary parts which compose these systems are known as organs.

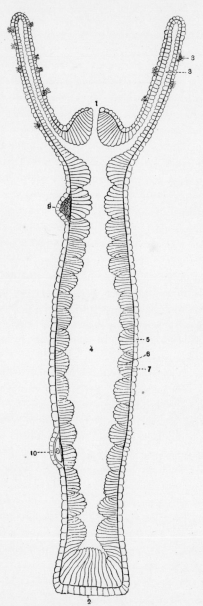

Fig. 2. Diagrammatic longitudinal section through *Hydra*, a tubular animal showing cellular differentiation of a simple kind. (From Shipley and MacBride.) 1, mouth; 2, foot; 3, tentacle; 4, digestive cavity; 5, outer layer of cells or ectoderm; 6, inner layer of cells or endoderm; 7, structureless jelly between the two latter; 8, groups of cells specialised for offensive purposes and containing structures which can be ejected; 9, testis; 10, ovary.

The following are the principal systems of the body in a higher animal: (1) the digestive system; (2) the circulatory system; (3) the respiratory system; (4) the excretory system; (5) the muscular system; (6) the nervous system; and (7) the reproductive system. In addition to these are the organs of special sense, such as the eye and ear, and the various organs of internal secretion.

Digestive System. In such lowly forms of life as the amoeba, food is taken in at any point on the surface, and is then assimilated, the indigestible residue being cast out at some other part of the surface. But in man and in all the other higher animals there is a differentiation of function, food being taken in only at a definitely located mouth, whence it passes down an alimentary canal which is divided into several portions. In some of these the digestible material is absorbed, passing through the wall of the canal and into the neighbouring lymph vessels or blood vessels, whence it is distributed throughout the body. The indigestible residue is expelled at a definite anus, which is placed at the hind end of the body. The actual digestive process takes place through the action of various glands such as the salivary glands, the gastric glands, the liver and the pancreas, all of which pour out juices having a digestive or solvent action on the food stuffs.

Circulatory System. To enable the food which is absorbed from the alimentary canal to be distributed to all the organs of the body a circulatory medium is provided, and this medium is the blood. In all higher animals the blood is kept in motion by a central organ of propulsion, the heart. In a mammal the heart is divided into four chambers—a right and a left auricle, and a right and a left ventricle. Each chamber communicates with the adjoining ones by valves, which only permit of the blood passing in one direction. The circulation is maintained by the heart alternately contracting and dilating, the compressing force being supplied by the muscular wall of the organ. The heart communicates with an elaborate system of vessels, those which carry the blood away from it being called arteries, while those which bring the blood back are called veins. The arteries possess thicker and more elastic walls than the veins. The arteries become divided up in the peripheral parts of the body into a number of much smaller vessels, the capillaries, which permeate the tissues. Some of the fluid of the blood transudes through the walls of these vessels, becoming the lymph which bathes the cells. The capillaries unite again to form the veins, which transport the blood back to the heart. If the web of a living frog's foot be examined under the microscope, the circulation of the blood in the capillaries may be observed quite easily.

The red colour of blood is due to the presence of innumerable little red discs known as corpuscles, which float in a yellowish-coloured semi-transparent fluid, the blood plasma. In addition to these red corpuscles, blood also contains a relatively small number of white corpuscles or leucocytes, which have the power of independent movement and resemble the unicellular amoebae referred to above. One of their functions is to eat up and so destroy the germs of disease.

As already mentioned, some of the products of digestion are absorbed into vessels containing lymph which is a colourless fluid resembling blood plasma. The lymph that bathes the cells re-enters the circulation by the lymph vessels or lymphatics. These communicate with veins so that the substances present in lymph eventually enter the blood system.

Respiratory System. In order to keep an animal alive it is necessary to supply it with oxygen, for, as we have seen, every animal is dependent for its source of energy upon the slow oxidation of the material which it builds up out of its food supply. As a result of this oxidation process it is continually giving off carbon dioxide. In the higher vertebrates the organs which are concerned in this gaseous exchange are the lungs; but in the lower forms of life the entire surfaces of the body serve to effect the interchange of oxygen and carbon dioxide; while in many other animals, which live in water (e.g. fishes), the respiratory organs take the form of gills.

The lungs of an animal are connected with the exterior by the windpipe or trachea, which opens into the back of the mouth at the root of the tongue. This tube at its lower end divides into the two bronchi, and these subdivide again and again within the lungs like the branches of a tree. Their finest divisions widen out into air sacs which are in close relation to a meshwork of capillaries, the air in the air sacs and the blood in the vessels being separated from one another by only a very thin layer of protoplasm. These air sacs and capillaries form an essential part of the structure of the lungs. Here the gaseous exchange is effected, the blood taking up oxygen from the air sacs and giving off carbon dioxide. When the blood passes to the tissues this process is reversed, the carbon dioxide being taken up from the tissue cells, while oxygen is given off to these cells. The arterial blood, or blood which is being circulated to the tissues after having been to the lungs and heart, is bright-red in colour owing to the presence of a compound called oxyhaemoglobin, which contains oxygen in loose combination: whereas venous blood which is in process of being returned to the heart and lungs is purple, the oxyhaemoglobin having been reduced, in part at least, to haemoglobin, thereby causing a change in the colour of the corpuscles. The complete course of the circulation in a mammal is as follows: Right auricle of heart, right ventricle, pulmonary arteries, lungs, pulmonary veins, left auricle, left ventricle, arteries (excepting pulmonary arteries), capillaries, veins (excepting pulmonary veins), and so back to the heart.

The interchange of gases which takes place between the lungs and the external air is effected by the alternate expansion and contraction of the chest wall, the air passing through the windpipe in opposite directions in the acts of inspiration and expiration. In this way the excess of carbon dioxide in the lungs is got rid of, and a supply of oxygen from the external air is able to take its place.

Excretory System. We have seen that the protoplasm of which an animal is composed consists principally of protein. This consists of carbon, hydrogen, oxygen, nitrogen, and sulphur. As a result of katabolism these elements must be got rid of. A great part of the waste carbon and oxygen is disposed of by the lungs in the form of carbon dioxide as just described. The hydrogen and a further proportion of oxygen are excreted in the form of water vapour both through the lungs and the skin. The waste nitrogen, however, and also the waste sulphur are got rid of for the most part by the kidneys, which are commonly described as excretory organs. For just as the cells of the body discharge their waste carbon dioxide into the blood, so also do they dispose of their nitrogenous products, and these are carried to the kidneys. In the latter the blood capillaries are separated by only a single cellular layer from the cavity which communicates with the exterior. The cells of this layer absorb the waste products and excrete them into the kidney tubules, together with water and some salts in solution. These form the urine, which flows down a duct termed the ureter into the bladder, from which it is expelled at intervals to the exterior in the act of micturition.

Muscular System. A muscle is an especially contractile organ which is either circular (as in sphincter muscles) or straight. The latter is the more usual form among the higher animals. Such a muscle, upon contracting, reduces the length between its two farthest points. One of these points is usually called the origin of the muscle and the other its insertion. The majority of muscles are attached to bones, and these by their movements may become inclined to one another at various angles. In the case of the limbs these angles are opened and closed, thereby causing progression, and the mechanical aid which is introduced to effect this is that of the lever. The muscles themselves are fleshy masses composed of fibres. Some muscles, such as those of the limbs, are under the direct control of the will and are consequently often called voluntary muscles; whereas others, like the muscles surrounding the intestines, which are not under the control of the will, are termed involuntary muscles. The voluntary muscles form a considerable part of the body, and constitute the flesh or meat on an animal. Broadly speaking, the muscular system is that part of the body in which the energy set free by the oxidation of the food material is converted into motion and so carries on work.

Nervous System and Sense Organs. In the lowest forms of animal life the protoplasm is uniformly irritable and contractile; but in the higher types, as just shown, the organs of movement are concentrated in a motor or muscular system, while there are also definite organs of sense (eye, ear, etc.). Such division of labour necessitates a means of communication between the various organs, and this function is fulfilled by the nervous system. The nerves consist of strands of a peculiar kind of tissue constituting the nerve fibres, and these connect together the sense organs and muscles and all the various parts of the body. The nervous system is presided over by the brain and spinal cord. The former of these is contained within the skull, while the latter consists of a hollow tube enclosed by the backbone or vertebral column. The brain and spinal cord together constitute the central nervous system. The other nerves are differentiated into afferent (sometimes called sensory) nerves, in which the impulses pass from the sense organs to the central nervous system, and efferent (sometimes called motor) nerves, in which the impulses travel outwards from the central nervous system to the muscles or other organs to which a message is to be sent. All actions which are under the control of the will are presided over by the brain, from which the voluntary nervous impulses are transmitted. But there is another class of actions in which either the brain or spinal cord is concerned, but which are involuntary. These are called reflex actions. For example, if a frog after being deprived of its brain be hung up by its jaw and one of its toes pinched, its leg is drawn up. Such an act is involuntary, and in this case is controlled by that part of the central nervous system which is still intact, namely the spinal cord. If this be destroyed the reflex action can no longer take place. It is clear, therefore, that such an act involves a succession of processes, which are as follows. The pinching of the toe supplies a stimulus which is transmitted as a nerve impulse by an afferent nerve to the spinal cord. Another nerve impulse is then transmitted by an efferent nerve in the opposite direction, passing from the spinal cord to the muscles of the limb, and this causes them to contract. There are also cerebral reflexes, which are likewise involuntary. For example, the secretion of the saliva and the secretion of the gastric juice are reflexes which are induced by the introduction of food into the mouth, messages being transmitted in the first place in an afferent direction from the mouth to the brain, and then in an efferent direction from the brain to the secretory glands of the mouth and stomach. It is interesting to note that different sets of nerves are concerned in transmitting the impulses in opposite directions. Every reflex is presided over by a special centre in the central nervous system, these centres being the parts of the brain and spinal cord that receive the afferent impulses and dispatch the efferent ones which are concerned in the reflexes in question. In the body of a higher animal a close succession of reflex actions is continually going on, and it is in this way that the individual organism is able to react to environmental changes, and so fit itself to its surroundings.

Reproductive System. In the unicellular organisms like the amoeba, reproduction is carried on by simple cell division. In the higher animals, however, there are certain special cells set apart for reproduction, the ova in the female and the spermatozoa in the male. The ova and spermatozoa are produced respectively in the ovaries and testicles. Their function is to unite together, a single ovum fusing with a single spermatozoon and giving rise to a conjugated cell or oösperm, which by a long succession of cell divisions develops into a new individual. In each of these divisions the cell nuclei also divide so that each product of division always contains a nucleus. In the mammal the development of the unborn young takes place in a special organ, the uterus, 'womb' or 'bed', whence they are expelled in the act of parturition or giving birth.

Organs of Internal Secretion. In addition to the various systems described above, we find also certain organs that have the power developed to a special degree of altering the composition of the blood by secreting into it chemical substances which are elaborated for the advantage of other parts of the body, whither they are conveyed in the blood stream. Many of the organs referred to above which subserve the functions already mentioned are in addition internally secreting glands, thus fulfilling more than one purpose. Such organs are the liver, the pancreas, the ovary, and the testicle. The liver, besides secreting bile, stores up a supply of carbohydrate in the form of glycogen, and when required liberates it into the blood as sugar. The pancreas also controls the carbohydrate metabolism, since after its experimental removal sugar makes its appearance in the urine, thereby indicating an excess of sugar in the blood. But there are certain other organs, which appear to be solely organs of internal secretion. Such are the suprarenal bodies, which are situated just in front of the kidneys, one on either side. These secrete into the blood a substance known as adrenalin, which acts on the muscles, particularly those of the blood vessels. If these organs are removed extreme weakness, associated with muscular collapse, results, and is followed sooner or later by death. The thyroid and pituitary are also internally secreting or endocrine organs since they secrete into the blood chemical substances or hormones which have a definite function in the economy of the organism.

CHAPTER II

HISTOLOGY

Histology is the study of the minute structure of the tissues of the body. Since it is carried out by means of the microscope it has been described as Microscopic Anatomy.

The tissues of which the different organs are composed may be divided into four main groups as follows:

(1) Epithelial tissues. (3) Muscular tissues.
(2) Connective tissues. (4) Nervous tissues.

The tissues are named partly according to structure and partly according to function.

(1) Epithelial Tissues.

An *epithelium* may be defined as a cellular membrane bounding a free surface. There is a certain amount of cementing substance present between the cells, but this is reduced to minimal proportions. There are two main kinds of epithelia, simple and compound.

In *simple epithelia* the cells form one layer only. They may be cubical in shape like those lining the tubules of certain glands such as the pancreas, or columnar like some of the cells lining the inside

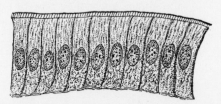

Fig. 3. Columnar epithelium from intestinal villus (from Gray).

of the stomach or intestine. They may be provided with cilia or fine filaments, as with the cells of the uterus, in which case we speak of a ciliated epithelium. Moreover the lining membrane may consist of a layer of thin cells arranged in the manner of flat paving-stones closely fitted together such as we find surrounding the air sacs of the lungs. Such a tissue is described as a pavement epithelium.

In *compound epithelia* the tissue consists of more than one layer of cells. When the cells are arranged in two, three or four superimposed layers the epithelium is frequently called transitional, but if the number of layers is considerable, we speak of a stratified

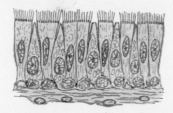

Fig. 4. Ciliated epithelium, from trachea of rabbit.

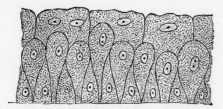

Fig. 5. Transitional epithelium (from Gray).

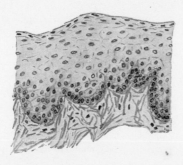

Fig. 6. Stratified epithelium, from œsophagus of sheep.

epithelium. The tissue lining the urinary bladder is a transitional epithelium; that forming the epidermis or superficial portion of the skin is a stratified epithelium. In addition to these kinds of epithelia there are the more specialised forms present in secreting glands, and certain sense organs, besides those structures like horn, tooth enamel, etc. which are of the nature of modified epithelia. These are described later in dealing with the physiology of the organs concerned.

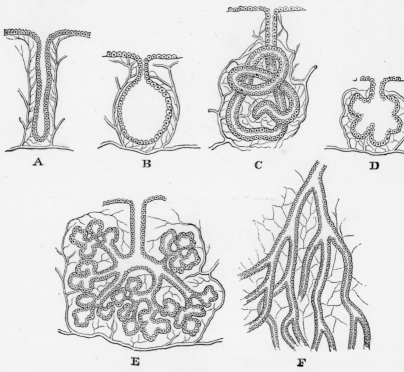

Fig. 7. Diagram illustrating development of different kinds of glands (from Sharpey's diagram in Quain). *A*, simple gland; *B*, sacculated gland; *C*, convoluted tubular gland; *D* and *E*, racemose glands; *F*, compound tubular gland.

(2) Connective Tissues.

The connective tissues are found throughout the whole body lying between and binding together the different organs or parts of the same organ. Their function is to act in a purely mechanical manner giving support where required and at the same time admitting of the necessary amount of elasticity or rigidity. In embryonic development they have an identical origin, and there are all gradations between the various kinds of connective tissue. They agree further in having a large amount of intercellular cementing substance, and in this substance fibres are developed. Although

situated outside of the cells this intercellular substance in the first
instance was derived from the cells.

One of the commonest kinds of connective tissue is called *areolar
tissue*, which is found in great abundance just under the skin. It
consists largely of a close meshwork formed of bundles of fibres
which are white in colour and very fine and wavy. Elastic fibres
are also present. These are generally thicker than the white fibres;
they are yellowish in colour, and as a rule much straighter. In
addition to the fibres there is a clear ground substance containing
several kinds of cells which can be seen lying amid the fibres. The
cells, which contain easily discernible nuclei, are in many cases

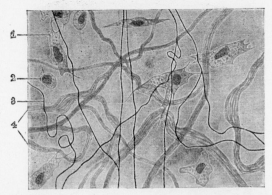

Fig. 8. Areolar tissue (after Szymonovicz, from Halliburton). 1, branched cell;
2, white blood corpuscle emigrated from a neighbouring vessel; 3, elastic fibres;
4, white fibres.

flattened and branched, but there are other kinds of cells which
resemble or are identical with some of the white corpuscles of the
blood.

Fibrous tissue which we find in tendon or sinew is almost wholly
composed of white fibres. In *elastic tissue* which occurs in ligaments
as well as in the lungs and the walls of the blood vessels elastic
fibres are the chief constituent. Otherwise both these kinds of
connective tissue resemble areolar tissue.

Cartilage, commonly called gristle, is a modified form of fibrous
tissue, which occurs at the ends of bones where these take part in
forming joints. It is firm, and at the same time elastic and to a
certain extent yielding so that it saves the bones from the effects
of concussion and the body from the jar which would otherwise

result. It occurs also in the wall of the windpipe, in the nostril, and in the external ear, besides supplying firm but elastic connections between the vertebrae, and between the ribs and the sternum.

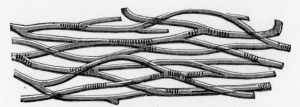

Fig. 9. Elastic fibres (from Schafer).

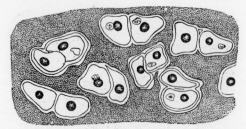

Fig. 10. Hyaline cartilage (from Gray).

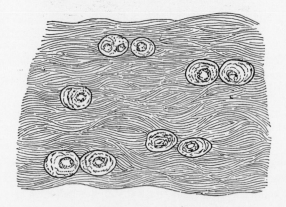

Fig. 11. Fibro-cartilage (from Gray).

Moreover, most of the bones are first laid down in embryonic development as cartilage and only become ossified in later life.

All cartilage consists of a matrix or ground substance containing cells scattered within it. There are three principal kinds of cartilage, *hyaline cartilage* in which the matrix is almost clear and transparent, *white fibro-cartilage* in which the matrix contains white fibres, and *elastic fibro-cartilage* in which elastic fibres are present.

Bone is a form of tissue produced by the ossification of connective tissue. It may be divided into two classes according to its origin, cartilage bone and membrane bone. Bone of the latter kind is formed by the deposition of lime salts in the ground substance of embryonic connective tissue. In this way such bones as the maxillary bone are produced. Cartilage bones (e.g. the limb bones) are formed through the activity of the cartilage cells. These become enlarged and arranged in rows, and give rise to fibrous lamellae which afterwards undergo calcification. The tissue becomes ex-

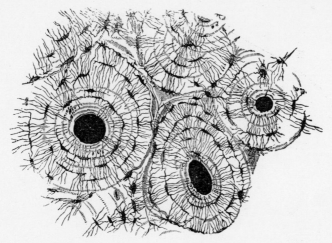

Fig. 12. Compact tissue of bone (after Sharpey, from Quain).

cavated by small holes through which blood vessels, arising from the periosteum or covering vascular membrane, pass into and through the bone. A fully formed bone is seen to be composed of lamellae, consisting of fine fibres which are calcified, lying in a matrix which is also calcified, and contains the bone corpuscles or cells of the tissue. Bone may be either compact as in the shaft of a long bone (e.g. the femur) or cancellous as in the ends of such a bone. In compact bone the blood vessels are contained in little canals—the Haversian canals—which are very numerous throughout the bone; in cancellated bone the vessels run in the interstices into which the bone marrow extends. The marrow is contained chiefly in the hollow cavity which extends throughout the length

of the shaft but is not continued into the enlarged ends. The
marrow consists largely of fat, but often contains a considerable
amount of blood, which then gives it a characteristic red colour.

Reticular tissue also occurs in bone marrow, as well as in the
liver, spleen, lymphatic glands, and various other parts of the
body. It is essentially a connective tissue in which the intercellular
substance has partly disappeared or been replaced by fluid, but it
contains white fibres, and sometimes elastic fibres.

Lymphoid tissue may be described as reticular tissue or areolar
tissue in which the meshes are packed with large numbers of small
round cells called lymphocytes or lymph corpuscles. It occurs in

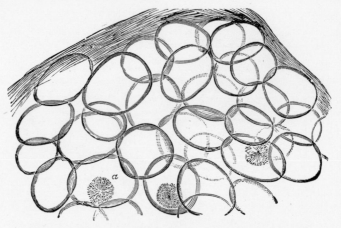

Fig. 13. Adipose tissue (after Gray). *a*, crystals of fatty acids.

the spleen, tonsils, and thymus, and in all lymphatic glands. (For
figures of spleen and thymus see pages 200, 201.)

Adipose tissue is connective tissue containing a large proportion
of fat in its cells. The fat globules are at first very small, and then
gradually increase in size so as to coalesce, pushing the cell protoplasm with its nucleus to the periphery or chiefly to one side, so
that there comes to exist a single fat globule surrounded by a thin
layer of cell substance, a portion of which contains the nucleus.
Adipose tissue is found mainly just beneath the skin, and in other
places where it serves as a packing, holding the organs in position
and protecting them from injury. It helps to give the limbs their
characteristic contour. It provides a store of nutriment for the
bodily requirements, besides acting as a non-conductive layer

under the skin, and so helping to retain the bodily heat. In fat animals adipose tissue occurs in great quantity in the abdominal cavity, especially in the region of the kidneys, as well as between the various muscles; sometimes also the muscles are themselves penetrated by fat, the flesh becoming marbled in appearance.

(3) Muscular Tissues.

Muscular tissue consists mainly of fibres in which all the primitive functions of the cell have become subservient to the function of contractility. There are three kinds of muscular tissues, which differ from one another both in their histological structure and in the functions which they perform.

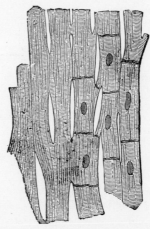

Fig. 14. Striated muscle showing capillary vessels (from Schafer).

Fig. 15. Cardiac muscle (from Schweigger-Seidel). (Cell divisions and cell nuclei omitted in left of drawing.)

In *voluntary* or *striated muscle* the fibres are long and cylindrical with characteristic cross striping, consisting of alternate dark and light bands. Each fibre has an elastic sheath, called the sarcolemma, which insulates the cells from one another and assists in forming the attachment of the muscle to the bone. In addition to the sarcolemma and striated substance, a muscle fibre has also a number of oval nuclei generally associated with a little undifferentiated cell protoplasm. This protoplasm, together with the interstitial substance between the elements composing the fibre, is the remains of the protoplasm of the cells which originally gave rise to the muscle fibres. Striated muscles are attached to the bones of the body and are under the control of the will; hence they are also called skeletal muscles, or, as already mentioned, voluntary muscles.

Cardiac or heart muscle also shows a transverse striation, but the cells are short and squat, and have branches which unite them with those of neighbouring fibres, and there is no sarcolemma. Each cell has a central nucleus.

Involuntary, non-striated, smooth, or *plain muscle* is devoid of striations. The cells are usually fairly long and taper at both ends. The nucleus which is elongated is situated centrally. Connective tissue is present (as in the case of heart muscle) but there does not appear to be a true sarcolemma. Smooth muscle occurs in the walls of the alimentary canal, the trachea, the urinary bladder, the uterus, and various other organs, the movements of which are not under the control of the will. It is well developed also in the middle coats of arteries, veins, and lymphatics, besides occurring in parts of the skin in association with sweat glands and hair follicles.

(4) Nervous Tissues.

The minute anatomy of the nervous tissues is most conveniently described in dealing with the nervous system. Here it will suffice to give a brief account of the different kinds of nerve fibres and the cells from which they arise.

If we cut across a nerve trunk, and examine a section of it under the microscope, we find that it is made up of a large number of nerve fibres which are held together by connective tissue. If we confine our examination to one of these fibres we find that it consists of a central strand or core, known as the axis cylinder or axon, and an outer portion consisting of the medullary sheath and the neurolemma, the latter being a fine membrane which surrounds the sheath. The axon is concerned with the conduction of the nerve impulse; the medulla, which is not quite complete but is broken at intervals, is of the nature of a protective covering and is com-

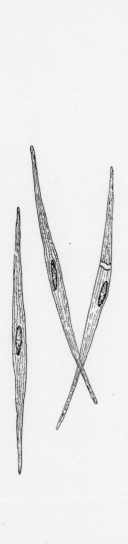

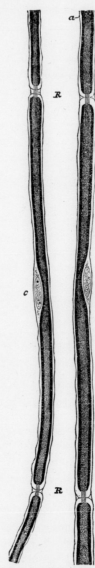

Fig. 16. Unstriated muscle fibres from bladder of frog (highly magnified). Note the spindle-shaped nuclei and the longitudinal fibrillation.

Fig. 17. Medullated nerve (J. E. Neale, from Schafer) showing nodes of Ranvier, R, where medulla is broken, the axon passing through. a, neurolemma outside of medulla; c, nucleus and protoplasm between primitive sheath or neurolemma and medulla.

posed of a phosphorised fatty substance. Such nerve fibres are called *medullated fibres*. Intermingled with these are other fibres in which the medullary sheath is lacking. These are called *non-medullated fibres*. They are especially common in the so-called sympathetic nerves. These non-medullated fibres appear to possess numerous nuclei but the nuclei belong actually to a very thin investing sheath.

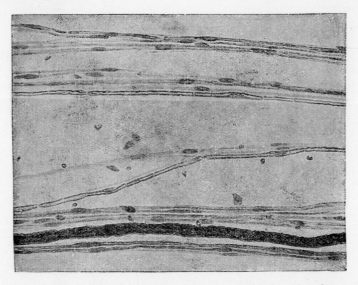

Fig. 18. Non-medullated nerve fibres from osmic acid preparation of vagus of cat (photograph from Schafer).

If we follow a nerve fibre along its entire length we finally come, either in one direction or the other, to the nerve cell of which the axon of the fibre is in reality a part. For the nerve cells give off prolongations, sometimes a great many and sometimes only a few, and these prolongations become the axons of the nerve fibres. A nerve cell possesses a nucleus like all other cells and external protoplasm which contains characteristic fibrils and granules. The name *neuron* is applied to the nerve cell together with all its various prolongations, including the axons of the nerve fibres. (See fig. 49, p. 148.)

CHAPTER III

THE CHEMISTRY OF FOODS. THE PROTEINS

Feeding stuffs in common use for animals are very diverse in character and composition. From a farmer's standpoint they may be roughly classified into three main groups:

(1) succulent feeding stuffs; examples: grass, green fodder crops, roots and silage;

(2) fibrous feeding stuffs; examples: hay and straw;

(3) concentrated feeding stuffs; examples: oilcakes and meals, cereal meals and grains, and by-products from sugar, cheese, beer, whisky and butter manufacture.

From the chemical point of view, all feeding stuffs are regarded as being built up from the following constituents—water, proteins and other nitrogenous compounds, fats and oils, carbohydrates, ash, and a group of chemical substances comprised under the general term vitamins.

The Proteins. Protein is a general term used to denote a large class of nitrogenous substances of which albumin, the chief ingredient of egg white, is typical. Protein is the most important ingredient of all living cell material, both plant and animal.

A substance is classified as a protein if it possesses certain properties and conforms to certain tests. For instance, proteins are colloids, and as such do not form true solutions or dialyse through membranes such as bladder or parchment paper. Their properties are also dependent to a large extent on their surroundings, especially on the content of acids, salts or alkalis in the water with which they may be in contact. They are also dissolved by certain specific enzymes secreted by plants and animals. Proteins when heated char and give off a characteristic odour, and if heated in contact with air burn, forming carbon dioxide and water. Heated in contact with soda-lime they give off ammonia. Treated with strong nitric acid and warmed a yellow colour is produced which becomes orange on addition of ammonia. When dissolved in excess of sodium hydrate solution proteins give a violet colour on addition of a drop of dilute solution of copper sulphate. A substance which conforms to all or nearly all of these tests is assumed to be a protein.

But although proteins possess all or nearly all these general properties, they show great variation in other respects, notably in their solubilities in various solvents. They are usually classified into well-defined groups according to solubility and other special characteristics. These groups are

(1) Protamines. Proteins strongly basic in character, and found only in the spermatozoa of certain fish.

(2) Histones. These proteins are similar in character to protamines, have a limited distribution and are found in fish roes and globin, the protein derived from blood pigment.

(3) Albumins. These proteins are soluble in water and are abundant in animal tissues and plants, e.g. egg albumin, blood albumin and various plant albumins. Their solutions are coagulated by heat and acids.

(4) Globulins. These proteins are insoluble in water, but soluble in dilute neutral salt solutions. They are abundantly distributed in plant and animal tissues and their solutions are coagulated by heat and by acids.

(5) Glutelins. Vegetable proteins insoluble in water or dilute salt solutions but soluble in dilute alkalis and acids, e.g. oryzenin of rice and wheat glutenin.

(6) Prolamines. These proteins are insoluble in water, salt solutions, dilute acids and alkalis, but are characterised by being soluble in 70–90 per cent. alcohol. Wheat gliadin and hordein from barley and zein from maize are examples of this class.

(7) Scleroproteins. These proteins are derived from the skeletal and connective tissues, and include keratin (from hair, horn, feathers, etc.), gelatin and elastin.

(8) Conjugated proteins. This group includes four important classes:

(a) nucleoproteins, consisting of nucleic acid combined with protein;

(b) chromoproteins, consisting of a colouring matter combined with protein, e.g. haemoglobin;

(c) phosphoproteins, consisting of phosphoric acid combined with protein, e.g. caseinogen;

(d) glucoproteins, consisting of protein combined with a carbohydrate radicle, e.g. mucin.

(9) Derived proteins. This class includes the proteins that arise during the treatment of proteins with acids, alkalis, or ferments,

and are known, according to their descending order of complexity, as metaproteins (acid and alkali albumins) proteoses, peptones and polypeptides.

Although the various groups into which the proteins are classified differ considerably in properties, their elementary composition is the same within narrow limits as shown below:

> Carbon from 51 to 55 per cent.
> Hydrogen about 7 per cent.
> Nitrogen from 15 to 17 per cent.
> Sulphur from 0·4 to 2·5 per cent.
> Oxygen from 20 to 30 per cent.

The simplest formula which corresponds to these figures is $C_{240}H_{370}N_{65}SO_{70}$. This formula is not suggested as the probable formula of any protein, but is given to indicate the great complexity of the protein group.

When a chemist wishes to study the chemical constitution of an unknown substance, his first step is to obtain the substance in a state of purity. In the case of colloid substances such as proteins this is an extremely difficult matter, but after repeated attempts methods have been devised which have been successful, and a considerable number of proteins have been isolated in a state of purity, in some cases, such as globulins and albumins, the proteins have actually been prepared in crystalline form. Having succeeded in preparing a pure specimen of protein, the chemist may proceed in two ways to investigate its chemical constitution. He may either attempt to synthesise similar substances by combining together several simpler compounds of known constitution, or he may attempt to decompose or analyse the complex protein into simpler compounds which can be separated and identified. It is by the second or analytical method that our knowledge of the chemical constitution of proteins has been mainly gained.

It had long been known that proteins could be decomposed by the long continued action of ferments or by prolonged boiling with dilute hydrochloric or sulphuric acids. Both these methods bring about the decomposition by the addition of water and are therefore known as hydrolysis. As long ago as 1820 gelatine had been decomposed by acid hydrolysis, and from the resulting decomposition products a crystalline substance had been obtained called glycocoll or sugar of glue, from its sweet taste. This substance was subsequently shown to be amino-acetic acid, and is now usually called glycine. In the same year a white crystalline compound called leucine was separated from the decomposition products resulting from the acid hydrolysis of flesh protein, and this substance is now known to be α-amino-isocaproic acid. Between 1820 and 1899 by means of similar experiments no less than ten separate crystalline compounds were isolated and identified. These compounds, by name glycine, alanine, valine, leucine, phenylalanine, tyrosine, serine, cystine, aspartic acid and glutaminic acid all have one point in common; they are mono-amino acids containing one NH_2 group combined with the carbon atom next to the acid group,

They are therefore neither strongly acid nor strongly alkaline.

In 1889 a compound of a new type, called lysine, was obtained from the decomposition products of casein. This compound was shown to be a di-amino acid containing two NH_2 groups and to be α-ε-di-amino-caproic acid. By virtue of the second NH_2 group which is widely separated from the acid group lysine possesses strongly basic properties. Shortly after the discovery of lysine two other basic compounds, arginine and histidine, were separated from the products of decomposition of proteins.

Although by this time some dozen or more crystalline compounds had been isolated from the products of protein decomposition, their discovery represented a series of interesting but disconnected observations.

In 1899 Emil Fischer began a series of studies of the properties of the various amino-acids obtained in the decomposition of proteins. When proteins are boiled for some time with hydrochloric acid in a flask fitted with a reflux condenser hydrolysis of the protein results, the hydrolytic digest containing the mixture of amino-acids resulting therefrom. Emil Fischer found that these amino-acids could be converted into their ethyl esters which could be distilled *in vacuo*. By this method he succeeded in separating the various mono-amino acids from one another and in determining approximately the quantitative proportions in which they occur in several pure proteins. The method also resulted in the discovery of several new compounds. It was found that the mono-amino-acids varied very much in the relative proportions in which they occur in proteins, and in certain proteins one or more of the amino-acids were found to be absent. Methods have also been devised for the separation of di-amino acids and their products, and considerable improvement in the technique of the methods devised by Fischer has resulted from the work of Levene and Van Slyke in America, and Foreman in England. Proteins may be regarded, therefore, as being built up from a series of amino-acids. Amino-acids are crystalline, colourless substances, and, with the exception of tyrosine and cystine, easily soluble in water. The di-amino acids are alkaline in reaction, the dicarboxylic acids are acid in reaction, whereas the mono-amino acids, as mentioned on p. 26, are neutral in character. The simplest amino-acid of this series is amino-acetic acid, or glycine, $CH_2(NH_2).COOH$. The amino-acid is derived from its constituent acid by the replacement of a hydrogen atom by an amino group (NH_2), i.e.

$$
\begin{aligned}
\text{acetic acid} &= CH_3.COOH, \\
\text{amino-acetic acid} &= CH_2(NH_2).COOH, \\
\text{propionic acid} &= CH_3.CH_2.COOH, \\
\text{amino-propionic acid} &= CH_3.CH(NH_2).COOH.
\end{aligned}
$$

A protein consists of a large number of amino-acids linked up in the following manner:

glycine + glycine   = glycyl-glycine + water,

$CH_2(NH_2).CO \boxed{OH + H} HN.CH_2.COOH$
$$= CH_2(NH_2).CO(NH).CH_2.COOH + H_2O,$$

one hydrogen atom of the amino group combining with an hydroxyl group (OH) of the carboxyl group to form water. This linkage, (CO-NH) which occurs when amino-acids are combined is known as the 'peptide linkage' and such bodies are called peptides. Dipeptides contain two amino-acid radicles, tripeptides contain three amino-acid radicles, and Emil Fischer has succeeded in producing complex polypeptides by combining a large number of amino-acids. Such polypeptides give many of the reactions associated with peptones. It will be noted that in the synthesis of polypeptides the amino-acids are linked together as anhydrides, water being eliminated. In the hydrolysis of proteins by mineral acids the reverse process takes place, amino-acids being formed from their anhydrides by the addition of water.

The following is a list of the principal amino-acids obtained by the hydrolysis of proteins:

(A) Mono-amino-monocarboxylic acids.

(1) Glycine, α-amino-acetic acid:

$$CH_2(NH_2).COOH.$$

(2) Alanine, α-amino-propionic acid:

$$CH_3CH(NH_2).COOH.$$

(3) Valine, α-amino-isovalerianic acid:

$$\begin{matrix} CH_3 \\ CH_3 \end{matrix} \rangle CH.CH(NH_2).COOH.$$

(4) Leucine, α-amino-isocaproic acid:

$$\begin{matrix} CH_3 \\ CH_3 \end{matrix} \rangle CH.CH_2.CH(NH_2).COOH.$$

(5) Isoleucine, α-amino-β-methyl-β-ethyl-propionic acid:

$$\begin{matrix} CH_3 \\ C_2H_5 \end{matrix} \rangle CH.CH(NH_2).COOH.$$

(6) Norleucine, α-amino-caproic acid:

$$CH_3.CH_2.CH_2.CH_2.CH(NH_2).COOH.$$

(7) Phenylalanine, β-phenyl-α-amino-propionic acid:

$$C_6H_5.CH_2.CH(NH_2).COOH.$$

(8) Tyrosine, β-p-hydroxyphenyl-α-amino-propionic acid:

$$OH.C_6H_4.CH_2.CH(NH_2).COOH.$$

(9) Serine, β-hydroxy-α-amino-propionic acid:

$$OH.CH_2.CH(NH_2).COOH.$$

(10) Cystine, the union of two molecules of amino-thio-lactic acid:

$$HOOC.CH(NH_2).CH_2.S - S.CH_2.CH(NH_2).COOH.$$

(11) Methionine, γ-methylthiol-α-amino-butyric acid:

$$CH_3.S.CH_2.CH_2.CH(NH_2).COOH$$

(B) Mono-amino-dicarboxylic acids.

(12) Aspartic acid, amino-succinic acid:

$$\begin{matrix} CH_2.COOH \\ | \\ CH(NH_2).COOH. \end{matrix}$$

(13) Glutamic acid, α-amino-glutaric acid:

$$HOOC.CH_2.CH_2.CH(NH_2).COOH.$$

(14) Hydroxy-glutamic acid, α-amino-β-hydroxy-glutaric acid:

$HOOC.CH_2.CH(OH).CH(NH_2).COOH.$

(C) Di-amino-monocarboxylic acids.

(15) Arginine, δ-guanidine-α-amino-valerianic acid:

$$NH = C\begin{cases} NH_2 \\ NH.CH_2.CH_2.CH_2.CH(NH_2).COOH. \end{cases}$$

(16) Lysine, α-ϵ-di-amino-caproic acid:

$H_2N.CH_2.CH_2.CH_2.CH_2.CH(NH_2).COOH.$

(D) Heterocyclic compounds (compounds containing rings other than the benzene ring).

(17) Histidine, β-iminazole-α-amino-propionic acid:

$$\begin{array}{c} CH \\ HN \quad N \\ | \quad | \\ HC = C.CH_2.CH(NH_2).COOH. \end{array}$$

(18) Proline, α-pyrrolidine-carboxylic acid:

$$\begin{array}{c} CH_2{-}CH_2 \\ | \quad \quad | \\ CH_2 \quad CH.COOH. \\ \diagdown\diagup \\ NH \end{array}$$

(19) Hydroxyproline, γ-hydroxy-pyrrolidine-carboxylic acid.

$$\begin{array}{c} CHOH{-}CH_2 \\ | \quad \quad | \\ CH_2 \quad CH.COOH \\ \diagdown\diagup \\ NH \end{array}$$

(20) Tryptophane, β-indole-α-amino-propionic acid:

$$\begin{array}{c} C.CH_2CH(NH_2).COOH. \\ C_6H_4 \quad CH \\ \diagdown\diagup \\ NH \end{array}$$

[NOTE. The α, β, γ, δ, ϵ, etc. refer to the exact position of linkage in the carbon chain of the group that follows: thus

Lysine = α-amino-ϵ-amino-caproic acid

$$\overset{\epsilon}{CH_2(NH_2)}.\overset{\delta}{CH_2}.\overset{\gamma}{CH_2}.\overset{\beta}{CH_2}.\overset{\alpha}{CH(NH_2)}.COOH.$$

Similarly $CH_3.CH(NH_2).COOH = \alpha$-amino-propionic acid.]

General Characters of the Proteins. The proteins are colloid substances containing carbon, hydrogen, nitrogen, oxygen and sulphur. In addition the phosphoproteins and nucleoproteins contain phosphorus. Except in a few cases, proteins cannot be obtained in a crystalline form. They are precipitated from their solutions by the addition of strong acids or the salts of the heavy metals. In addition they give characteristic colour reactions which are due to the presence of certain amino-acids or to certain linkages. Thus solutions of proteins treated with nitric acid become bright yellow. This colour becomes orange when the solution is neutralised by strong ammonia solution. The reaction, called the xanthoproteic reaction, is due to the presence of a benzene nucleus. Proteins containing tyrosine or phenylalanine will therefore give this colour reaction. Similarly, a solution of proteins heated with a mixture of mercuric and mercurous nitrates gives a brick-red coloration, if tyrosine is present. This reaction is given by all aromatic substances containing a benzene ring to which a hydroxyl group is attached. Similarly, a violet colour is developed when a few drops of dilute copper sulphate solution are added to a protein solution made strongly alkaline by the addition of sodium hydrate. This reaction, known as the biuret reaction, is associated with the presence of 'peptide linkages' in the protein, and is given by other substances than proteins. Thus the residue left when urea is heated will also give this reaction. Again, solutions of proteins containing tryptophane give a violet coloration when treated with concentrated sulphuric acid and reduced oxalic acid. Hopkins and Cole have shown that this reaction with tryptophane is due to glyoxalic acid which is formed when oxalic acid is reduced by magnesium powder and acetic acid is added to the resultant solution.

The annexed table gives the approximate distribution of amino-acids in the commoner proteins. The figures for casein, swede-turnip protein, and linseed protein are derived from analyses carried out by Foreman.

Consideration of the table reveals the fact that the sum of the percentage of amino-acids determined in any protein rarely approaches, and in one case exceeds, the expected value of 100 per cent. This is partly due to the experimental difficulties involved in the quantitative analysis of the products of protein decomposition and partly, no doubt, to the fact that the com-

	Protamines (Salmine)	Histones Globin	Thymus histone	Albumins Egg albumin	Globulins Serum globulin	Edestin from hemp seed	Globulin from linseed	Prolamines Hordein	Gliadin from wheat	Zein	Scleroproteins Gelatin	Elastin	Keratin	Phosphoproteins Caseinogen	Protein from swede turnip
Glycine	—	—	0·5	0·0	3·5	3·8	+	0·0	0·4	0·0	16·5	25·8	4·7	0·5	0·3
Alanine	—	4·2	3·5	2·1	2·2	3·6	1·0	1·4	0·3	2·2	0·8	6·6	1·5	1·9	3·6
Valine	4·3	—	—	—	+	+	12·7	1·4	0·0	0·3	1·0	1·0	0·9	7·9	10·0
Leucine	—	29·0	11·8	6·1	18·7	20·9	4·0	7·0	4·1	18·6	2·1	21·4	7·1	9·7	9·0
Phenylalanine	—	4·2	2·2	4·4	3·8	2·4	4·1	5·5	1·0	4·9	0·4	3·9	0·0	3·9	4·5
Tyrosine	7·8	1·3	5·2	1·1	2·5	2·1	0·7	4·0	1·9	3·6	0·0	0·4	3·2	4·5	2·9
Serine	11·0	0·6	—	—	—	0·4	—	0·1	—	0·6	0·4	—	0·6	0·5	—
Cystine	—	0·3	—	0·3	0·7	0·3	+	—	—	—	—	—	10·0	0·0	+
Proline	—	2·3	1·5	2·3	2·8	1·7	2·9	5·9	4·0	6·5	5·2	1·7	3·4	7·6	4·2
Hydroxyproline	—	1·0	—	—	—	2·0	—	—	—	—	3·0	+	—	0·2	—
Aspartic acid	—	4·4	0·0	1·5	2·5	4·5	1·7	1·3	0·7	1·4	0·6	0·8	0·3	4·1	7·0
Glutamic acid	—	1·7	0·5	8·0	8·5	6·3	11·6	41·3	24·0	18·3	0·9	—	3·7	21·8	3·2
Hydroxyglutamic acid	—	0·0	—	—	—	—	—	—	—	—	0·0	—	—	10·5	—
Tryptophane	—	—	—	+	+	+	+	—	+	0·0	0·0	0·3	—	1·5	+
Arginine	87·4	+	15·5	—	—	11·7	6·1	3·2	4·4	1·2	7·6	—	—	3·8	3·1
Lysine	0·0	5·4	6·9	—	—	1·0	1·2	0·0	2·2	0·0	2·8	—	—	7·6	4·4
Histidine	0·0	4·3	1·5	—	—	1·1	1·7	0·5	1·2	0·4	0·4	—	—	2·5	3·0
Ammonia	—	11·0	—	—	—	—	—	4·4	2·5	3·6	0·4	—	—	1·6	—
	110·5	69·7	49·1	25·8	45·2	61·8	47·7	76·0	46·7	61·6	42·1	61·9	35·4	90·1	55·2

plete history of the protein hydrolysis products is still not yet known. The figures, however imperfect they may be, yet reveal certain important facts. They show that proteins derived from animal substances yield on decomposition a fairly evenly balanced mixture of amino-acids, with the notable exception of gelatin, whereas the vegetable proteins, particularly those of the alcohol-soluble type, differ widely from the typical animal proteins in the nature and proportions of the amino-acids present, and contain certain amino-acids such as glutamic acid in large proportion. On the other hand, edestin from hemp seed, linseed globulin and the protein of swede turnips yield a well-balanced mixture of all the amino-acids not widely different from the mixtures yielded by the typical animal proteins.

In view of the importance of amino-acids to the animal (see p. 302) it is clear that all proteins are not of identical value in the nutrition of animals. Thus a pound of gliadin, for instance, would not go so far for tissue repair as a pound of linseed globulin or swede protein. On the other hand, it is clear that the distinction generally made that vegetable proteins are inferior to animal proteins for the nutrition of farm animals is not true in every case.

Non-Protein Nitrogenous Compounds. In the analysis of feeding stuffs the nitrogenous compounds are arbitrarily grouped together as 'crude protein', and crude protein includes many other nitrogenous compounds than protein. Plants synthesise proteins from the nitrates or ammonium salts they take up from the soil solutions. If a ripe seed be examined, it will be found that the nitrogenous compounds present are largely in the form of protein; in an immature or growing plant, however, only a small proportion of the nitrogenous compounds present is protein. A small proportion of these non-protein nitrogenous compounds may be nitrates, the larger proportion consisting of crystalline compounds called amides, which are closely related to amino-acids. For instance, in mangolds before Christmas one-third of the total nitrogen is present as nitrate, one-third as protein and one-third as amide. An amide may be defined as the compound formed when one hydrogen of ammonia is replaced by an acid radical (acyl group).

The amides of mangolds have been examined. Their chief constituent is glutamine, the amide of glutamic acid; asparagine,

the amide of aspartic acid, is also present, and a substance known
as betaine. Their structural formulae are as follows:

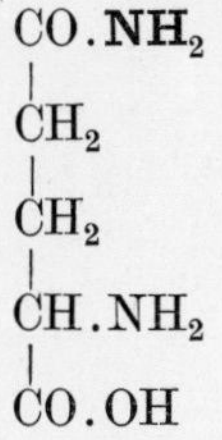

$$CO.\mathbf{NH_2}$$
$$|$$
$$CH_2$$
$$|$$
$$CH_2$$
$$|$$
$$CH.NH_2$$
$$|$$
$$CO.OH$$

glutamine

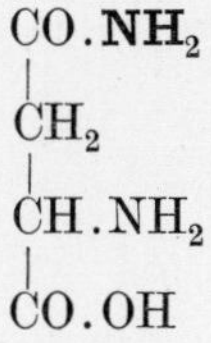

$$CO.\mathbf{NH_2}$$
$$|$$
$$CH_2$$
$$|$$
$$CH.NH_2$$
$$|$$
$$CO.OH$$

asparagine

$$\begin{array}{c} O \\ \diagup \diagdown \\ (CH_3)_3N \quad CO \\ \diagdown \diagup \\ CH_2 \end{array}$$

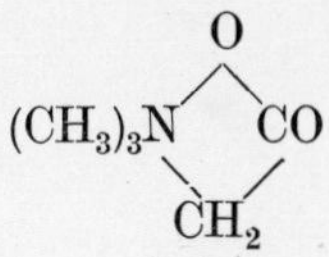

betaine

CHAPTER IV

THE FATS

In dealing with the chemistry of fats, it is necessary, first of all, to define as well as we can what we mean when we use the term 'fats'. Alcohols behave like metallic hydroxides when treated with acids, and form salts. The compound formed by the combination of an alcohol with an acid is called an ethereal salt or *ester*. For instance, ethyl alcohol combines with acetic acid to form ethyl acetate, and ethyl alcohol combines with sulphuric acid to form ethyl hydrogen sulphate, in accordance with the following equations:

$$C_2H_5.OH + CH_3.COOH = C_2H_5.OOC.CH_3 + H_2O,$$
$$C_2H_5.OH + H_2SO_4 \quad = C_2H_5.HSO_4 + H_2O.$$

In the first reaction given it will be noticed that the hydroxyl group (OH) of the alcohol reacts with hydrogen of the carboxyl group (COOH) to form water. Now fats consist of the esters formed by the reaction of the trihydric alcohol, glycerol, with a group of acids known as fatty acids. Such esters, if liquid at ordinary temperature, are called 'oils', if solid, 'fats'. It must be remembered that the term 'oil', as used in the popular sense, includes liquids such as paraffin oil, etc., which are not oils in the chemical sense of the word. In using the terms fat and oil it must be carefully borne in mind that the terms are used in the chemical sense and not in the popular sense. Esters formed by the union of fatty acids with alcohols other than glycerol are called 'waxes'. A similar confusion of nomenclature occurs here, the term 'wax' being used in some cases for substances that are really fats, such as Japan wax, and sometimes for substances which are hydro-carbons, e.g. paraffin wax.

We have already seen that a fat consists of glycerides of various fatty acids, in which fatty acid radicals replace the hydroxyl groups of glycerol. It is obvious, there being three hydroxyl groups in glycerol, that any or all of these groups may be replaced by a fatty acid radical. Taking butyric acid, $C_3H_7.COOH$, as an example of a fatty acid, we shall obtain monobutyrin, dibutyrin and tributyrin, according as 1, 2 or 3 hydroxyl groups are replaced. Thus:

$$\text{Monobutyrin} = \begin{array}{l} CH_2.OOC.C_3H_7 \\ | \\ CH.OH \\ | \\ CH_2.OH \end{array}$$

$$\text{Dibutyrin} \quad = \begin{array}{l} CH_2.OOC.C_3H_7 \\ | \\ CH.OH \\ | \\ CH_2.OOC.C_3H_7 \end{array}$$

$$\text{Tributyrin} \quad = \begin{array}{l} CH_2.OOC.C_3H_7 \\ | \\ CH.OOC.C_3H_7 \\ | \\ CH_2.OOC.C_3H_7 \end{array}$$

It is also obvious that any fatty acid radical may replace any hydroxyl group, so that in a triglyceride we might have three different fatty acid radicals present.

Fats as they occur in nature consist of mixtures of several glycerides together with varying quantities of an alcohol of the nature of cholesterol or phytosterol, cholesterol being associated with fats of animal origin, and phytosterol with those of plant origin.

A fat when boiled with caustic soda yields glycerol and the sodium salts of the fatty acids present. Soap of commerce consists of sodium and potassium salts of fatty acids. On treatment with water under high pressure and at a temperature of about 200° C., fats undergo hydrolysis, yielding the constituent fatty acids and glycerol. When boiled with sodium or potassium hydroxide a fat yields glycerol and the sodium or potassium salts of the fatty acids present; as may be represented by the following equation:

$$C_3H_5(C_{17}H_{35}.COO)_3 + 3NaOH = C_3H_5(OH)_3 + 3C_{17}H_{35}.COONa.$$

glyceryl tristearate   glycerol   sodium stearate

The decomposition of fats by alkalis is known as saponification because the resulting sodium or potassium salts possess the property of lathering when shaken with soft water, and are in fact soaps.

The organic acids which enter into the composition of fats and oils belong to various series. Many of them are included in the higher members of the acetic series of saturated acids, as for instance stearic acid, $C_{17}H_{35}$.COOH, whose glyceryl salt is an important constituent of the harder fats such as beef or mutton suets: palmitic acid, $C_{15}H_{31}$.COOH, whose glyceryl salt is an abundant constituent of palm oil. Some of the lower members of the acetic series are also found in fats, notably butyric acid, C_3H_7.COOH, which is present in butter.

Unsaturated acids are also commonly found, chiefly in the softer fats, or oils. Oleic acid, $C_{17}H_{33}$.COOH, whose glyceryl salt is the predominant constituent of olive oil, and is also present in most animal fats, is an unsaturated acid, containing two less hydrogen atoms than the corresponding saturated fatty acid, stearic acid, $C_{17}H_{35}$.COOH.

Linoleic acid, $C_{17}H_{31}$.COOH, whose glyceryl salt is a characteristic constituent of linseed oil, is still more unsaturated, containing four hydrogen atoms less than the corresponding stearic acid. Its glyceryl salt, being so highly unsaturated, combines readily with oxygen on exposure to air, forming an insoluble varnish-like compound. It is this capacity of linseed oil to 'dry' or to cover any surface over which it is spread with an impervious film that renders it so valuable as a basis for the manufacture of paints.

Fats are lighter than water, insoluble in water, but soluble in such organic solvents as ether, benzene, or petrol. Although they differ considerably in chemical composition, the fats which are used for foods all have approximately the same elementary composition, containing 76 per cent. of carbon, 12 per cent. of oxygen and 12 per cent. of hydrogen. All fats burn readily with the formation of CO_2 and H_2O; thus:

$$2C_3H_5(C_{17}H_{35}.COO)_3 + 163O_2 = 114CO_2 + 110H_2O.$$

From this equation it is evident that when fats are burnt the ratio of the volume of CO_2 formed to the volume of O_2 required for oxidation is $\frac{114}{163} = 0.7$. This ratio (known in physiology as the respiratory quotient) is obviously the same, whether the fat is oxidised by burning or by the slower chemical processes of oxidation that occur in the animal body. The respiratory quotient obtained by the oxidation of fat in the animal body will therefore be 0.7.

The heat of combustion of pure fat is 9.3 kilocalories per gram, but since in feeding stuffs the so-called fat or ether extract is estimated by extracting the feeding stuff in question with a solvent such as ether, substances such as chlorophyll and waxes are included. The inclusion of these substances in the figure for fat reduces the heat of combustion figure, so that the heat value per gram of 'fat' in feeding stuffs should be taken as 8·3 kilocalories and not 9·3 kilocalories, which is the figure for pure fat.

The following fatty acids commonly occur in nature:

Fat	Occurrence
Saturated fatty acids	
Formic acid, CH_2O_2	Sweat, urine and meat juice
Acetic acid, $C_2H_4O_2$	Sweat, muscles, liver faeces, urine
Propionic acid, $C_3H_6O_2$	Sweat and faeces
Normal butyric acid, $C_4H_8O_2$	Sweat, faeces, urine and butter
Normal caproic acid, $C_6H_{12}O_2$	Faeces, butter, coconut and palmnut oils
Caprylic acid, $C_8H_{16}O_2$	Sweat, butter, coconut and palmnut oils
Capric acid, $C_{10}H_{20}O_2$	Milk of cows and goats, coconut and palmnut oils and wool washings
Lauric acid, $C_{12}H_{24}O_2$	Milk and coconut and palmnut oils
Myristic acid, $C_{14}H_{28}O_2$	Milk and palmnut oil
Palmitic acid, $C_{16}H_{32}O_2$	Animal and vegetable fats and waxes
Stearic acid, $C_{18}H_{36}O_2$	Solid animal and vegetable fats
Unsaturated fatty acids	
Hypogaeic acid, $C_{16}H_{30}O_2$	Peanut oil and maize oil
Oleic acid, $C_{18}H_{34}O_2$	Most fats and oils and in milk
Linoleic acid, $C_{18}H_{32}O_2$	Linseed oil, pig's liver fat, and cottonseed oil

It will be noted that all the fatty acids of high molecular weight occurring in nature are characterised by possessing an even number of carbon atoms, and that a fat often contains a large number of different fatty acids. Thus, the fat of cow's milk, in addition to containing as esters large amounts of oleic, stearic and palmitic acids, contains about 7 per cent. of butyric acid, 3 per cent. of caproic acid and nearly 10 per cent. of myristic acid, together with traces of caprylic, capric, lauric and arachidic acid.

CHAPTER V

THE CARBOHYDRATES

Carbohydrates are, like the fats, compounds of carbon, hydrogen, and oxygen. The name carbohydrate is given to this group of compounds because they consist of carbon combined with hydrogen and oxygen in the same proportions as these elements exist in water. From this point of view therefore they may be regarded as compounds of carbon and water or hydrates of carbon. Carbohydrates are present in small amount in animal tissues, but bulk largely in plants and animal dietaries, and are consequently of considerable importance in animal physiology. The carbohydrates of agricultural interest comprise (1) sugars, (2) starches, (3) cellulose, (4) gums. The sugars are all soluble in water, are all crystalline and capable of diffusing through animal or vegetable membranes. They are all white or colourless, and all are more or less sweet to the taste. The starches are insoluble in water but form opalescent colloidal solutions when their suspensions in water are heated. The celluloses, on the other hand, are insoluble in water, but can be rendered soluble by treatment with certain reagents, such as cupric ammonium hydrate. When the celluloses and the starches are heated with mineral acids, hydrolysis occurs and sugars can be identified in the resultant solution, indicating that the more complex starches and celluloses are built up from sugars. A sugar is designated by the suffix -ose, and sugars are divided into several groups according to their chemical constitution. The simplest sugars are those in which the 'carbon' and the 'water' of the carbohydrate molecule are equal in value, the number of atoms of carbon in the molecule ranging from two upwards. Thus, a sugar containing two atoms of carbon is a biose sugar, three a triose, four a tetrose, five a pentose, and one containing six a hexose. In animal physiology, the hexose group is most important, and the pentose group also takes part in physiological processes. The simple sugars are called monosaccharides, thus arabinose ($C_5H_{10}O_5$, a pentose sugar) and glucose ($C_6H_{12}O_6$, a hexose sugar) are both monosaccharides. The monosaccharides may be considered chemically as aldehydic or ketonic alcohols. Regarding the monosaccharides as units, disaccharides are formed when two units combine with the elimination of a molecule of water, trisaccharides are formed when three units combine with the elimination of two molecules of water, and so on. The more complex carbohydrates (starches, gums and celluloses) have the general formula $(C_6H_{10}O_5)_n$ and are called polysaccharides. Thus in the hexose group—glucose, $C_6H_{12}O_6$, is a monosaccharide; sucrose, $C_{12}H_{22}O_{11}$, is a disaccharide; and raffinose, $C_{18}H_{32}O_{16}$, is a trisaccharide.

Polysaccharides, trisaccharides and disaccharides, when heated with mineral acids, are broken down to the simpler monosaccharides, water being added in the process. This process takes place in stages. Thus starch solution, which is a colloidal solution, when heated with mineral acid forms soluble starch, then dextrin, then maltose and finally dextrose. Similarly maltose when heated with dilute mineral acid forms glucose in accordance with the following equation:

$$C_{12}H_{22}O_{11} + H_2O = 2C_6H_{12}O_6 .$$
$$\text{(maltose)} \qquad\qquad \text{(glucose)}$$

It will be convenient to group together in a table all the carbohydrates of physiological importance and the main facts relating to them.

Carbohydrate	Yields on hydrolysis	Occurrence
MONOSACCHARIDES:		
d-Glucose, $(C_6H_{12}O_6)$	—	Fruit juices
D-Galactose, $(C_6H_{12}O_6)$	—	In milk sugar, raffinose, gums and seaweeds in combined form
Laevulose, $(C_6H_{12}O_6)$	—	Fruit juices, chicory and Jerusalem artichoke
Xylose, $(C_5H_{10}O_5)$	—	In combined form in straw, oat hulls, wood, etc.
Arabinose, $(C_5H_{10}O_5)$	—	Gums such as gum arabic
DISACCHARIDES:		
Sucrose, $(C_{12}H_{22}O_{11})$	Glucose + laevulose	Reserve material in plant tissues
Lactose, $(C_{12}H_{22}O_{11})$	Glucose + galactose	Milk of all animals
Maltose, $(C_{12}H_{22}O_{11})$	Glucose + glucose	From hydrolysis of starch
TRISACCHARIDE:		
Raffinose, $(C_{18}H_{32}O_{16})$	Glucose + galactose + laevulose	In sugar beet, cottonseed meal
POLYSACCHARIDES:		
Starch, $(C_6H_{10}O_5)_n$	Glucose	Plant tissues and feeding stuffs
Inulin	Laevulose	Tubers of artichoke and dahlia
Glycogen, $(C_6H_{10}O_5)_n$	Glucose	In liver and muscles of animals
Celluloses and pentosans	Glucose and xylose	Woody fibre of feeding stuffs and plant tissues

If a solution of glucose is examined through a polariscope it will be found that it has the power of rotating the plane of polarised light. Such optical activity is associated with the presence of an asymmetric carbon atom in the molecule, i.e. a carbon atom which is combined with four different atoms or groups. Where this is the case, different arrangements of the structure of the molecule can be made, each arrangement being associated with a definite chemical compound. Thus several compounds can exist, all having the same general formula, such compounds being called isomers. In the case of the sugar $C_6H_{12}O_6$, no less than sixteen different isomers are possible.

Dextrose or *d-glucose* occurs in ripe fruits, especially grapes, and is often called grape sugar. As ordinarily met with in commerce it is a whitish somewhat sticky solid consisting of very small crystals bound together by a trace of sticky syrup. It can be purified by crystallisation from hot methyl alcohol, when it is obtained in small white needles. It is very soluble in hot or cold water. As already mentioned, dextrose in solution rotates the plane of polarisation to the right, its specific rotatory power being $+ 52°·5$. Freshly dissolved dextrose shows nearly twice this rotation, but the value falls to the above figure immediately on boiling or in 24 hours at the ordinary temperature. This phenomenon is known as mutarotation and is due to intramolecular change. The name dextrose was given to this sugar because of its power of rotating the plane of polarised light to the right, but owing to the fact that many other sugars having this property have since been discovered chemists now call it glucose. Moreover, since two forms of glucose are known, dextrose, which has a specific rotatory power of $+ 52°·5$ and another which has a specific rotatory power of $- 52°·5$, dextrose is now known as d-glucose, the other form being known as l-glucose, being laevo-rotatory. Like all the hexoses glucose is a reducing agent.

Laevulose or *Dl-fructose* occurs in many ripe fruits, and is produced together with dextrose by the hydrolysis of cane sugar. It is most readily obtained by boiling with water the substance known as inulin, a reserve carbohydrate present in the tubers of the artichoke and dahlia. It is not so easily obtained in the crystalline form as dextrose. Its solution rotates the plane of polarised light to the left. Like dextrose, its name is connected with its optical activity, and owing to the recognition of many sugars possessing the power of rotating the plane of polarised light to the left, chemists now call it Dl-fructose[1]. Two forms of fructose are known, the laevo-rotatory naturally occurring form Dl-fructose or laevulose, and the dextro-rotatory synthetic form Ld-fructose.

D-Galactose, the third hexose sugar of agricultural interest, is not found as such. It arises, in association with dextrose, during the hydrolysis of lactose, or milk sugar, and is found together with various other sugars in the hydrolytic products of certain vegetable gums. It is dextro-rotatory, its specific rotatory power being $+81°$. The hexose sugars already described are alike in most of their properties, but they differ in their action on polarised light. This difference is due to the different arrangement of their constituent atoms, as will be seen by consideration of their structural formulae:

$$
\begin{array}{cccc}
\text{CHO} & \text{CHO} & \text{CHO} & \text{CH}_2\text{OH} \\
| & | & | & | \\
\text{H—C—OH} & \text{HO—C—H} & \text{H—C—OH} & \text{C—O} \\
| & | & | & | \\
\text{HO—C—H} & \text{H—C—OH} & \text{HO—C—H} & \text{HO—C—H} \\
| & | & | & | \\
\text{H—C—OH} & \text{HO—C—H} & \text{HO—C—H} & \text{H—C—OH} \\
| & | & | & | \\
\text{H—C—OH} & \text{HO—C—H} & \text{H—C—OH} & \text{H—C—OH} \\
| & | & | & | \\
\text{CH}_2\text{OH} & \text{CH}_2\text{OH} & \text{CH}_2\text{OH} & \text{CH}_2\text{OH} \\
\text{dextrose} & l\text{-glucose} & D\text{-galactose} & \text{laevulose} \\
d\text{-glucose} & & & Dl\text{-fructose}
\end{array}
$$

These sugars are all reducing agents and in virtue of this property give a red precipitate of cuprous oxide (Cu_2O) when boiled with Fehling's solution. Fehling's solution is a deep blue fluid obtained by adding sodium hydrate to copper sulphate solution and then dissolving the cupric hydrate precipitate thus formed by means of sodium potassium tartrate solution. It is virtually an alkaline solution of cupric oxide CuO, half the oxygen of which is removed by reducing agents forming the bright red Cu_2O which is insoluble in alkaline tartrate. Standard Fehling solution is used in the quantitative estimation of reducing sugars. A solution of silver oxide dissolved in ammonia is reduced to metallic silver when boiled with solutions of hexose sugars. Heated with potassium or sodium hydroxide, hexose sugar solutions become yellow. The above tests serve to determine the presence of one or other of these hexoses in solution.

[1] For explanation of nomenclature, see note on p. 46.

Xylose and *arabinose* are two pentose sugars; xylose being obtained by the hydrolysis of wood gum, arabinose by the hydrolysis of cherry gum. On boiling with mineral acids, these sugars yield furfurol or its derivatives.

Disaccharides.

Lactose, $C_{12}H_{22}O_{11}$, the sugar found in milk, is a white crystalline solid, less soluble than cane and much less sweet. It is dextro-rotatory and reduces both Fehling's solution and ammoniacal solution of silver oxide. Milk sugar is obtained by the evaporation of whey, the liquid which remains after the separation of the curd from milk in cheese making. It is used as a basis for medicinal powders and tablets, and for humanising cow's milk intended for infant feeding.

Cane sugar, $C_{12}H_{22}O_{11}$, is a common constituent of the cell sap of plants and is obtained commercially from sugar beet and sugar cane. It is a soluble white crystalline substance, dextro-rotatory, and is not a reducing agent. On hydrolysis with weak mineral acids it yields dextrose and laevulose. The mixture resulting from hydrolysis is laevo-rotatory and is known as invert sugar. A ferment in yeast which inverts cane sugar is called invertase. It is estimated quantitatively either by calculation from the amount of Cu_2O produced after inversion and treatment with Fehling's solution or by optical methods, taking advantage of the change in rotation of its solution after inversion.

Maltose or malt sugar, $C_{12}H_{22}O_{11}$, is found in certain parts of plants at certain stages of growth, particularly in germinating cereal grains. It is produced by the process of malting, in which plant ferments present in cereal grains convert the reserve starch present in the seed into maltose during the process of germination. In malting, barley grains or other suitable grains are induced to germinate by being kept at favourable conditions of temperature and moisture on a malting floor. When the plumules and radicles have reached about a half-inch in length, the grains are dried to prevent further growth. When dry, the sprouts, called malt coombs, are rubbed off and the grain is ground and forms malt. The malt contains diastase (see p. 53), maltose and much starch. To convert this starch into maltose the malt is soaked, or, as it is called, mashed in warm water. The diastase converts the remaining starch into sugar, and the liquor which is separated from the husks and other insoluble material is now called wort, which is generally used for beer or whisky production by the aid of yeast. Pure maltose crystallises into fine white needles, is dextro-rotatory and reduces Fehling's solution and ammoniacal silver oxide solution. On hydrolysis with acids it yields dextrose.

Polysaccharides.

Starch, $(C_6H_{10}O_5)_n$, is the most abundant constituent of plant cells, and forms the chief reserve store material of plants. Although non-crystalline, it possesses a definite organised structure, consisting in the plant tissues of grains built up in concentric layers round a central nucleus or hilum. Starch grains of different origin can often be assigned to the tuber or seed from which they originate by the differences in structure they present on microscopical examination. On treatment with hot water, starch grains swell up and form an opalescent solution, which gives a characteristic blue colour with iodine in neutral or acid solution. A blue additive compound of free iodine and starch is formed, and if the blue compound is heated the colour disappears, to reappear on cooling. By the action of the enzyme maltase, starch is converted into maltose, but on hydrolysis with mineral acids the reaction proceeds a stage further with the production of glucose. Intermediate products, called dextrins, are formed during hydrolysis, such dextrins being used as gums. By controlled hydrolysis with weak mineral acids, the conversion of starch to sugar can be stopped at the dextrin stage.

Inulin, which occurs in dahlia tubers, and bulbs and roots of many plants, is a white solid somewhat like starch and dissolves in water, giving a yellow colour with iodine. On boiling it is gradually converted into laevulose.

Glycogen, or animal starch, is a starch-like compound found in animal tissues, in certain fungi and in molluscs. By rapidly cutting out the liver of an animal fed on carrots and warming it with a strong solution of potassium hydroxide the tissue is dissolved. The glycogen is then precipitated from solution by the addition of alcohol. It is a white solid, soluble in water, and its solution gives a cherry red colour with iodine. Diastatic ferments convert it into dextrin, maltose, and glucose.

Cellulose, $(C_6H_{10}O_5)_n$, is a white substance, and enters into the composition of most plant cell walls. It is insoluble in water, but dissolves in certain reagents, such as a strong solution of zinc chloride in water or hydrochloric acid, cupric ammonium solution, or strong sulphuric acid.

By alternate treatment with dilute mineral acid and alkali a crude impure preparation of cellulose is obtained, called 'crude fibre'.

Vegetable gums, mucilages, and pectins. Many plants contain all or some of their carbohydrates in the form of gummy or mucilaginous substances, the chemical constitution of which is still uncertain. They are present in the seed coats of linseed and cress, which exude these substances when soaked in water, forming a mucilaginous mass. The mucilages are soluble in water, the gums insoluble. Gums also exist in combination with cellulose in succulent roots and fruits. These gums are readily hydrolysed by dilute mineral acids with the formation of a mixture of one or more acid substances and sugars, pentose sugars such as xylose and arabinose often being present. The pentose sugars are not readily retained by the animal organism, although pentose sugars form a normal constituent of nucleo-protein found in animal tissues. The pentose sugar associated with nucleo-protein is the dextro-rotatory sugar d-ribose:

$$
\begin{array}{c}
\text{CHO} \\
| \\
\text{H—C—OH} \\
| \\
\text{H—C—OH} \\
| \\
\text{H—C—OH} \\
| \\
\text{CH}_2\text{OH}
\end{array}
$$

In the case of ruminants, pentose sugars given in the food readily appear in the urine. In pathological conditions in man, pentose sugar appears in the urine, the condition being known as pentosuria, the pentose sugar in this case being arabinose. There is evidence to show that this pentose sugar under such conditions originates from the hexose sugars, and not from the pentose radical present in nucleo-proteins. The pectins are white, amorphous gelatinous substances present in many succulent fruits and in sugar beets. They are closely related to the gums and mucilages, form colloidal solutions in water, and are of great importance in jam-making owing to their peculiar property of setting to a jelly in the presence of fruit acids. On hydrolysis they yield galactose, dextrose and pentose sugars such as arabinose.

Glucosides. Closely allied to the carbohydrates are the class of compounds known as glucosides. As the name implies, glucosides are compounds in which glucose is one of the constituents. From the agricultural point of view, two kinds of glucosides are important, the cyanogenetic or prussic acid yielding glucosides, and the mustard oil glucosides.

The cyanogenetic glucosides are of importance, because under certain circumstances they may yield prussic acid and this may cause either illness or death. The best known glucoside of this class is amygdalin, which is present in almonds and in the kernels of peaches, plums and most rosaceous fruits. It is a white crystalline substance soluble in water and is bitter to the taste. When brought into contact with emulsin, a ferment occurring with it in almonds and rosaceous fruits, or when heated with dilute hydrochloric or sulphuric acids, amygdalin is hydrolysed, and yields glucose, benzaldehyde, and prussic or hydrocyanic acid, thus

$$C_{20}H_{27}O_{11}N + 2H_2O = 2C_6H_{12}O_6 + C_6H_5 . CHO + HCN.$$

amygdalin   glucose   benzaldehyde   prussic acid

Another glucoside, linamarin or phaseolunatin, is found in linseed and in a certain species of bean called *Phaseolus lunatus*. This glucoside, when acted upon by the ferment occurring with it or by boiling dilute mineral acids, yields glucose, acetone and prussic acid.

Cases of poisoning have occurred in animals through eating *Phaseolus lunatus* and with calves fed on linseed meal. The glucoside and the ferment are present in separate cells in the seeds, and when these are masticated and swallowed, the cells are broken, and the glucoside and ferment thus brought into contact react together under the favourable conditions of warmth and moisture present in the paunch, with the resultant development of free prussic acid.

The mustard oil glucosides are typical constituents of the Cruciferae, particularly of white and black mustard. The glucoside of black mustard, sinigrin, is hydrolysed by the ferment present with it into glucose, allylsulphocyanide and acid potassium sulphate thus:

$$C_{10}H_{16}O_9NS_2K + H_2O = C_6H_{12}O_6 + C_3H_5 . CNS + KHSO_4.$$

The allylsulphocyanide or mustard oil possesses an extremely pungent smell and taste.

It is a remarkable fact that the substances occurring with glucose in glucosides are almost invariably antiseptic or disinfectant in character. This suggests that the function of glucosides in plants is protective in character, since on injury occurring to the plants, the ferment and glucoside are set free from the injured cells and react together. The antiseptic component thus liberated prevents or checks the invasion of the injured tissues by fungi or bacteria. The bitter taste of the glucosides themselves also discourages attack by animals.

Note. In the naming of the sugars, the monosaccharides are referred back to the two optically active glucoses in accordance with their structural relationship to them. Two families are thus recognised, the *d* family in which the spatial arrangement of the —CHOH group adjacent to the terminal —CH_2OH is similar to *d*-glucose, i.e.

$$H—C—OH$$
$$|$$
$$CH_2OH,$$

and the *l*-family in which the spatial arrangement is similar to *l*-glucose, i.e.

$$HO—C—H$$
$$|$$
$$CH_2OH.$$

Since it is desirable that the *d* and *l*, where used, should denote whether the sugar named is dextro-rotatory or laevo-rotatory, the nomenclature adopted by Schmidt (*Organic Chemistry*, Julius Schmidt, English Edition by H. Gordon Rule, 1926, p. 256) has been followed. In this arrangement, the family relationships to the active glucoses are indicated by the large italics *D* and *L*, the small italics *d* and *l* being used for their usual function of denoting the nature of the optical rotation of the sugars concerned.

CHAPTER VI

THE DIGESTIVE ORGANS

The Mouth. The organs employed by animals for conveying the food to the mouth are the lips, tongue, and teeth, but the precise part played by each varies in the different species. A horse when feeding in a manger, for example, employs its lips for collecting the food, and for this purpose they are strong and thick and are richly supplied with end organs or organs of touch. The lips are not used by a horse when grazing, but are drawn back so as to allow the incisor teeth to bite off the grass. In the ox the lips play a small part, but the tongue is used freely, being first protruded and curled round the grass, and then withdrawn into the mouth, while the grass is cut off between the incisor teeth of the lower jaw, and the dental pad which takes the place of the teeth in the upper jaw. In the sheep and goat the upper lip is divided into two parts each of which is possessed of independent movement. As in the ox, the lower incisors bite against a pad in the upper jaw, there being no upper incisors. By reason of the cleft upper lip the sheep and the goat can bite more closely to the ground, and thus they can subsist where a horse or an ox could not do so. In all these animals the tongue is employed in pressing back the food to the hinder part of the mouth where it is brought under the action of the molar teeth. The tongue is assisted in most animals by grooves in the palate. In the ox there are papillae covering the inside of the mouth and inclining backwards. The object of these is believed to be to assist in preventing the food from falling out of the mouth.

The tongue differs considerably in the horse and the ox; in the former animal it is relatively smooth and swells out at the apex; in the latter it narrows from the base to the apex, being pointed; moreover it is very rough and well able to resist injury from coarse grasses. The movements of the tongue may be very extensive in the ox and the dog, but horses seldom protrude their tongues.

The process of mastication is very effectively carried out in all herbivorous animals, for the molar teeth, by reason of the alternation of hard enamel ridges and softer cement substance, wear with a rough surface, and are admirably adapted for grinding and crushing the food.

The lower incisor teeth in those animals in which there is a dental pad are placed obliquely in the jaw so that the pad is not injured when the mouth closes. For the same reason they are capable of free movement in their sockets. In the horse the incisors in both jaws are at first vertical, but become oblique with advancing age.

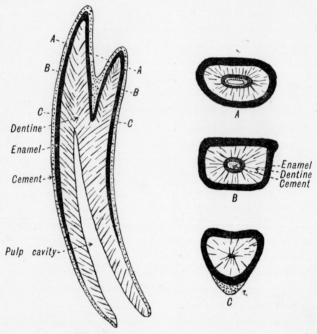

Fig. 19. Longitudinal and cross-sections of incisor tooth of horse. Cross-sections *A, B, C* illustrate the surface appearance of the tooth at various stages of wear. Note that the peripheral cement quickly disappears from the newly erupted tooth in situations subject to wear.

All the teeth are gradually pushed out from their sockets, the fangs becoming reduced in length; at the same time the teeth are ground down through wear and tear. By taking advantage of these facts the age of an animal can be determined after it has acquired its full mouth of permanent teeth. At an earlier period of life, the age can be ascertained by noting the number and arrangement of the temporary or milk teeth.

The movements which the jaws undergo to admit of mastication vary somewhat in different animals. In the dog there is a simple up-and-down movement of the lower jaw, and for this purpose the articulation of the jaw is of the simplest kind. Hardly any effort is required for opening the mouth, for this movement merely involves a depression of the lower jaw, but powerful muscles are provided for closing the mouth, that is, for elevating the jaw. This statement applies to the horse and ox and other animals besides the dog; but the horse, ox and sheep differ from the dog in being able to move the jaw laterally as well as up and down. Thus the articulation of the lower jaw in these animals is provided with a well-developed cartilaginous disc which is sufficiently yielding to admit of movement in different directions.

Mastication is very thoroughly performed in the horse, which may take as much as ten minutes to eat a pound of corn, or twenty minutes to eat a pound of hay. In ruminating animals mastication is performed principally after the cud has been returned to the mouth. In the dog the food is only very slightly masticated.

In the horse and ox and other herbivorous animals mastication only takes place on one side at a time. To facilitate this unilateral mastication the upper jaw is wider than the lower; otherwise the molar teeth would not properly meet during the process. A horse or an ox will masticate on one side only for many minutes at a time before transferring the food to the molars on the opposite side.

In drinking, the tongue is drawn backwards, while the lips are shut excepting for a small orifice in front which is placed under the surface of the water. The water is thus sucked in by the action of the tongue, the cheeks being drawn inwards at the same time. The act of sucking as performed by young animals is essentially similar, the size of the tongue being decreased in front and increased behind. A horse while drinking extends its head, moving its ears forward during each swallow and letting them fall back in the intervals between the swallows. Lapping as performed by the dog and cat is carried out by the animal curling its tongue and using it like a spoon and so conveying the liquid into the mouth, the tongue being withdrawn and extended in a succession of rapid movements.

Deglutition or the act of swallowing occurs normally in several stages, and has recently been reinvestigated by Barclay. The first stage consists in the closure of mouth, posterior nares and larynx. The larynx is pulled upwards and its entrance closed by the pressure

of the tongue on the cartilaginous epiglottis which guards the
entrance to the windpipe. At the same time the pharyngeal space
is obliterated by the raising of the larynx and the retraction of the
tongue. In the second stage the pharyngeal space is again opened
up, creating a negative pressure which extends to the oesophagus.
The food bolus, which has lain in a groove along the tongue is then
tipped over the back of the tongue, and, owing to the negative
pressure, is sucked through the pharynx into the oesophagus. In
the third stage of swallowing the food is carried down the oesophagus to the stomach by successive waves of muscular contraction.
Swallowing is facilitated by the presence of saliva, without which
it can only be performed with difficulty. It can be performed
against gravity since it is a definite muscular act, the peristaltic
waves of contraction passing along the oesophagus irrespective of
the position of the individual. In swallowing fluids the action is
very rapid and may be carried on at the rate of one swallow
every second.

The first act in the process of swallowing is voluntary, but the
second and third acts are purely reflex, being presided over by a
definite centre in the hind brain which is informed of the presence
of food by afferent nerves coming from the pharynx. Impulses are
then conveyed by efferent nerves passing to the different muscles
concerned in swallowing. Afferent impulses may be started by
touching the inside of the windpipe or the rim of the glottis and
the swallowing centre will be thereby stimulated.

The oesophagus in the horse differs from that of the ox and most
other mammals in one important respect. The thin red striated
muscle, which surrounds it throughout the greater part of its
length, gives place to thick, pale, non-striated muscle at its lower
end, where it is tightly contracted, the lumen being very narrow.
It is largely for this reason that horses experience such difficulty
in vomiting. In the ox and sheep the muscles of the oesophageal
wall are red and striated throughout, and the lumen of the organ
is widely distended at the lower end, thus easily permitting the
passage of food back into the mouth in the process of rumination.

The Salivary Glands. Just prior to and during mastication
saliva is secreted in considerable quantities and is poured into the
mouth where it mixes with the food. It is secreted in well-developed
racemose glands, situated a short distance from the cavity of the
mouth, into which the secretion passes by ducts leading away from

each gland. There are three pairs of salivary glands. (1) The parotid glands, so called because they lie in front of each ear. Their ducts communicate with the buccal cavity just opposite the upper molar teeth on each side. These are the glands which in man become characteristically swollen in the disease known as 'mumps', though the other salivary glands are also generally affected in this complaint. (2) The submaxillary glands, which lie in the lower jaw on each side. Their ducts open at the side of the root of the tongue.

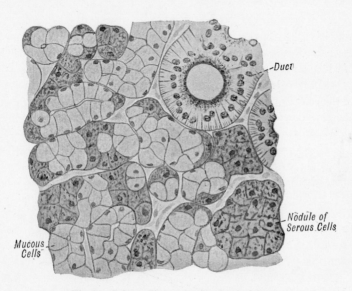

Fig. 20. Submaxillary salivary gland of dog.

(3) The sublingual glands, placed underneath the tongue in the floor of the mouth, with several ducts opening close together.

The salivary glands are developed in the embryo in the form of buds which spring from the epithelium lining the inside of the mouth. These buds are at first solid but gradually become hollowed out and undergo a process of ramification so as to form lobules which when fully developed are bound together with connective tissue. In their mode of origin and also structurally they may be regarded as typical of secreting glands generally.

Histologically there are two kinds of salivary glands, mucous glands and serous glands. The parotid glands are generally composed of purely serous cells, whereas the submaxillary and sublingual glands are mixed glands, containing both mucous and serous constituents.

Each lobule of a salivary gland is composed of saccular or tubular alveoli or acini from each of which a duct passes, uniting with similar ducts from other alveoli to form the main duct of the gland. The alveoli are enclosed by a basement membrane within which are the glandular epithelial cells. In the case of mucous alveoli these cells contain granules the number and position of which vary according to the condition of the gland, whether it is active or resting. The granules contain a substance called mucigen which is the precursor of the mucus to be discharged. In the resting state they are scattered over the greater part of the cell, the nucleus of which may be seen near one edge. During activity the granules are passed towards the lumen on the inside of the cell, leaving the rest of the cell relatively clear. In the cells of serous glands during rest the granular material is so abundant that the nuclei are occluded, only becoming visible when the gland passes into the active state. The nuclei are placed centrally. In the exhausted state the cells of serous glands retain only very few granules which are left on the inner edge near the lumen, which has grown larger, while the cells have become correspondingly smaller. The granules of serous glands, like those of mucous glands, represent the precursors of the secretion which is subsequently discharged. This account of the salivary glands is based on the observations of Langley upon the living glands and not merely upon glands which were preserved.

The salivary glands are as a rule well developed in herbivorous animals, but the submaxillary and sublingual glands are small and inactive in the horse. The parotid is four times the weight of the submaxillary and sublingual in the horse. The parotid in the horse is about half as heavy again as in the ox. (Ox 283 g. Horse 400 g.) The parotids (horse) secrete seven-tenths of the total salivary secretion. The parotid in all animals secretes more than the submaxillary or sublingual but it is not necessarily the largest in size. The amount of secretion discharged by the salivary glands depends upon the degree of dryness in the food, hay absorbing far more saliva than oats, and oats absorbing more than green fodder. Colin has estimated that a horse on an average will secrete 84 lb. of saliva in a day, and an ox 112 lb.

Mixed saliva is a viscid, turbid, colourless fluid with a slightly alkaline reaction. The viscidity is due to the presence of mucin, and the cloudiness to epithelial cells derived from the lining of the mouth, and to the salivary corpuscles. These are small granular cells, and may be altered leucocytes or lymphocytes derived from the tonsils. Saliva contains only about one per cent. of solid constituents altogether, and these include mucin (already mentioned) and other proteins in small quantities, a ferment called ptyalin (not always present), and some inorganic matter. The salts found in saliva are chiefly carbonate of lime, alkaline chlorides, and phosphates of lime and magnesia. Calcium salts in the saliva are responsible for deposition of 'tartar' on the teeth. In human saliva potassium sulphocyanide is also present. The gases of saliva are carbon dioxide, which is very abundant, and traces of oxygen and nitrogen. The ferment ptyalin, although present in human saliva and in the saliva of the pig, is absent from that of the dog, and its occurrence in the horse and other Herbivora is problematical. The function of ptyalin is to act on starch and convert it into maltose which is a sugar. Such starch-converting ferments are called diastases. Their action is permanently destroyed by a high temperature and inhibited by a low one; it is also partly inhibited by weak acids or alkalis and destroyed by a strong acid. The chemistry of starch conversion by ptyalin is dealt with later.

As already mentioned, the horse and ox and other Herbivora masticate on one side only at a time, and it is interesting to note that the parotid glands in these animals to a large extent secrete unilaterally, that is to say, that the gland on the side where mastication is taking place secretes two or three times as much saliva as the gland on the opposite side; on the other hand, the submaxillary and sublingual glands secrete equally on each side.

In addition to any ferment action which the saliva may possess, this secretion is of undoubted use in mastication and in deglutition. In the ox and sheep it is of use also in rumination.

The secretion of saliva is under the control of the nervous system, the process being brought about by a reflex mechanism. The afferent nerves are connected with the mucous membrane of the mouth, and the efferent nerves pass to the different salivary glands. Each gland has a double nerve supply, one from a branch given off the seventh cranial nerve and called the chorda tympani (in the case of the submaxillary and sublingual) or from the auriculotemporal (in the case of the parotid), and the other from the sympathetic or thoracic autonomic system. There are two sets of nerves in the chorda tympani and in the auriculo-temporal, vaso-dilator and secretory. Stimulation of the chorda promotes dilatation of the blood vessels supplying the gland as well as secretion of saliva, but that the two processes are separate (depending upon two sets of nerve fibres) is proved by injecting atropin, when stimulation of the nerve still produces all the vascular changes, but no saliva is secreted, the atropin having paralysed the secreting fibres without affecting the vaso-dilator fibres. The existence of a secretory process occurring independently of the vaso-dilator mechanism is further proved by the fact that the pressure of the saliva in the duct at the time of secretion may be greater than the blood pressure in the carotid artery, and consequently considerably greater than that in the capillaries of the gland. Moreover secretion may take place in the absence of blood, since after cutting off the head of a rabbit and immediately stimulating the chorda, salivary secretion can be induced. In the sympathetic two sets of fibres can also be demonstrated experimentally, these being secretory and vaso-constrictor, but the secretory fibres are comparatively few.

Further evidence of the existence of a definite secretory mechanism is afforded by the presence of mucigen granules, and the changes which take place during activity as described above, as well as by the fact that mucin and ptyalin do not exist as such in the blood, and therefore must be manufactured by the glands.

THE STOMACH.

The alimentary canal throughout its entire length is surrounded by several layers of tissue which have an essential similarity throughout its entire length. In those parts which lie freely in the body cavity there is an external serous or peritoneal coat consisting of fibrous tissue, and continuous with the mesentery or fibrous sheet which slings the gut in position and connects it with the inside of the body wall. Within the peritoneal coat are un-striated muscles arranged longitudinally and circularly, and within the muscular coat is connective tissue lined internally by a further thin muscular layer. The cavity of the alimentary canal is lined by an epithelium which varies in character in its different parts. In the mouth, pharynx and oesophagus, and in some cases the first part of the stomach, it is stratified and in function mainly protective, but in the secretory part of the stomach and in part of the intestine, the epithelium is columnar and depressed into tubular glands.

The stomach may be described as the dilated portion of the alimentary canal at the posterior end of the oesophagus. It acts partly as a storehouse for food and so in man and many animals obviates the necessity for nutriment being eaten at short intervals, but it is also an important digestive organ in which the food is acted upon by the gastric juice secreted by the glands in its

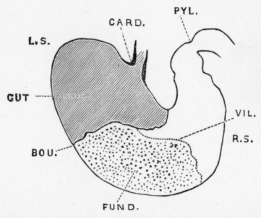

Fig. 21. Longitudinal section of stomach of horse (from Smith, Messrs Baillière, Tindall and Cox). *Card.* oesophagus; *Pyl.* pylorus; *L.S.* left sac; *R.S.* right sac (or pyloric portion); *Gut,* cardiac portion; *Vil.* villous coat; *Bou.* boundary between cardiac and villous portions; *Fund.* fundus or villous portion.

epithelial lining. The stomach is smallest and of least functional importance in carnivorous animals such as the dog which feed on flesh to be converted into other flesh. In the dog the stomach may be removed and the organ completely dispensed with, without appearing to impair the digestive processes or the health of the animal. In herbivorous animals in which the processes of digestion are necessarily more complicated since vegetable tissue has to be converted into animal tissue, we frequently find a very complex stomach, but this is not necessarily the case, for in the horse the stomach is small and simple, its place being taken functionally to a great extent by the extremely bulky large intestines which are reserved for the performance of digestive processes that in the ox and sheep take place in the rumen or first stomach. Thus maceration of vegetable fibre and decomposition of cellulose are carried out in the horse to a large extent in the colon and in the ox in the rumen.

It is noteworthy that the stomach of the pig is intermediate in character between that of the carnivorous dog and the herbivorous

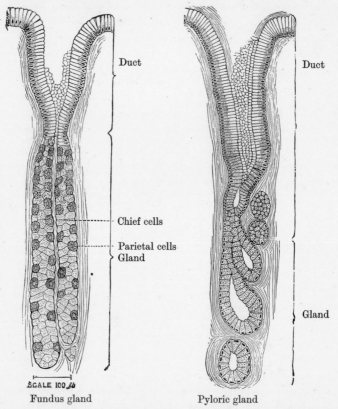

Fig. 22. Gastric glands (after Heidenhain from Smith, Messrs Baillière, Tindall and Cox). The parietal cells are the acid-secreting ones.

sheep, for the pig is not purely herbivorous, but, like man, can subsist on a very varied diet.

In the horse nearly one-half (the cardiac portion) of the internal lining of the stomach (that is, the mucous membrane) is merely of the nature of a continuation of the lining of the oesophagus. This part, which is sometimes called the proventriculus, comes to an abrupt end and is succeeded by the secretory part or fundus. Here the tubular glands which secrete the gastric juice are separated by finger-shaped villous processes protruding into the cavity. The villous part is followed by a smooth pyloric portion which opens into the duodenum or first part of the small intestine. As already mentioned, the horse's stomach is relatively small, its average capacity being from 35 to 40 pints. It lies some distance from the body wall, being supported by the colon which is a part of the large intestine. Its cardiac and pyloric openings are situated close

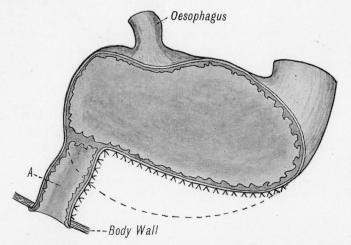

Fig. 23. Pavlov's fistula. The ∧ markings indicate the line of sutures. *A*, closed fundic sac. The broken line indicates the original outline of the stomach prior to operation.

together, and the former is tightly contracted so as to make vomiting an act of great difficulty.

Pure gastric juice has not been obtained from the horse's stomach since, owing to the distance between this organ and the body wall, it has been found impracticable to establish an artificial connection between the secretory stomach and the outside of the body as Pavlov and others have done in the case of the dog. Such a connection is called a gastric fistula, and the method of establishing it has been to make a cul-de-sac of the cardiac end of the stomach by reflecting the mucous membrane so as to form a diaphragm between the two cavities (that is the cavity of the cul-de-sac and the main cavity of the stomach), and to connect the cul-de-sac

with the abdominal wall so that it communicates freely with the
outside of the body in the manner shown in the diagram. The
vascular and nerve supply to the cul-de-sac portion are allowed to
remain intact. Pavlov also made an oesophageal fistula in the
dog, so that the food which was swallowed instead of entering the
stomach forthwith passed out of the body.

A dog so operated upon will eat with avidity and may continue
eating for hours, during which time gastric juice, free from admixture with other substances, passes out through the gastric
fistula. The juice thus obtained is found to be a clear fluid with an
acid reaction; it contains about 1 per cent. of solids and 99 per cent.
water. The solids consist of mucin, proteins, and inorganic salts.
It also contains two ferments, pepsin which acts upon proteins and
converts them into simpler substances, called proteoses and peptones, in the manner described later, and rennin, which changes
caseinogen (the phosphoprotein of milk) into casein. There is,
however, some reason to doubt whether rennin is in reality an
independent ferment, since evidence has been brought forward
suggesting that the conversion of caseinogen into casein may after
all be due to pepsin (see p. 85). This ferment can only act in an acid
medium. In the dog and in man the acid present is hydrochloric.
The lactic and other acids which are found in the gastric juice of
herbivorous animals are probably produced by the bacterial decomposition of the food they swallow. As in the case of other
ferments the activity of pepsin and rennin is permanently destroyed by boiling. The experiments by Pavlov described above
indicate that the normal stimulus for gastric secretion is the
presence of food in the mouth and that the process is of the nature
of a nervous reflex. The truth of this presumption is established
by the fact that secretion may not occur after the severance of the
two vagus nerves which supply the stomach, and the further fact
that electrical stimulation of these nerves is followed by secretion.
It is clear therefore that the efferent nerves concerned in the reflex
are the two vagi, while the afferent nerves are the sensory nerves
of the mouth, possibly assisted by the nerves of sight and smell.

There can be no doubt that the general principles underlying
the mechanisms of digestion just described apply as much to the
horse and other animals as to the dog. A further knowledge of the
digestive processes in the horse has been obtained by means of
feeding experiments.

It has been noted that under normal conditions in the horse the stomach is hardly ever empty. Even many hours after feeding, some food is still present, and it is not until a horse has been starved for twenty-four hours that its stomach is found to be really devoid of food. At the time of feeding, however, food usually passes out of the stomach into the small intestine with considerable rapidity, and when the stomach has become two-thirds full the rate of ingress of food and the rate of egress are equal. But as soon as the feed is finished the passage of the food into the intestine at once slows down.

The condition of the stomach during digestion varies somewhat according to the nature and quantity of the food, and the order in which it is supplied. Hay after mixing with about four times its weight of saliva and after mastication in the mouth passes into the stomach, and if it be empty, the hay comes to lie in the pyloric region. As the stomach gradually fills, the food is acted upon by the gastric juice, and some of it, in a partially digested state, commences to pass out into the intestine. At the end of the feed the material left in the stomach is found to be comminuted and to resemble green and yellow faeces, the colour being due to the acid of the gastric juice. The entire stomach is at this time generally acid throughout, and if any alkalinity can be detected it is caused by the swallowed saliva.

The duration of digestion of hay by the stomach has been worked out experimentally by Colin and by Smith. Colin found that the rate of digestion during the first two hours is rapid, but that it afterwards decreases so that at the end of eight hours some hay is still retained in the stomach. Smith starved a horse for twenty-hours and then gave it 6 lb. of dried grass; the horse was destroyed nine hours afterwards when the stomach contained $2\frac{1}{2}$ lb., showing that $3\frac{1}{2}$ lb. had been digested. Other experiments illustrated the same point, namely the increasingly slow rate of digestion the longer the time that had elapsed after a meal.

In digesting oats the same fact was observed. Smith found that in a horse which had received 2 lb. and was killed twenty hours later the stomach was not empty.

If a horse be fed with different foods in succession these arrange themselves in the stomach in the order in which they enter, and pass out in the same order without mixing unless the horse is watered after its meal. The effect of watering is to disturb the arrangement of the food and to wash a large part of it, in a very undigested state, into the small and large intestine where it may produce irritation and colic. Hence, the importance of watering a horse before feeding and not afterwards.

The acids which are present in the digesting stomach depend partly upon the nature of the food. It has been said that hay induces an outpouring of lactic acid and oats of hydrochloric, but as already mentioned, it is a matter of great doubt as to whether lactic acid is ever actually produced by the stomach itself, the suggestion being that its presence is due to the fermenting food. Hydrochloric acid is unquestionably produced by the gastric glands; nevertheless lactic acid appears to predominate in the

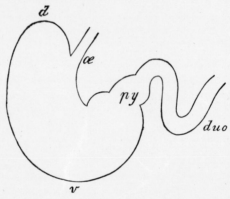

Fig. 24. Section through stomach of horse showing syphon-trap of duodenum (*duo*). *œ*, oesophagus; *py*, pylorus; *d*, left sac; *v*, fundus. (From Smith, Messrs Baillière, Tindall and Cox.)

horse's stomach during digestion. The secretory part of the stomach produces also a quantity of mucin which frequently forms a gelatinous coat over the surface.

The pyloric aperture, unlike the opening of the oesophagus, is usually wide, and beyond this the small intestine is dilated. The passage of food out of the stomach is regulated by a U-shaped curve (sometimes called the 'syphon-trap' of the duodenum). When the large bowels become distended they press against this portion of the duodenum and close the pyloric outlet from the stomach, and if fermentation is taking place in the stomach, its contents may be unable to escape since the oesophageal opening is also contracted as already described. In such cases rupture of the stomach may supervene.

The stomach of the pig, as already mentioned, represents a transition stage between the simple stomach of the dog and the complex stomach of ruminants. There is an oesophageal patch without glands, which corresponds to the proventriculus of the horse, and according to some authorities the rest of the stomach is divisible into three or four zones in which the number of glands and the secretory activity are somewhat different. Ellenberger and Hofmeister have found that the swallowed saliva has a strong amylolytic action on the carbohydrates in the pig's stomach and that conversion of starch into dextrin and sugar takes place to a marked extent, the sugar so formed becoming further converted into lactic acid. The cardiac end of the stomach is utilised for digesting starch while the pyloric half digests albumen, but the latter process begins at a later stage than the starch digestion and continues after it is over.

Rumination. In the ox and sheep and all ruminating animals the food after being swallowed for the first time does not ordinarily reach the true or digestive stomach until it has been first re-gurgitated to the mouth where it undergoes a second and more complete mastication. This process is called rumination or the chewing of the cud. It involves a complicated system of oeso-phageal enlargements which will now be described.

The food after being submitted to a slight chewing passes down the oesophagus and into a receptacle of great size called the rumen or paunch, the histological structure of which is indicated in Fig. 25. Here it undergoes a churning movement and is acted on by the saliva which is swallowed with it. In the rumen cellulose is said to be digested through fermentative processes to as much as 60 or 70 per cent. This is due to the action of bacteria present in the food, for the rumen possesses no glands. Thus it corresponds functionally with the large intestine in the horse, as will be made clearer later. The reticulum, which, from the ridges arranged in a honeycomb pattern on the inside of its walls, is often called the honeycomb bag, is an extension of the rumen. It receives the heavy matter in the food and acts as a reservoir of liquid which moistens the food before it is passed back into the mouth. The reticulum, the histological structure of which is seen in Fig. 27, is not essential for rumination since Flourens showed that its excision did not inhibit the process.

The oesophagus is continued along the side of the rumen and

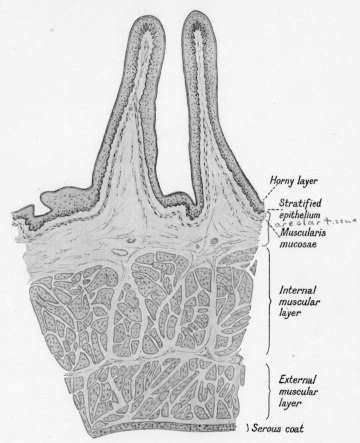

Horny layer

Stratified epithelium

areolar tissue

Muscularis mucosae

Internal muscular layer

External muscular layer

Serous coat

Fig. 25. Rumen of sheep.

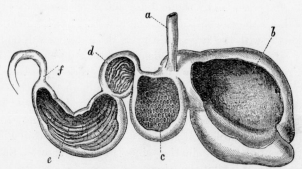

Fig. 26. Stomach of ruminant (from Flower and Lydekker). *a*, oesophagus; *b*, rumen; *c*, reticulum; *d*, omasum; *e*, abomasum; *f*, duodenum.

reticulum in the form of a groove with lips or pillars which when
relaxed admit of its communicating with the rumen and reticulum.
During the churning movement which takes place in the rumen
the food becomes pressed against the lips of the groove. This sets
up a spasmodic contraction of the muscles of the abdomen and
diaphragm, as a result of which some of the food enters the lower

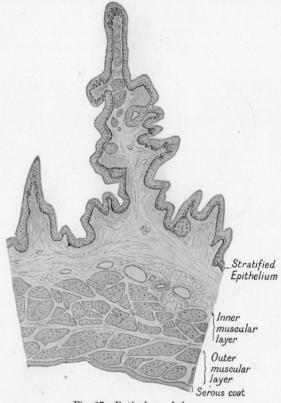

Stratified
Epithelium

Inner
muscular
layer

Outer
muscular
layer

Serous coat

Fig. 27. Reticulum of sheep.

part of the oesophagus and is carried upwards in a fluid by peristaltic
waves passing upwards along the muscles of that organ. In this
way the food is regurgitated to the mouth. The liquid part of it is
at once reswallowed, but the more solid part is masticated afresh
for a minute or longer, during which time it is acted on by the
parotid saliva. It is then swallowed a second time and after being
carried down the oesophagus, according to Wester, again enters

the rumen and reticulum. Then, if fine enough, the food passes into
the omasum or third stomach, frequently called the manyplies
owing to the wall being thrown into folds which resemble the leaves
of a book. Some of the food, however, may return once more to
the rumen. Whether the food is to enter the rumen or the omasum
appears to be determined by its condition. It is only allowed to
pass into the third stomach if it is in a sufficiently divided condition. Its entry is said to be effected by the contraction of the
lips of the groove, but according to Wester, the lips only close in
young animals and not in adults, this reflex being gradually lost

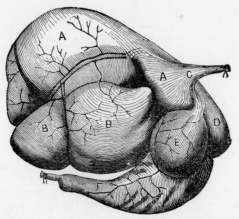

Fig. 28.   Stomach of ox (from Smith, Messrs Baillière, Tindall and Cox). *A* and *B*,
rumen; *C*, oesophagus; *D*, reticulum; *E*, omasum; *F*, abomasum.

as the animal grows up. When the lips are closed the rumen and
reticulum are shut off and the oesophagus communicates directly
with the omasum.

This compartment is not concerned in the process of rumination.
Its chief characteristic is its strong muscular leaves lined with
coarse stratified epithelium as shown in Fig. 29. These act as a
triturator and strainer, and prevent food substances passing into
the abomasum or fourth stomach until they are in a sufficiently
fine state of division.

The abomasum is the true digestive stomach corresponding with
the fundus portion of the horse's or pig's stomach. In it are the
glands which secrete the gastric juice containing pepsin, and the
other substances which are present in the gastric juice of the horse.
It is interesting to note that in the sucking ruminant (e.g. the calf

and lamb) the abomasum is the only compartment which is functional, the first three stomachs being comparatively undeveloped. This is because the young animal does not ruminate, and has no need for bulky receptacles for cellulose digestion.

Rumination is a reflex act, the centre for which is in the medulla. The efferent nerves are the sensory nerves of the rumen. The

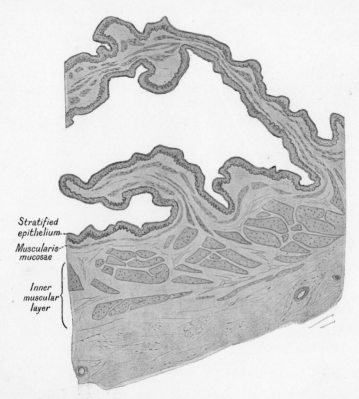

Fig. 29. Omasum of sheep, outer muscular layer and serous coat not shown.

process depends on the united action of the diaphragm, stomach and abdominal muscles. The amount of food contained in each ascending bolus in the ox is about $3\frac{1}{2}$ to 4 ounces. The formation of the bolus and its ascent to the mouth occupy 3 seconds; the actual process of chewing the ascended cud generally lasts about 50 seconds; and the descent of the bolus $1\frac{1}{2}$ seconds. Colin has estimated that out of 24 hours, about 7 are occupied by rumination. According to Wester, however, there are typically about eight ruminating periods in the day, each period lasting for half an hour.

Rumination commences usually about half an hour after feeding, but the time varies according to the diet. After eating hay rumination is said to begin at once. After finely comminuted food there is hardly any rumination at all. The process cannot occur in the absence of water.

During rumination the animal lies slightly on one side, and rests partly on its chest and partly on its abdomen, its fore limbs being bent under its chest, and its hind limbs brought forward so as to lie partly under its body. This is the familiar attitude of cows chewing the cud. They are usually very timid, and any slight disturbance causes them to get up, and rumination is brought temporarily to an end. So also fatigue, or the occurrence of slight maladies or excitement due to oestrus, may interfere with rumination, and the longer it is delayed the more difficult it is to resume, since the food becomes dry and closely packed, so that it is liable to set up local irritation.

The Small Intestine and the Glands
communicating with it.

The intestinal canal or alimentary canal beyond the stomach is divided into two main parts, the small intestine, and the large intestine. The small intestine is comprised of the U-shaped *duodenum* which immediately succeeds the pyloric end of the stomach, and the *ileum* which is considerably longer and is usually much coiled. The middle portion of the small intestine is sometimes called the *jejunum*.

The small intestine is composed of the same four coats as the stomach, serous or peritoneal, muscular, submucous, and mucous, the latter being lined internally by a columnar epithelium. There are numerous vascular villi confined to the mucous membrane. These are provided with vessels containing lymph, and each villus is covered by a columnar epithelium resting on a fine basement membrane. This epithelium is continuous with that lining the rest of the mucous membrane. Beneath the basement membrane is a rich supply of blood vessels.

There are two kinds of glands in the small intestine, the so-called

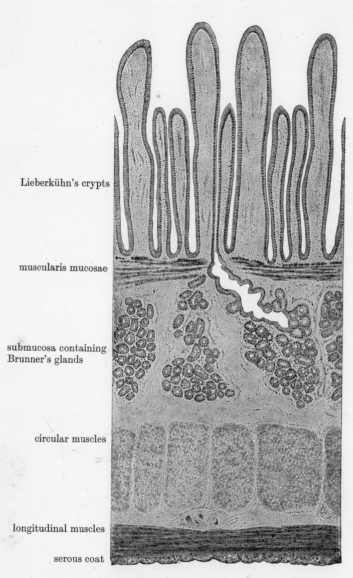

Lieberkühn's crypts

muscularis mucosae

submucosa containing
Brunner's glands

circular muscles

longitudinal muscles

serous coat

Fig. 30. Section through wall of duodenum (from Schafer).

crypts of Lieberkühn and Brunner's glands, but the latter are
restricted to the duodenum, not being found in the ileum. The
crypts are tubular depressions in the mucous membrane, and
occur also in the large intestine, being very numerous throughout
the greater part of the intestinal canal. Brunner's glands are
situated in the submucous tissue of the duodenum and communicate with the lumen by ducts which traverse the mucous membrane. They are especially numerous in the horse. We also find
numerous patches of lymphoid tissue in the mucous coat of the
small intestine. These are similar to the tonsils which are two
larger lymphoid masses at the entrance to the pharynx. Those
occurring in the small intestine are known as Peyer's patches.

Lieberkühn's and Brunner's glands secrete the succus entericus
or digestive juice of the small intestine. The ferments or enzymes
present in this juice and their action on the different classes of
food are described below.

The Liver. Communicating with the duodenum by the bile
duct is the liver, which is the largest gland in the body. It is com-

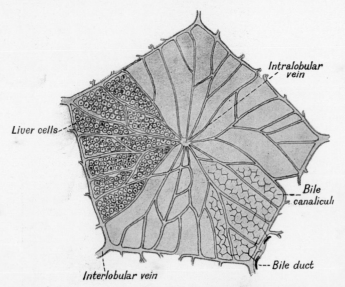

Fig. 31. Diagram of liver lobule.

posed of round, oval or polyhedral lobules consisting of the liver
cells among which ramify the branches of the bile duct and

numerous blood vessels and lymph vessels. The lobules are separated by connective tissue, and in the pig this separation is complete, but in man and many animals is incomplete; the lobules however become more perfectly divided as a result of certain diseases such as alcoholism, in which case the liver in man comes to resemble that of the pig. The blood supply of the liver is peculiar, for besides receiving arterial blood from the hepatic arteries it is provided with a large quantity of venous blood which is brought to it by the portal vein from the stomach, spleen and alimentary region. It is obvious, therefore, that a great variety of metabolic products must be brought to the liver, and correlated with this fact we find that the liver discharges a number of important functions connected with the general metabolism of the body. It stores up carbohydrate material in the form of glycogen, releasing it into the blood as sugar, the percentage of which is thereby kept constant; it makes urea and uric acid, which are discharged as waste products by the kidneys; and it manufactures bile, which is poured out into the small intestine and utilised there for digestive purposes.

The bile contains the waste products of the liver which result from its other activities. Nevertheless when associated with pancreatic juice it is of considerable importance in the process of fat digestion; moreover it promotes intestinal peristalsis, its absence leading to constipation. Bile is an alkaline fluid of a slimy consistence and with a bitter taste; in herbivorous animals it is yellow-green or dark green, in the pig reddish-brown, and in carnivorous animals golden red. The differences in colour depend on the bile pigments of which bilirubin and biliverdin are the chief. Its composition is approximately as follows:

Water, 85 parts,
Bile salts, 10 parts (glycocholate and taurocholate of soda),
Fats, lecithin and cholesterin, 1 part,
Mucus and pigments, 3 parts,
Inorganic salts, 1 part.

The secretion of bile occurs under a pressure lower than that of the blood, and in this respect is different from the salivary secretion. There is no evidence that nerve fibres are concerned with bile secretion, which seems to be controlled by the composition of the blood carried to the liver and by the activity of the liver cells

There is some evidence that the secretion is stimulated by the reabsorbed bile salts as well as by a substance called secretin which is liberated from the wall of the duodenum and is of the nature of a hormone or chemical excitant. This substance, however, acts chiefly upon the cells of the pancreas, as will be described below.

The bile is either conveyed directly by the bile duct into the duodenum or by the cystic duct into the gall bladder, in which it is retained until required; it is then poured out into the duodenum by the bile duct. The latter opens a short distance from the pyloric end of the stomach. In some animals there is no gall bladder. This was pointed out long ago by Aristotle who records its absence in the horse, ass, deer and roe. It is also absent in the elephant, tapir and rhinoceros, and is imperfectly developed in the camel. In the ox, sheep, pig, and all Carnivora it is present. In man it is present with a few individual exceptions, as noted by Aristotle, whose observations on this subject show a remarkable accuracy. It has been suggested that the gall bladder is absent in the horse because this animal in the natural state is constantly eating, and consequently the continual outpouring of bile into the intestine is beneficial, whereas its presence in the sheep and ox has been attributed to the fact that these are ruminating animals in which the passage of food into the duodenum only occurs at stated intervals when the presence of bile is desirable, the fluid being stored in the gall bladder between whiles. This explanation, however, is scarcely adequate in view of the facts recorded above that the deer and roe, which ruminate, have no gall bladder, whereas the pig, which does not ruminate, possesses one.

Obstruction of the bile duct, due, for example, to a flux of mucus leading to its closure, or to disease, causes the bile to pass into the blood, and this produces the disease known as jaundice.

The Pancreas. The sweetbread or pancreas is a diffuse gland lying in the loop of the duodenum and communicating with it by a duct which usually opens into its ascending portion. In the horse and the sheep there is a common aperture for both bile duct and pancreatic duct but in the ox, pig and dog the ducts open separately. In structure the pancreas presents a general similarity to the salivary glands, but in addition to the secretory alveoli it contains certain cells which have a different staining reaction and do not communicate with the secretory ducts. These constitute the islets of Langerhans and are referred to again later in describing the pancreas as an organ of internal secretion. The secretory cells of the alveoli contain granules which are probably zymogenic, that is, they form a preliminary stage in the production of the pancreatic secretion. They disappear after prolonged activity of the gland.

In an animal with a pancreatic fistula pancreatic juice, which is colourless and alkaline in reaction, makes its appearance between

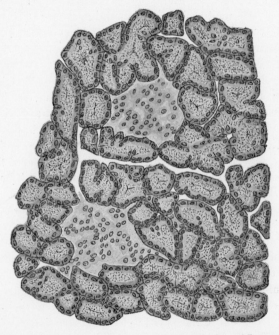

Fig. 32. Section of pancreas showing alveoli and islets of Langerhans.

five and twenty minutes after a meal. Two or three hours later its quantity is considerably increased and after five hours it ceases to flow. The time of maximal flow, therefore, is when the contents of the stomach are being passed out into the duodenum. Bayliss and Starling have shown that the main factor in producing pancreatic secretion is chemical, but it is possible that nervous action may play a very small part in the initial stages of secretion.

The Ferments of the Pancreas and Small Intestine. The ferments present in the pancreatic juice are of great importance.

They are as follows: (1) trypsin, which is a proteolytic ferment like pepsin but has the power of breaking down the protein molecule still further, and can change proteins into amino-acids of which leucine, tyrosine, and tryptophane are examples; (2) amylopsin, which, like ptyalin, acts on starches and converts them into sugars, and (3) steapsin or lipase, which splits fats into fatty acids and glycerin. The fatty acids are then able to unite with the alkalis of the bile salts to form digestible soaps.

The succus entericus contains the following ferments: (1) maltase, which converts maltose into dextrin and dextrose; (2) invertase, which converts cane sugar into dextrose and laevulose; (3) lactase, which converts lactose into dextrose and galactose, and (4) erepsin, which converts peptones into amino-acids. It also contains (5) enterokinase, which is a necessary factor for changing the trypsinogen present in the juice secreted by the pancreas into the active ferment trypsin. For trypsin does not exist as such in the juice produced by the pancreas, but is only present in pancreatic juice which has been brought under the influence of enterokinase.

Seeing that pepsin can convert proteins into peptones and erepsin can further change peptones into amino-acids, it has been suggested by Reynolds Green that trypsin is in reality composed of a pepsin-like ferment together with an erepsin-like ferment.

Erepsin is also manufactured by the pancreas, and according to Vernon all (or nearly all) the tissues of the body have certain ereptic properties and may therefore be regarded as forming this ferment to a greater or less extent.

The inlet and outlet to the small intestine are regulated by sphincters. The total length of the small intestine in the horse is about 70 feet; that of the ox is 130 feet, but the diameter is very much smaller. The small intestine in the sheep is 80 feet and in the pig 60 feet. It has been found that in the horse water takes from five to fifteen minutes to traverse the length of the small intestine; semi-digested food takes a much longer time.

The Large Intestines.

The large intestines comprise the colon, the coecum, and the rectum. Each of these parts is composed of the same four coats as the small intestine. Lieberkühn's crypts are represented, but there are no Brunner's glands and no villi (excepting in the coecum in the horse and some other animals), neither are Peyer's patches to be found. In man and some animals an ileocoecal valve at the entrance to the large intestine prevents a reflux into the small intestine. It is made up of two semi-lunar folds of the mucous membrane.

The coecum varies in importance according to the character of the food. In man it is a short wide pouch ending with the small appendix vermiformis which is largely composed of lymphoid tissue; it is this structure which is frequently removed surgically as a consequence of the inflammatory condition or infection known

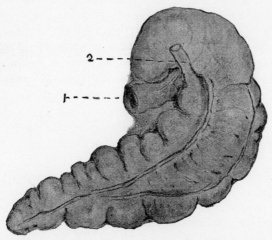

Fig. 33. Coecum of horse (from Smith, Messrs Baillière, Tindall and Cox). 1, beginning of colon; 2, end of ileum.

as appendicitis. In the Carnivora the coecum is likewise vestigial or absent. In all Herbivora, on the other hand, it is large and functional.

In the horse the capacity of the coecum is enormous, being about 8 gallons (while its length is 4 feet). It acts as a reservoir for intestinal digestion. Everything must traverse it in passing from the ileum to the colon. The two openings are placed near together, and the outlet is above the inlet, so that the substances it contains have to pass out against gravity in order to enter the colon. The contents of the coecum are always fluid and sometimes watery; their reaction is alkaline. Its main function is probably to store water required for intestinal digestion and for the general wants of the body, but the digestion of cellulose is undoubtedly one of its functions. This substance undergoes churning, maceration and decomposition and is thereby reduced to a condition in which it can be absorbed. Ellenberger has shown that in the horse the entire 'feed' reaches the coecum at some time between twelve and twenty-four hours after entering the stomach, that it may remain in the coecum for twenty-four hours, during which time 20 per cent. of the cellulose may disappear. There can be no doubt that absorption occurs in the coecum to some extent. Poisonous products are removed from it and carried by the blood to the liver.

In the ox and sheep, in which cellulose digestion is known to take place in the rumen, the coecum is much smaller than in the horse. In the pig it is still smaller relatively to the size of the animal.

The colon in the Carnivora is of small importance, acting chiefly as a reservoir for the excrement which becomes somewhat drier as it passes along it. In the Herbivora, and particularly in the horse, it is the main absorbing part of the gut. Its glands liberate mucus, but do not produce ferments. It also has an excretory function, for metallic salts leave the body by this channel.

Digestion continues in the colon and is therein terminated, but the process is carried on either by ferments passing into it along with the food from the anterior part of the gut or else by bacterial disintegration as happens in the horse. It has been shown that bacteria may hydrolyse cellulose, and that in the case of oats there is evidence that a digestive ferment is present in the food itself. In the horse particles of corn and other comparatively unaltered food substances are found in the first part of the colon, but as we pass on the food becomes more and more fluid, then firmer again, and in the last part the contents are like thick pea soup containing finely comminuted particles. In ruminants the function of the colon is only subordinate, since, as already mentioned, cellulose digestion is carried on at the anterior end of the gut. In the pig also the colon is of relatively small importance.

It remains to describe the colon of the horse, in which animal this portion of the gut is better developed than in any other. It begins by being very narrow, but rapidly swells out to an enormous size. The first part is high up, lying a little below the vertebral column and to the right side. It then passes downwards to the floor of the abdominal cavity, where it is very large, as just mentioned. It next ascends in the direction of the pelvis, and makes

a curve of two right angles. The curved part being very small, it
then passes forwards and on top of the part already described.
Near the diaphragm it passes first downwards and then upwards
and backwards again, meanwhile increasing in size to form the
enormous double colon; the calibre of which is greater than that of

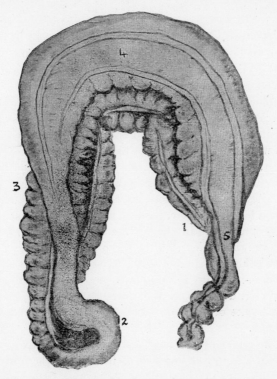

Fig. 34. Colon of horse (from Smith, Messrs Baillière, Tindall and Cox). 1, first
colon; 2, pelvic flexure; 3, suddenly enlarges; 4, diaphragmatic flexure; 5, commencement of single or small colon.

any other part. Finally it suddenly contracts, becoming the single
colon. It is obvious that such a large and complicated structure
must be of great importance functionally, and there is every
evidence that this is actually the case. Its huge capacity, which is
five or six times that of the stomach, admits of its retaining great
quantities of food substances and fluids which are brought into
contact with a large absorptive area of the lining of the gut
wall.

The following are the dimensions of the colon in the domestic animals:

		Feet	Maximum diam.
Horse	Great colon	10 to 12	8 to 10 inches
	Small or single colon	10 to 12	3 to 4 ,,
Ox		35	5 to 2 ,,
Sheep		15	2 to 1 ,,
Pig		11 to 14	

The Rectum. The faeces, consisting of indigestible residue, collect in the lower part of the colon and then pass into the rectum from which they are ejected through the anus. In all animals they vary to a greater or less extent according to the diet, and according to the amount of the excretory products of the digestive tract. If no food is given, they consist solely of the latter, and the same statement holds good if the food is completely digested, as may happen with the dog when somewhat underfed on an exclusively meat diet.

In the horse the faeces are generally firm and brownish-red in colour. They contain cellulose, husks of grain, vegetable tubes, starch and fat globules, etc. together with bile pigments and other excretory products. In the ox the faeces are semi-solid and greenish-brown in colour. In the sheep they are small solid balls, black or dark green. In the pig the faeces are generally semi-solid and human-like with a variable colour and very disagreeable smell. In the dog they are very variable, being often grey owing to the presence of lime salts (due to eating bones) and dense in consistency.

As to the amounts of faecal matter passed, the ox averages a very large amount, as much as 75 lbs. a day, the horse passes 30 lbs. a day (the maximal amount being over 70 lbs. a day), the sheep about 4 lbs. and the pig approximately the same. The quantity passed relatively to the amount of food is less in the Carnivora.

Defaecation is usually in animals a reflex act due to the presence of faeces in the rectum. It is brought about by the rectal muscles assisted by the muscles of the abdomen, though these are not essential, since horses can defaecate while trotting. The centre for defaecation is in the lower part of the spinal cord. The sphincter of the anus is relaxed during the process. It contains striated muscles, showing that defaecation may be partly a voluntary process.

The volume of the stomach and that of the rest of the alimentary canal in the different animals, according to Colin, are as follows:

	Stomach		Intestinal canal	
Horse	31	pints	340	pints
Ox	440	,,	183	,,
Sheep	52	,,	26	,,
Pig	14	,,	34	,,
Dog	6½	,,	14	,,

These results are in general agreement with the statements of more recent authorities.

The movements of the musculature of the alimentary canal are under the control of a network of nerve fibres and ganglia, and although they are capable of going on in the absence of any connection with the spinal cord, are normally under the subordination of the central nervous system through autonomic nerves. The cranial autonomics through the vagus nerve supply the whole of the alimentary canal excepting the hind part of the colon and the rectum. Impulses transmitted along them excite muscular movement and increase peristalsis. In the hind part of the gut they are replaced by sacral autonomics. The whole of the gut is supplied by sympathetic or thoracic autonomic nerves which in a general way act antagonistically to those above mentioned. Impulses transmitted along them decrease muscular movement, and by constricting the blood vessels reduce the blood supply. The gut is also supplied with sensory nerves conveying the sensations of hunger, pain, etc.

The whole of the gut is well supplied by blood vessels bringing arterial blood from the aorta. The veins of the alimentary tract, as already described, unite to form the portal vein, so that the blood drained from the gut cannot reach the heart and join the general circulation without first traversing the liver.

The lymphatic vessels discharge their contents either into the large thoracic duct which opens into the left innominate vein at the junction of the subclavian and internal jugular veins or else into the corresponding smaller right lymphatic trunk (not always present) which communicates with the right innominate vein. Through these vessels the lymph is passed into the blood vascular system.

CHAPTER VII

THE DIGESTIVE APPARATUS OF THE FOWL

Before passing on to deal with the processes of digestion and absorption in mammals it has seemed desirable to devote a short chapter to the digestive apparatus in the fowl in which, in common with other birds, the organs concerned differ considerably, both structurally and physiologically, from the digestive organs of mammals.

The alimentary canal of the fowl is anatomically divided into the following consecutive organs or parts: mouth, pharynx, upper oesophagus, crop, lower oesophagus, proventriculus, gizzard, small intestine, large intestine and cloaca. The tongue is shaped like an arrowhead with the points directed backwards, and is covered with a horny epithelium. The oesophagus is a muscular tube composed of four coats; a mucous membrane consisting of stratified epithelium, a submucous coat containing numerous mucous glands, a muscular coat divided into an inner circular muscular layer and an outer longitudinal layer, and an outer sheath made up of fibrous connective tissue. The crop, a sac-shaped organ, which physiologically can be distinguished as bilobed, is similar in general structure to the oesophagus, and may be regarded as an outgrowth of it. The lower oesophagus ends at the proventriculus or glandular stomach, which is fusiform in shape. The inner mucous coat is lined with columnar epithelium, and the numerous openings of the ducts from the gastric glands may be distinguished on the surface by naked-eye inspection. The gastric glands proper are tubular in character, and are grouped together into lobules, the numerous tubular glands opening into the cavity of the lobule which communicates with the lumen of the proventriculus proper by the ducts already referred to. The underlying muscular coat consists of two outer thin longitudinal muscular layers with a middle circular muscular layer interposed between them. The outermost coat consists of the serous coat. The gizzard, or muscular stomach, is a lenticular-shaped organ, the walls of which consist of three coats, the mucous coat, the muscular coat and the serous coat. The mucous coat has an internal horny layer, underlying which is a glandular layer consisting of simple tubular glands, which secrete a glutinous thick secretion which, on hardening, forms the horny lining membrane of the gizzard. The muscular coat is extremely well developed. The oesophageal and pyloric openings into the gizzard are placed side by side, and the pyloric opening is guarded by a valve formed by a fold of the mucous membrane. The small intestine is similar in structure to that of other animals. The large intestine has the usual four coats; an inner mucous, a submucous, a muscular, and a serous coat, the mucous coat being plentifully supplied with tubular glands containing columnar epithelium. The two caeca, which originate at the junction of the large and small intestines, are well developed in the fowl. Each is differentiated into a narrow neck portion, and a long saccular body portion. The mucous layer is lined with columnar epithelium, and nodules of lymph tissue are frequently present. The muscular coat consists of two longitudinal layers, between which lies a central circular muscular layer.

Digestion. Although salivary glands are present in the mouth of the fowl, the saliva contains no digestive ferments. The glands secrete chiefly a watery fluid containing mucin, and this is supplemented by similar secretions from the numerous mucous glands present in the oesophagus and the crop. While in the crop, the food that is swallowed becomes moistened, and the only digestion that occurs is that brought about by the ferments in the food itself or by the activity of bacteria in the crop. When passing through the proventriculus, the food becomes soaked with the gastric juice which contains hydrochloric acid and pepsin. After trituration in the gizzard, the food enters the small intestine and becomes mixed with the pancreatic juice and the bile. The three characteristic ferments of the pancreatic juice, a diastase, a lipase and trypsin have been shown to be present. The bile juice of the fowl differs in chemical composition from that of the Mammalia, and the exact relation of this fluid to the digestion of food nutrients, particularly fat, needs investigation. Under the action of the ferments of the proventriculus and the pancreas, aided possibly by the bile juice, the food nutrients are converted into dextrose, amino-acids and fatty acids and glycerin, and are absorbed by the villi of the intestine. Digestibility determinations have shown that the digestion of food nutrients by the fowl is just as efficient as by the pig, except in the case of crude fibre. Crude fibre is but poorly digested by the bird. Mangold and his associates have shown that fibre is digested to a certain extent by the fowl, and they assign as the seat of digestion, the caeca.

Movement of Food through the Alimentary Canal. The passage of food through the alimentary canal of the fowl has been studied both by X-ray methods and by mechanical methods. Barclay has shown that the passage of food from the mouth to the oesophagus is a suction effect, due to the setting up of a negative pressure in the pharynx. The food thus swallowed enters the upper third of the oesophagus, and then passes by a peristaltic muscular contraction of the oesophagus either down into the crop or straight on to the gizzard. Observations by Barclay and Halnan showed that the bolus of food, as a general rule, if the gizzard was empty as during a fast, passed straight to the gizzard. The time taken for the passage of the food from the mouth to the gizzard varied from 15 to 21 seconds, a pause of nil to 7 seconds occurring when the bolus reached the proventriculus. This pause was doubtless associated with the fact that the muscular movements of the proventriculus and the gizzard are co-ordinated, the length of the pause depending upon the exact phase of contraction or relaxation of the gizzard at the time the bolus reached the proventriculus. As soon as the gizzard has received its normal complement of food (three or four boluses of mash or seven to ten grains of corn), a nerve block appears to be set up at the entrance of the crop, and food subsequently swallowed drops down into the crop, which then gradually fills. The muscular walls of the crop then undergo slow rhythmical contractions, and from time to time a bolus of food passes from the crop to the gizzard. The chief function of the crop is clearly, therefore, to act as a food reservoir for the supply of food material to the gizzard. The gizzard undergoes slow rhythmical contractions, strong contractions of the muscular walls themselves exerting great pressure on the food contents of the organ; while at the same time the gizzard itself undergoes a slow oscillatory movement. Mangold and Kato estimated the average pressure exerted by the gizzard of the hen to be in the neighbourhood of about 6 lb. Each phase of contraction of the gizzard varies from 15 seconds to 30 seconds according to whether the bird has been recently fed or is in a state of hunger. After leaving the gizzard the food passes along the intestine by peristaltic movements, a contraction wave of the duodenum following each contraction of the gizzard, but the food does not appear to undergo segmentation as in the Mammalia. The caeca themselves undergo a slow rhythmical filling of the fluid intestinal contents, followed at approximately eight-hour intervals by an expression of the caecal contents. According to Mangold and his associates, the functions assigned to the caeca are (1) water absorption, (2) absorption of nitrogen containing compounds, (3) digestion of crude fibre. The large intestine itself undergoes rapid writhing snake-like movements which result in the filling of the saccular cloaca. The bolus of faeces is then suddenly expelled by muscular contraction, which in the case of the goshawk is almost explosive in character. A bolus of food swallowed by a bird, if not delayed by residence in the crop, passes through the alimentary canal in less than two hours. It can readily be understood, therefore, that the power of digestion of fibre by the bird is extremely limited, since digestion of fibre necessitates bacterial action, and the time of such action is severely limited except in the case of such of the food contents as enters the caeca, or the crop. With regard to the crop, the chief change that occurs from bacterial action appears to be the formation of lactic acid from carbohydrates, there being no evidence to support the view that digestion of fibre occurs in this organ. This lack of fibre digestion emphasises the importance of the efficient functioning of the gizzard, which by aid of the grit contained in it crushes the plant cells and so sets free the cell contents, which can then be acted on by the bird's digestive juices. Indeed, Mangold has given definite proof that unless grit is present in the gizzard a certain amount of the food material given to the bird escapes digestion.

CHAPTER VIII

THE DIGESTION AND ABSORPTION OF FOOD

The Passage of Food through the Alimentary Canal. Food taken into the mouth is first thoroughly masticated, the muscles of the tongue, lips and cheeks serving to keep the food in a position suitable for the efficient action of the teeth upon it, and to place it, when masticated, into a position suitable for swallowing. In the horse and man, the food is thoroughly masticated before swallowing, in the dog and the Carnivora generally, little if any mastication takes place prior to swallowing, and in the ruminants thorough mastication takes place only during rumination, when the food, hastily swallowed during grazing, is regurgitated in boluses into the mouth for further mastication. During this period the food is thoroughly moistened by the digestive juices poured into the mouth from the salivary glands. We have already noted that the act of swallowing is initiated as a voluntary act, but its completion is quite involuntary, a wave of contraction of the oesophagus forcing the food down before it into the stomach. The food remains in the stomach several hours, and by slow rhythmical contractions of the muscular walls the food in the stomach is thoroughly churned and mixed with the gastric juices secreted by gastric glands. Both the oesophageal and pyloric openings of the stomach are guarded by sphincter muscles, which prevent the egress of the stomach contents. As the result of this gastric activity, the food is reduced to the consistency of a thin creamy mass. The action of the musculature of the stomach is to press the food mass against the pyloric sphincter, which, however, remains closed if the food mass is not thoroughly broken up into a cream. At intervals, the pyloric sphincter relaxes, and a portion of the acid food material is shot into the duodenum. The effect of the presence of the acid in the duodenum is to cause the closure of the pyloric sphincter until the alkalinity of the duodenum is once more restored, when the pyloric sphincter is again relaxed and more of the stomach contents is shot into the duodenum. In this way, the food in the stomach is gradually passed into the small intestine in a state of fine subdivision. The muscular coats of the small intestine

consist of two layers, an inner circular coat and an outer longitudinal coat. Between the two coats and in the submucous coat lie
plexuses of nerves, which play an important part in the muscular
movements of the intestine. These movements are of two kinds,
a rhythmical or pendular movement and a peristaltic movement.
The rhythmic movement is confined to that part of the intestine
in which the food mass lies, and consists in a series of rhythmical
contractions of the circular muscular layer. These contractions
occur at points along the line of the food mass and result in the
food mass breaking up into small masses during the contractions.
As soon as relaxation of the muscles occurs, these masses re-unite.
Contractions of the circular muscular layer again occur at different
points, again separating the united food mass into small separate
portions. The combined effect of these movements is to cause the
food mass to be thoroughly mixed with the intestinal secretions
and to ensure that every particle of food comes in turn in close
contact with the intestinal wall, thus favouring digestion and
absorption.

This rhythmical movement does not change the position of the
food mass in the intestine, the progressive movement of the food
mass along the intestine being effected by peristaltic contractions.
The peristaltic movement of the intestine is of a peculiar character,
and is governed by the nerve plexuses present in the intestinal
wall itself. If an isolated portion of intestine be observed, it will
be noticed that slow waves of contraction pass down the intestine.
Close observation will also show that immediately in front of the
zone of contraction is a zone of relaxation, so that the lumen of the
intestine becomes larger than normal in front of the constricted
portion. If a solid object is introduced into the lumen of the
intestine at any point, the stimulus caused by its contact with the
intestinal wall gives rise to a dilatation in front of the object and
a contraction immediately behind, the dilatation and contraction
passing down the intestine as a slow wave. The net effect of this
will be to cause the object to travel down the intestine. At the
junction of the small and large intestine is the ileo-caecal valve,
by the operation of which the passage of the food mass from
the small intestine to the large intestine is regulated. The
muscular movements which take place in the large intestine are
similar to those occurring in the small intestine, with peculiar
differences not shown under normal conditions in the small

intestine. The large intestine can be divided physiologically into two portions. In the first portion antiperistaltic movements occur as well as peristaltic movements, so that the liquid food mass gradually travels backwards as well as forwards in this portion. During the time this is occurring, the liquids are gradually absorbed. The more solid portion remaining, which constitutes the food residue or faeces, then moves on through the latter portion of the large intestine and eventually reaches the rectum, when defaecation takes place.

The Nature of the Changes undergone by Food during its Passage through the Alimentary Canal. During its passage through the alimentary canal, the food comes into intimate contact with several digestive juices. In the mouth it is thoroughly mixed with saliva, in the stomach it receives the gastric juices, and in the intestine it becomes mixed with the bile, the pancreatic juice, and the succus entericus. The function of these juices is to convert the protein, fat and carbohydrates of the food into forms suitable for absorption by the walls of the alimentary canal. This preparation for absorption is achieved by the action of enzymes present in the digestive juices. In chemistry we have met with two distinct classes of reactions, those which occur instantaneously, such as the formation of silver chloride by the interaction of a chloride and silver nitrate, and those which take an appreciable time for the completion of the reaction, such as the saponification of an ester by an alkali. In the latter class of reactions, substances exist which alter the rate of change of the reaction, causing it to come to finality sooner or later than would be the case if the substance had not been introduced. Such substances, provided they are recoverable unaltered at the end, are called catalysts, and the reaction is referred to as 'catalysis'. The chemical reactions that go on in the body and during digestion are largely effected by substances of this nature. The catalysts which play the important part in the chemistry of digestion are bodies of a colloidal nature, are destroyed by heat, and are called 'enzymes'. Owing to their sensitivity to heat, enzymes exhibit the phenomenon of an 'optimum temperature', and the temperature at which the velocity of the reaction is at its greatest coincides with the normal blood temperature of the body. Since the reactions in which enzymes play a part are reversible ones, it is obvious that enzymes can act in a synthetic sense as well as in an analytical sense. Enzymes are generally designated by the suffix -ase joined to the substrate on which they work. Thus the enzyme which acts on maltose, converting it into glucose, is called 'maltase'. Owing, however, to the fact that many enzymes were discovered before the chemistry of enzymes was thoroughly understood, this general rule is not always followed, as will be evident in the table that follows. Another property of enzymes is their specificity, i.e. maltase acts on maltose only, and invertase acts on cane sugar only. It must be remembered, however, that this 'specificity' is not absolute, and evidence has already been brought forward which shows the possibility of certain enzymes, at least, influencing the velocity of reaction of more than one compound. For instance, Kuhn has demonstrated that invertase, which acts on cane sugar, is equally effective in raffinose solutions.

The enzymes present in the various digestive juices may be grouped into proteoclastic or proteolytic enzymes, lipoclastic enzymes, and amyloclastic or amylolytic enzymes according to whether they effect the splitting up of proteins, fats or carbohydrates. For the convenience of description, the enzymes which take part in the digestive processes may be grouped together in a table:

Enzyme	Origin	Class	Function
Ptyalin	Salivary secretion	Amyloclastic	Converts starch into maltose
Amylopsin	Pancreatic ,,	,,	,, ,, ,,
Maltase	Succus entericus	,,	,, maltose into dextrose
Lactase	,, ,,	,,	Converts lactose into dextrose and galactose
Invertase	,, ,,	,,	Converts sucrose into dextrose and laevulose
Pepsin	Gastric juice	Proteoclastic	Converts proteins into peptones and proteoses
Trypsin	Pancreatic juice	,,	Converts proteins into polypeptides and amino-acids
Erepsin	Succus entericus	,,	Converts peptones into amino-acids
Steapsin or Lipase	Pancreatic juice	Lipoclastic	Converts fats into acids and glycerol

In addition to the above enzymes, the presence of another enzyme, called rennin, has been assumed in gastric juice. One of the earliest phenomena noticed with regard to gastric juice was its power of clotting milk, and this power was attributed to the presence of an enzyme called rennin. Pavlov and Parastschuk in

1904 brought forward experimental evidence to support the view that the clotting of milk was due to the action of pepsin, the calcium salt of caseinogen acting on the substrate. Further investigators have supported this view, and there appears to be no reason for assuming the presence of a specific enzyme, rennin, for the fulfilment of this function by gastric juice.

The Correlation of Food Supply with Secretion of Digestive Juices. The synchronisation of the secretion of the various digestive juices with the presence of the food mass in the alimentary canal forms an interesting story. The flow of saliva is under control of the nervous system (see p. 53) and the glands are brought into activity by psychical phenomena such as sight or smell of savoury food, and by the sensory effect on the nerves of the mouth and tongue produced by the presence of food in the mouth. Pavlov has shown that the preliminary secretion of gastric juice is nervous in origin, and is due to sensory stimuli arising in the mouth and nostrils from the sensations of eating. It has been further demonstrated that the mechanical stimuli caused by the presence of food in the stomach have no effect on the secretory activity of the gastric glands. Subsequent production of gastric juice is due to either the presence of substances called secretogogues present in the food mass itself or in the products of digestion of the food mass arising from the action of the first psychical secretion of gastric juice on the food mass. This latter secretion is chemical in nature. Edkins has shown that extracts of the pyloric mucous membrane of the stomach made by extracting the mucous membrane with boiling peptone solution, when injected into the blood stream, cause marked increase in the flow of acid gastric juice, whereas neither the peptone solution alone, nor an extract of the pyloric mucous membrane with water, has any such effect. Edkins suggests therefore that the secretogogue, acting on the pyloric mucous membrane, produces a 'hormone' called gastric secretin, which circulating in the blood stream stimulates the gastric glands into further activity. The secretion of the pancreatic juice is also brought about both by nervous and chemical means. Dolinsky in 1895 had shown that acid brought into contact with the duodenal mucous membrane caused immediate secretion of pancreatic juice, and it was thought that the acid, acting on sensory nerves in the duodenum, caused the flow of pancreatic juice to take place through secretory fibres present in the pancreas.

It was shown, however, that the flow of juice occurred even after all nervous connections to the gland had been severed, and Bayliss and Starling, as the result of their work, have arrived at the following explanation.

The acid present in the food mass, when passing the pyloric sphincter into the duodenum, comes in contact with the duodenal mucous membrane and acts with a substance called 'pro-secretin' present in the mucous membrane to form a substance called 'secretin', which is conveyed in the blood stream and stimulates the pancreatic gland to activity. This substance, 'secretin', is not destroyed by heat and belongs, like gastric secretin, to the class of substances called 'hormones', which may be defined as chemical substances produced by glands, which when conveyed by the blood stream to certain other glands cause secretory activity or some other physiological effect. They are, in other words, chemical messengers and effect co-ordination of activity between two glands. With regard to the secretion of bile, although in some animals it is being produced continuously by the liver cells, there is evidence to show that the actual passage of bile into the duodenum synchronises with the passage of food from the stomach to the duodenum. The opening of the common bile duct with the duodenum is guarded by a sphincter, so that when this sphincter is closed the bile secreted by the liver passes into the gall bladder. On the passage of food into the duodenum, the sphincter relaxes and the stored bile is passed into the duodenum. In such animals as the horse in which there is no gall bladder, the stimulus for the secretion and pouring out of the bile is probably the reabsorbed bile salts, assisted possibly by secretin (see p. 70). The secretion of 'succus entericus' from any portion of the intestines appears to be excited by the presence of pancreatic juice in the preceding portion. There is consequently a natural co-ordination between the supply of food and the supply of the digestive juices; and by the methods already described above, the various digestive juices are secreted as and when the food mass is in a position where the action of these juices may be most effective.

Digestion and Absorption of Proteins. The digestion of the proteins occurs both in the stomach and the small intestine. The gastric juice is an acid secretion, the acidity being about 0·3 per cent. in human gastric juice, and this acidity is due to hydrochloric acid. The HCl is derived from chlorides, and is definitely secreted by the 'oxyntic' or acid secreting cells present in the gastric glands. The proteoclastic enzyme responsible for the gastric digestion of proteins is pepsin, an enzyme which works only in an acid medium. The main effect of the peptic activity is to carry the hydrolysis of the protein to the 'peptone' stage. On entering the duodenum, the acid food mass is neutralised and rendered faintly alkaline by the sodium carbonate present in the pancreatic juice, this alkalinity being a necessary preliminary to further digestive action, since the 'trypsin' can only act in an alkaline medium. The presence of pancreatic juice in the intestine stimulates the mucous membrane of the small intestine into activity, and an intestinal secretion called 'succus entericus' is formed. The proteoclastic enzyme 'trypsin' is produced by the interaction of an enzyme secreted by the 'succus entericus' called 'enterokinase' and the trypsinogen produced by the pancreas. Trypsin converts the native proteins and peptones into amino-acids and complex polypeptides; such polypeptides as are resistant to the action of trypsin being converted to amino-acids by the proteoclastic enzyme 'erepsin' present in the succus entericus. The effect of the action of these proteoclastic enzymes is to convert the colloidal proteins into the crystalline soluble amino-acids. This conversion is very complete, and but little protein remains unconverted under normal conditions.

Absorption of the proteins. The conversion of proteins into amino-acids is a gradual process, and begins immediately the food mass passes the pylorus. Although the conversion of the proteins into amino-acids is a gradual one, it is by no means a slow process, since Jauney in 1915 found that the time required to effect digestion of the complex protein molecule and to metabolise the amino-acids produced is but little longer than that required for the absorption and elimination of dextrose. Although evidence has been brought forward to support the view that absorption of protein can and does take place in the stomach, there is little doubt that under normal conditions no gastric absorption of proteins takes place. It has even been demonstrated that amino-acids given *per os* are not absorbed in the stomach, and that absorption first occurs in the duodenum. Observations made on a patient with a fistula at the end of the small intestine showed that 85 per cent. of the food protein had disappeared by the time the food mass reached this point. There is, therefore, little doubt that rapid absorption of the amino-acids produced during digestion takes place in the small intestine. The earlier theory was that the amino-acids were absorbed by the intestinal epithelium and were there resynthesised into native protein. This view was upheld owing to the failure of earlier workers to demonstrate the presence in the blood stream of amino-acids during digestion of a meal. The failure was due, no doubt, to the fact that the formation and absorption of amino-acids is a gradual process, so that but small quantities of amino-acids reach comparatively large quantities of blood at one time. In addition, the presence of large amounts of coagulable proteins in the blood interfered with the attempt to demonstrate the presence of amino-acids, which are also being rapidly removed by the cells of the tissues. Improvement in technique enabled Leathes, Howell, Folin and others to demonstrate that the amino-acid nitrogen of the blood increases during absorption, and there is now little doubt that the food proteins reach the blood stream as amino-acids.

The Digestion and Absorption of Fats. In 1900 Volhard demonstrated that, under certain conditions, fats could undergo digestion in the stomach, although previous to this the general view held was that no digestion of fat occurred in the stomach. In Volhard's experiments as much as 30 per cent. of the fat was hydrolysed in a few hours. These results were confirmed by later workers, and in 1917 Hull and Keeton demonstrated the presence of a fat-splitting enzyme in the gastric juice. It was shown that this enzyme was very sensitive to the presence of acid, 15 minutes exposure to a 0·02 per cent. solution of hydrochloric acid being sufficient to destroy it. Furthermore, it is necessary for the fat to be presented in an emulsified form for this lipase to have much effect, so that, except under abnormal conditions, or in the case of suckling animals, the rôle played by gastric lipase is insignificant and may be disregarded. This view is supported by the fact that practically no gastric digestion of fat takes place in dogs when fat is given in the form of beef fat, butter or lard. The chief action that occurs in the stomach is the setting free of the fat of the food from its enclosing connective tissue membranes. As has already been shown, the acid food mass of the stomach reaches the duodenum in the form of a creamy mass. The first stage in the intestinal digestion of fat consists of emulsification. The acid food mass is rapidly made alkaline by admixture with pancreatic juice and bile, the salts of the pancreatic juice responsible for its alkalinity being principally the phosphates and carbonates of sodium. If a drop of neutral olive oil be placed in distilled water, the olive oil retains its spherical form, but the addition of minute traces of sodium carbonate rapidly causes the olive oil to break up into a partial emulsion. The bile salts, sodium glycocholate, and sodium taurocholate, have the property of lowering the surface tension of any fluid in which they are dissolved, and their solutions also act as solvents for fatty acids.

The presence of pancreatic juice and bile in the food mass consequently produces favourable conditions for the emulsification of fats. The pancreatic lipase (steapsin) attacks the fat in the food, converting a portion into fatty acid and glycerol. The fatty acid thus formed reacts with the sodium carbonate forming a soap. The presence of the soap leads to a remarkable lowering of the surface tension of the food contents, and this lowering of the surface tension, combined with the agitation caused by the mechanical movement of the intestines, causes the fats to break up into a very fine emulsion, each small particle of fat being separated from its neighbour by a soap film. The surface area of fat thus presented to the action of steapsin is consequently enormously increased, and rapid conversion of fat to fatty acid and glycerol results. Since steapsin, like other enzymes, can only work at the free surfaces of the substrate, this preliminary emulsification of fat is extraordinarily important.

Two fat-splitting enzymes have been demonstrated in the intestinal contents, one being present in the pancreatic juice and the other in the succus entericus. Claude Bernard in 1870 first demonstrated the lipoclastic action of the pancreatic juice, and Berthelot a year later demonstrated the nature of the reaction.

Absorption of fat. The digestion of fat, as we have seen, takes place mainly in the small intestine, and consists in the hydrolysis of fats to fatty acids and glycerol. Digestion and absorption takes place *pari passu*, and work by Levites has established the fact that whereas in the upper portions of the small intestine the absorption of the products of the hydrolysed fats proceeds practically as fast as they are formed, in the lower portion of the intestine the rate of absorption is apt to lag behind the rate of hydrolysis. If the lacteals of the villi be examined in an animal several hours after it has been given a fat-rich meal, they will be

found to contain a lymph resembling milk in colour, and microscopical and chemical tests on this lymph will show that the
milkiness is due to the presence of small particles of neutral fat.
On the other hand, if the lacteals from a starving animal be
examined, the lymph will be clear and examination will show that
fat is absent.

It is clear that the fat found in the lacteals of the villi is derived
from the food fat, and it becomes of interest to ascertain how the
transport to the lacteals and the formation of neutral fat from
the fatty acids and the glycerol of the intestinal food contents take
place. Our knowledge on this problem is mainly due to the
researches of Immanuel Munk. It was formerly believed that
only enough fat was converted into a soap to enable a fine
emulsion to be formed, and that the main portion of the fat
was absorbed by the intestinal epithelium in a particulate form.
Munk found that fatty acids in the presence of protein and with
the addition of a little soap would form a fine emulsion, and
thinking that the fatty acids might be absorbed in a similar way
to that of fats, proceeded to give an emulsion of free fatty acids
to dogs. On testing the chyle in the thoracic duct of these dogs,
he was surprised to find that only neutral fats were present,
showing that during the process of absorption the free fatty
acids had in some way been resynthesised to fat.

Subsequent experiments by Moore showed that the synthesis of
the fat had occurred at an early stage of absorption, since the
lacteals of the villi themselves contained neutral fat. Examination
of the intestinal mucous membrane during the height of fat absorption revealed the presence of fats and fatty acids, thus demon-
strating that the resynthesis occurred in the mucous membrane
itself. Munk, as the result of his work, came to the conclusion that
fats were absorbed in a particulate form as fatty acids by the
epithelial cells of the villi. Histological evidence by staining
methods showed that although fat could be demonstrated in the
body of the epithelial cell, it could not be demonstrated in the free
borders of the cell. It has, however, been shown that whether fat
will stain or not depends upon the degree of dispersion, and that
particles of fat, if sufficiently dispersed, will no longer react to
osmic acid or other fat staining reagents. The absence of fat in
the free borders of the cells could not, on histological evidence
alone, be regarded as proved, and attempts were therefore made

to ascertain whether any fatty acid solvent was present in the intestinal fluids.

It had already been demonstrated that bile acted as a solvent for fatty acids, and in cases of disorder resulting from occlusion of the bile duct, fatty material was excreted in the faeces. Since this fatty material consisted almost entirely of fatty acids and not of fats, it was obvious that the accumulation of the fatty acids in the faeces was not due to failure of the pancreatic lipase, but was due to a failure of absorption of the fatty acids produced during digestion. Moore and Parker showed that, whereas bile salts alone only dissolved fatty acids or their salts to a slight extent, this solvent power was increased if lecithin were present. The presence of lecithin in bile is therefore significant, and the story of fat absorption becomes clear. The normal course of events is as follows:— The fats in the intestine are converted partly to soaps but mainly to fatty acids and glycerol. The fats are then absorbed in solution partly as soaps and partly as fatty acids dissolved in bile. The bile salts thus absorbed return to the liver and are used again, the fatty acids and glycerol being resynthesised in the intestinal epithelium to form neutral fats. Further support to this theory is found in the fact that paraffins and similar bodies, even when given in the state of a fine emulsion, are not absorbed by the intestinal epithelium. Moreover, ethyl esters of the higher fatty acids are absorbed in the intestine but are only recovered as triglycerides in the chyle. If absorption took place in a particulate form, one would expect to recover the ethyl esters unchanged, and one would also expect absorption of fine emulsion of paraffin to take place.

Experiments have also demonstrated the fact that, by the time the ileo-colic sphincter is reached absorption of fat is complete. Absorption of fat is therefore confined to the intestinal epithelium of the small intestine. The fine droplets of neutral fat present in the epithelium are transferred to the central lacteals, pass along in the lymphatic system to the thoracic duct, and then enter the blood stream, by an opening at the junction of the left internal jugular and left subclavian veins. It is interesting, to note that food fat, after absorption, unlike the absorbed protein and carbohydrate, reaches the blood by a path which avoids traversing the liver substance.

Digestion and Absorption of Carbohydrates. The carbohydrates present in food consist chiefly of monosaccharide and disaccharide sugars, and polysaccharides of varying complexity of structure. The two chief polysaccharides of interest are starch and cellulose. During their passage through the alimentary canal, the carbohydrates are subjected to the action of several amyloclastic ferments, the ptyalin of the saliva, the amylopsin of the pancreatic juice, the invertase, maltase and lactase of the succus entericus. The two former enzymes convert starch to disaccharide sugar, the three latter convert disaccharide to monosaccharide sugars. The enzyme ptyalin just mentioned is present in the saliva of certain animals but not in all saliva (see p. 53). This enzyme works in an alkaline medium, and is destroyed readily by acids. During mastication the food is broken up and thoroughly mixed with saliva. The food mass thus reaches the stomach in an alkaline condition, and the ptyalin begins to attack the starch present, breaking it down to the disaccharide maltose. If the stomach contents be examined during digestion, it will be found that the acidity, due principally to the secretion of hydrochloric acid, lies between 0·2 and 0·5 per cent., an acidity which is sufficient to effect the destruction of ptyalin. It is important, therefore, to ascertain to what extent digestion of starch occurs in the stomach. Grützner, by feeding rats with foods coloured with different dyes, established the fact that the food material in the fundic end of the stomach is unaffected for a long time by the muscular movements of the stomach. It is probable, therefore, that under these conditions, the interior of the food mass escapes for some time admixture with the acid gastric juice, thereby enabling the ptyalin to effect the conversion of some part, at least, of the starch to maltose.

It may, therefore, be assumed that partial conversion of starch to maltose occurs in the stomach during the time that elapses between the entry of the food into the stomach and the penetration of the food mass by the acid gastric juice. The carbohydrate material, as it reaches the small intestine, consists therefore of starchy material and disaccharide sugars, together with any monosaccharide sugars that may have been present in the original food material. The amylopsin of the pancreatic juice now comes into play, and the remainder of the starchy material is converted into maltose. Examination of the blood leaving the vessels of the small intestine reveals the fact that the sugars present consist entirely of monosaccharide sugars, and in experiments in which disaccharide sugars, such as cane sugar and maltose, have been injected into the blood stream it has been shown that these are excreted unchanged. It is obvious, therefore, that sugars are absorbed from the intestine only in the monosaccharide form, and further digestive changes must occur in the intestine which result in the production of monosaccharide sugars from disaccharide sugars. Experiment has shown that such a digestion does take place, and the conversion of disaccharide sugars to monosaccharide sugars has been traced to the action of enzymes present in the succus entericus. Thus cane sugar, by the action of invertase, is converted to glucose and laevulose; maltose, by the action of maltase, is converted into glucose; and lactose, by the action of lactase, is converted into glucose and galactose.

The net effect of the digestive action on the carbohydrates is the production of glucose or its isomers. The main seat of absorption is the intestinal mucous membranes, little, if any, glucose being absorbed in the stomach. The absorption of sugar is complete by the time the ileo-colic valve is reached, so that, under normal conditions, no absorption of sugar occurs in the large intestine. Under conditions of rectal feeding, however, it has been shown that alcohol and glucose are both readily absorbed in the large intestine.

Digestion of Cellulose, and Effect of Bacterial Action in the Alimentary Canal. In the case of Carnivora, little or no cellulose-containing material is eaten, but in the case of farm animals, a considerable proportion of the feeding stuffs eaten contain cellulose. Digestibility experiments have shown that during digestion some part, at least, of the cellulose disappears, and evidence has been brought forward to show that the energy of the cellulose that disappears becomes available for the animal's needs. The presence of a cellulose-splitting enzyme has not been demonstrated in the digestive tract of the higher animals, although cellulose-splitting enzymes have been shown to occur in certain seeds, in the 'liver' of the snail, and in the alimentary canal of the mealworm. Apart from the cellulose enzymes that may be taken in by the animal with the food, the conversion of cellulose into simpler disaccharides must be sought for in some other direction.

Microscopical examination of the fibrous portions of food at various stages of digestion has shown that the pure cellulose disappears during its passage through the alimentary canal, lignine

and the encrusting materials which protect the cellulose walls of
the plant tissues showing the greatest resistance to change. Wildt
in 1874 showed that solution of cellulose occurs principally in those
portions of the alimentary canal in which the food material lies
quiescent for some time, i.e. the rumen in ruminants, and the
coecum and the colon in the horse and the pig. Tappeiner
showed that this disappearance of cellulose was due to the activity
of bacteria, and Kellner demonstrated that the disappearance
of the cellulose was correlated with an increase in the production
of methane. It is probable, therefore, that the digestion of cellulose
that occurs in the alimentary canal, particularly of ruminants,
is not a digestion in the true sense but rather a destructive
fermentation. This fermentation leads to the production of gases
such as methane, carbon dioxide and hydrogen, with the further
production of lactic, acetic and butyric acids. The extent to which
the animal profits from this bacterial action is still unknown.
Kellner found that digestible fibre was of equal value to digestible
starch for fat production in ruminants. Woodman, in a critical
survey of the subject, came to the conclusion that if the bacterial
fermentation of cellulose in the animal normally proceeded to the
final stage of gas and fatty acid production Kellner's result would
be difficult of acceptance. Pringsheim in 1912 had demonstrated
that the sugars cellobiose and glucose were formed as intermediate
products in the destructive fermentation of cellulose by bacteria,
and Woodman and Stewart, by controlled fermentation, using a
thermophilic bacterium isolated from well-rotted dung, proved
that the formation of glucose from cellulose does take place
by this means under appropriate conditions. They concluded that
the formation of glucose takes place at a later stage of fermentation by the action of enzymes elaborated and secreted by the
bacteria at an earlier stage of fermentation. Woodman postulated
the theory that in the normal process of cellulose digestion in the
ruminant by bacteria the cellulose is broken down to cellobiose
and glucose, thus rendering possible the absorption and utilisation
by the animal of the glucose not utilised by the bacteria for their
own metabolic processes. Such a hypothesis would account
for Kellner's discovery that digestible fibre and digestible starch
are of equal value in the ruminant for productive purposes.
Lohrisch, in a study of the utilisation of cellulose by man, obtained
evidence that part at least of the cellulose becomes available to the

organism, and he suggests that part of the cellulose is utilised firstly as carbohydrate, and secondly as fatty acid derived by bacterial action from the cellulose.

General effect of bacterial activity in the alimentary canal. As is well known, the digestive tract is the seat of bacterial activity, the chief nutrients attacked by the bacteria being proteins and carbohydrates. In the small intestine fermentation of some portion of the carbohydrates takes place, giving rise to a number of organic acids such as lactic and acetic acids and gases such as methane and hydrogen. In the large intestine putrefactive fermentation of any protein that has escaped digestion occurs. Such fermentation is associated with the production of ammonia compounds, skatol and indol derivatives, and such gases as methane, carbon dioxide, hydrogen and hydrogen sulphide. The indol and skatol derivatives are largely absorbed, and appear in the urine as ethereal sulphates. The extent to which these latter substances appear in the urine indicates the extent to which putrefactive fermentation of protein in the large intestine is occurring.

CHAPTER IX

THE BLOOD AND THE ORGANS OF CIRCULATION

Every part of the body, with few exceptions, is to a greater or less extent vascular, that is to say, it is permeated by vessels through which the blood is continually circulating. The blood is the medium by which nutritive substances, water, salts, and oxygen are conveyed to all parts of the body, and it is through this same medium that the waste products are carried away to be eventually disposed of by the organs of excretion or respiration. Moreover, the sub-

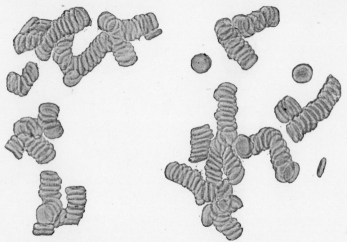

Fig. 35. Human red blood corpuscles (from Schafer).

stances manufactured by the internally secreting glands, together with other chemical bodies, are likewise transported by the blood. Lastly, by circulating rapidly through all the tissues, the blood helps to keep the temperature of the animal approximately the same throughout.

As seen in quantity blood is a red opaque fluid, but when examined in thin layers under the microscope it is found to consist of corpuscles of two kinds floating in a yellowish coloured liquid, the blood plasma. The erythrocytes or red corpuscles (appearing yellow when looked at singly) are by far the most numerous, there being about 500 of these to one leucocyte or white corpuscle in normal human blood. The erythrocytes in nearly all mammals are minute, circular, biconcave discs. They have no nuclei. They consist of an alkali-soluble protein material containing a red-coloured substance called haemoglobin, which itself can be resolved into a protein, globin, and an iron-containing substance termed haematin. The haemoglobin of the blood of most animals forms characteristic crystals of oxyhaemoglobin if treated by appropriate means, and both the crystalline structure and the elementary chemical analysis of the oxyhaemoglobin differ according to the animal from which it is derived. The content of iron in all cases is, however, approximately the same, i.e. 0·336 per cent. The red

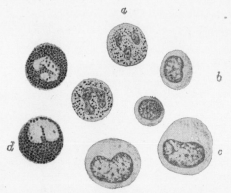

Fig. 36. White corpuscles or leucocytes from blood (from Schafer). *a*, polymorph; *b*, lymphocyte; *c*, macrocyte; *d*, eosinophil.

blood corpuscles, after circulating through the blood vessels for a variable period, eventually undergo destruction, chiefly in the haemolymph glands and the spleen. The haemoglobin is disso-ciated in the liver into globin, and haematin, the haematin being further broken down to bile pigment, which is secreted in the bile, and iron, which is stored in the liver for further use. The leucocytes are generally slightly larger, but vary in size according to the variety to which they belong; they are round or amoeboid in shape, and may have one or more nuclei, and they possess the power of independent movement. Some of them are phagocytic and can ingest bacteria or other foreign bodies after the manner of an amoeba. They tend to congregate in any area of inflammation or disturbance, and one of their main functions is undoubtedly to protect the organism against disease or the results of injury. They have different staining reactions according to kind, some having acid and some basic affinities.

The red corpuscles are produced in bone marrow, which is richly supplied with vessels. Certain kinds of white corpuscles also have their origin in bone marrow, but others are formed from the lymphocytes of the lymphatic glands.

Blood which has been recently shed also contains platelets, which are circular bodies smaller than corpuscles. They have been supposed to represent nuclei extruded from erythrocytes in the process of their development, but it is uncertain whether they are really present in normal unaltered blood.

The blood plasma contains about 92 per cent. water, and the remaining 8 per cent. consists of proteins, fats, carbohydrates, salts and gases, and all the various products of metabolism which need to be transported to or from the different parts of the body. The proteins consist largely of albumin and globulin together with fibrinogen, which as mentioned below plays an important part in the process of clotting. The reaction of blood plasma is alkaline.

If blood is withdrawn from the body and allowed to stand in a vessel for a short time (three or four minutes for a man or a little longer for a horse) it becomes thick and eventually coagulates or clots. After a space of a few hours the clot shrinks like curd of milk, and finally we get a tangled mass containing the corpuscles enmeshed in it, floating in a colourless fluid which is called serum. The network of the tangled mass or clot consists of fibrin, a protein substance white and stringy in appearance, and produced by the alteration of fibrinogen under the influence of another substance of unknown composition called thrombin. Thus, pure fibrinogen obtained by repeated precipitation is without the property of spontaneous coagulation, but if a little serum be added coagulation proceeds to take place, since the serum contains thrombin. Moreover, serum from the pericardial or other cavities will sometimes not clot spontaneously, but on the addition of other serum coagulation sets in. This again is explained on the assumption that the pericardial serum did not contain thrombin, but that this substance was introduced in the addition of other serum. It seems certain that thrombin is not a ferment, since its activity is not permanently destroyed by boiling.

Thrombin, like fibrin, is not present in the blood as such, but in the form of a precursor called prothrombin or thrombogen, from which it is converted through the agency of thrombokinase in the presence of lime salts. Normally, however, if lime salts are not present (e.g. if they have been precipitated out from freshly shed blood, as by adding potassium oxalate) the blood will not clot. The thrombokinase, which is formed in injured animal tissues and escapes into the blood, brings about the union of the lime salts with prothrombin, the resulting product being thrombin. This explains why it is that blood clots readily when in contact with broken or torn vessels, but does not easily do so in uninjured tissues, since thrombokinase does not occur (at any rate in any great quantity) in normal healthy tissues. To recapitulate, when a vessel is ruptured so that blood escapes from it, the injured vessels will liberate thrombokinase. This thrombokinase enters into the blood, and there it finds all the necessary factors for the production of thrombin; it finds prothrombin and calcium salts. Thrombin is therefore formed, and this causes the fibrinogen to coagulate very quickly. This clotting helps to stop bleeding, and if the injury is slight allows the wound to heal without further loss of blood.

The Heart. The blood is kept in constant circulation through the vessels by the heart which acts as a double pump, the right and left portions of which have no direct communication with each other. The heart is situated between the lungs in a chamber called the pericardium. This is of the nature of a double bag, one covering forming a thin layer closely adherent to the heart itself, while the other or outer one envelops the heart more loosely. Between these two coverings is the pericardial fluid which is a form of lymph. The right and left portions of the heart referred to above each consist of an auricle and a ventricle. These are divided from one another by a movable transverse partition and communicate with one another by valves which admit of the blood flowing in one direction only, namely from the auricle to the ventricle. The apex of the heart is at the end of the ventricular portion which has a much thicker wall than either of the auricles. The valves just mentioned are of the same type on each side of the heart, but, whereas the one on the right side has three flaps (the tricuspid valve), that on the left side has only two flaps (the mitral valve). Each flap is fastened at the base to the auriculo-ventricular junction, while its free end points towards the ventricle. The free edges of the flaps are connected by tendons, the chordae tendineae, to muscular processes (the musculi papillares) on the inner walls of the ventricle, and these prevent the flaps from being carried backwards into the auricular cavity when the ventricle becomes full of blood. Consequently, whereas increased pressure in the auricle forces the blood to flow into the ventricle by the flaps opening, the reverse process cannot take place excepting in certain kinds of heart disease when the valves are damaged or do not properly close. Coming away from each ventricle there is an artery (pulmonary artery on right side and aorta on left) which is provided with valves of another type. These are of the nature of pouches, three in number, and having their free edges inside pointing away from the ventricle. These free edges separate under pressure and admit of the passage of the blood from the ventricle, but close together when the pressure is in the opposite direction, the pouches being then distended. The name semilunar valves has been given to them owing to their shape.

The blood is kept in motion mainly by the rhythmical contraction and dilatation of the heart, the alternating periods or conditions being called systole and diastole. Systole begins with the great venous trunks (the two superior venae cavae and the inferior vena cava) and then passes to the right auricle which undergoes a sharp contraction. The left auricle into which the pulmonary veins open contracts simultaneously with the right auricle. The wave of contraction then extends through the tissue dividing the auricular from the ventricular part of the heart to the ventricles which contract very powerfully, forcing the blood into the pulmonary arteries on the right side and the aorta on the left. The heart then expands previous to another contraction. As is well known, the movements of the heart are entirely involuntary. Nevertheless the organ is well provided with nerves, there being two chief sources of supply, those from the vagus or tenth cranial nerve, and those arising from the sympathetics. The former are inhibitory, checking or controlling the heart's activity, while the sympathetic nerves are accelerator in function. There is a cardio-inhibitory centre in the hind brain, and when this is stimulated to excess (as in fainting or sudden emotion) it temporarily (or sometimes permanently) stops the heart's action. On the other hand stimulation of the sympathetic supply quickens the heart beats and may induce palpitation. Apart, however, from the nerve

supply, it is the essential property of heart muscle to undergo
rhythmical contractions, as may be seen when the organ is withdrawn from the body and placed in a glass vessel, while at the same
time it is perfused with a fluid resembling blood serum (e.g. Ringer's
solution). Under these conditions the heart will continue to beat
in the same manner as it does normally when fulfilling its usual
bodily functions. Moreover, in the case of some animals (e.g.

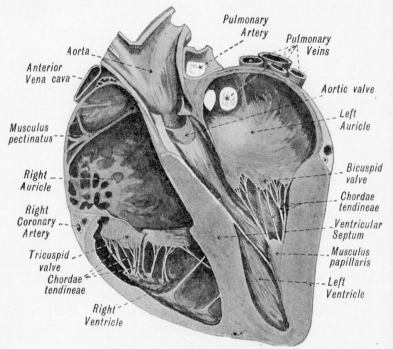

Fig. 37. Section through heart of horse.

tortoises) even small pieces of heart muscle will continue to undergo
contractions after being removed from the rest of the heart.

In the horse, and various other Ungulata, in addition to the
chordae tendineae there are other bands of tissue traversing the
ventricles. These are the moderator bands; they pass from wall to
wall, and their function is to restrain the ventricles from undergoing undue distention. For this purpose they are especially well
developed in antelopes and other animals which are fleet of foot,
and in which cardiac strain might be supposed to be exceptionally
great.

The complete course of the circulation in a mammal may now be described. The venous blood coming from all parts of the body enters the right auricle by the superior and inferior venae cavae. It passes through the tricuspid valve to the right ventricle; thence it proceeds by the pulmonary artery which gives off a branch to each lung; in so doing it is forced through the semilunar valves. In the lungs the blood undergoes the gaseous exchange which is an essential part of the respiratory process, yielding up the waste carbonic acid gas, and absorbing oxygen. The purified or oxygenated blood then traverses the pulmonary veins which convey it to the left auricle; from this chamber it goes through the mitral valve to the left ventricle, and thence through the aorta, being driven through the semilunar valves. The aorta gives off numerous arteries, which further divide many times and convey the blood to all the organs and parts of the body. The smallest arteries give off still smaller vessels called capillaries, and having a diameter hardly greater than that of a red corpuscle. It was in the capillaries of the lung of the frog that Malpighi in 1664 first demonstrated the fact previously discovered by Harvey in 1616 that the blood circulates, and the observation may be repeated by anyone who examines the web of the foot of a living frog with the low power under the microscope. The capillaries reunite together to form the veins through which the blood is conveyed back to the heart. The veins form an elaborate branching system resembling that of the arteries, the smallest veins being those formed by the junction of capillaries.

The arteries have thicker walls than the veins, and excepting the aorta and the pulmonary artery do not possess valves. The veins, on the other hand, may have valves which admit of the blood passing in the direction of the heart but not in the opposite direction. The wall of an artery consists typically of three coats, the inner consisting of elastic tissues with a thin endothelium lining the lumen, the middle of unstriated muscle fibres, and the outer of fibrous tissues. The wall of a vein contains less muscular and elastic tissue but is otherwise not dissimilar to that of an artery.

The lymph. A capillary has a still thinner wall than a vein, and through this wall the blood plasma transudes, forming the lymph which is contained in the loose connective tissue and bathes the cells of the body. It is this intimate relation between the lymph and the tissues which admits of the process known as 'tissue respiration' (that is to say, the gaseous exchange between the tissues and the blood) and of nourishment being supplied from the blood to the tissues, and of waste products being removed. From the unenclosed spaces in the tissue the lymph is collected in thin-walled vessels which join together forming the lymphatics. These vessels, which, like the veins, may possess valves, communicate eventually with the thoracic duct or with the right lymphatic trunk which open into the large veins near the heart, as already described (see p. 77). Placed in the course of the lymphatic vessels are the so-called lymphatic glands which consist of areolar tissue packed with lymphocytes. When in a position where the vessels connected with them are receiving lymph from an inflamed area, these glands tend to become swollen and may cause a considerable amount of discomfort or pain. If owing to one cause or another (local obstruction of vessels or partial failure of the heart to discharge its functions through valvular disease) the lymph increases in the tissues to a quantity beyond the normal, a condition of oedema or dropsy is produced.

The pulse. The alternate contraction and dilatation of the heart makes itself felt in the arteries as the pulse. When an artery is situated near the surface of the skin and there is a bony background present, the pulse or pressure wave produced by the heart beat can be recorded by an instrument known as a sphygmograph which is placed over the artery and responds to the varying pressure. A tracing can then be obtained by allowing a piece of smoked paper to pass across the recording needle of the instrument, the movements of the needle being regulated by the beats of the pulse. A typical pulse tracing obtained in this way is shown in the figure. The straight upstroke represents the dilatation of the artery due to the increased blood pressure caused by the contraction of the heart. This is followed by a curved downstroke representing the period of arterial contraction, and this in turn is succeeded by another period of arterial expansion. The downstroke in the tracing is not a continuous curve, but is broken by a slight rise known as the dicrotic wave or notch. This has been shown to be due to the recoil of blood produced by the closure of the semilunar valves in the aorta, for in horses in which these valves have been destroyed experimentally there is no such recoil, the downstroke of the sphygmograph tracing being then continuous. In the veins there is normally no pulse.

The normal rate of the pulse (or of the heart beat) varies in different animals; it also varies under different conditions. Exercise increases the rate of the pulse, just as it increases the respiratory movements. The heart rate responds also to nervous excitement,

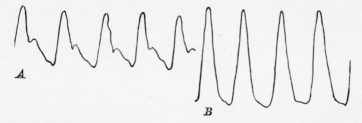

Fig. 38. Sphygmograph tracing from facial artery of horse (after Hamilton, from Smith, Messrs Baillière, Tindall and Cox). *A* before and *B* after destruction of aortic valves; in *B* the dicrotic notch has disappeared.

and it quickens when there is a rise of temperature as in febrile conditions. The increased rate is apparently due to reflex stimulation, and in the case of fevers the rise of temperature in the blood is probably the exciting cause. In young animals, except the fowl, the rate is always faster than in adults, and with the advance of old age the pulsations become still slower and at the same time weaker. The following are the average rates for the heart beat in man and fully grown animals:

Man	72 beats per minute		Pig	75 beats per minute
Horse	38 ,, ,,		Dog	95 ,, ,,
Ox	46 ,, ,,		Cat	130 ,, ,,
Sheep	75 ,, ,,		Fowl	300 ,, ,,

In the newly born foal or calf the average rate is about 110 beats per minute.

The velocity of the blood varies in the different parts of the body. In the carotid artery of the horse it has been shown to flow at the rate of 300 mm. per second (Volkmann). In the jugular vein of the dog it may flow at the rate of 260 mm. per second (Vierodt). In the smaller veins and arteries the rate of flow is much slower, and in the capillaries it is slowest of all, having been estimated at about an inch per minute. In no part of the body, however, does the blood traverse more than an extremely short distance through capillaries before being returned to a vein. Vierodt, by injecting potassium ferrocyanide into the jugular of a dog and awaiting its appearance at the other jugular, found that a complete circulation only took 16·32 seconds.

In the arteries the blood is kept in motion by the direct action of the heart. In the veins the flow is due to several causes. One of these is the back pressure due to the heart, but there are other contributing causes. Thus the expansion of the thorax in breathing results in a suction of blood along the large veins entering the heart, and the compression of the diaphragm assists in driving the blood in the same direction. Moreover, the movements of the muscles involved in exercise exert pressure on the veins, and tend to drive the blood onwards, the action of the valves assisting. In the same kind of way muscular movements cause the lymph to flow along the lymphatic vessels, which are also provided with valves. It is partly for this reason that exercise has a beneficial effect upon the circulation, and it is well known that horses whose legs have become swollen or oedematous through much standing may often be cured by moderate exercise.

Blood pressure. It is of course obvious that the blood is retained in the body under pressure. Thus, if we cut a large artery the blood flows out in a forcible stream and with spurts corresponding to the heart beats. Exact measurements of the degrees of pressure were first obtained *circa* 1733 by Hales who connected the left crural artery of a mare with a long glass tube in which the blood rose to a height of eight feet three inches and then remained approximately steady. This experiment showed that in the normal closed artery the blood was under a pressure or tension sufficient to support the weight of a column of blood (or water) to this height. He then performed a similar experiment with the jugular vein and found that the blood rose only to a height of 12 to 21 inches, showing that the blood pressure in the veins is very much less than in the arteries. Later experimenters have substituted a column of mercury for a column of blood, mercury being 13·5 times as heavy as blood (or water). Moreover, a manometer formed in this way may have its piston connected with a recording drum, and a permanent tracing of the variations in the blood pressure can be obtained.

The degree of arterial pressure is not due solely to the heart; it is also regulated by the action of the nerves supplying the arteries. These nerves are of two kinds. There are vaso-constrictor fibres belonging to the sympathetic system (on which the hormone adrenaline acts), and vaso-dilator fibres of different and diverse origin, which produce inhibition or temporary paralysis of the arterial muscles, and so cause the arteries to expand.

THE CHEMICAL COMPOSITION OF THE BLOOD.

The blood is the nutritive medium by which transport of food materials from one part of the body to another takes place, it plays an important part in the gaseous exchanges of the body, and lymph, the fluid which bathes all the living cells of the body, is derived from the blood by a process of filtration through the blood capillary cell walls.

The protein which forms the structural framework of the red blood corpuscle is regarded by Wooldridge as a compound of lecithin and a protein; by others, as a nucleo-protein. Defibrinated blood, warmed with glacial acetic acid containing sodium chloride, yields abundant reddish brown crystals of haemin, which is regarded as the hydrochloride of haematin. Both haemin and haematin, treated with concentrated sulphuric acid, yield an iron-free derivative called haematoporphyrin, which, according to Nencki and Sieber, is isomeric with the bile pigment, bilirubin. Oxyhaemoglobin and its derivatives exhibit characteristic absorption spectra whereby they may be identified. The blood plasma contains fibrinogen, a protein of the globulin class, and thrombogen, which we have already seen forms fibrin when blood is shed. In addition to these substances, proteins of the albumin and globulin class are also present, together with salts, hormones, food nutrients, and small quantities of waste products. The approximate percentage chemical composition of the blood of domestic animals, according to Nasse, is as follows:

	Horse	Ox	Pig	Fowl
Water	80·5	80·0	76·9	78·3
Corpuscles	11·7	12·2	14·6	14·5
Proteins	7·0	7·0	7·7	53·2
Fat	0·131	0·205	0·195	0·263
Alkaline phosphates	0·084	0·047	0·136	0·094
Sodium sulphate	0·021	0·018	0·009	0·010
Alkaline carbonates	0·110	0·107	0·120	0·035
Sodium chloride	0·466	0·432	0·429	0·539
Iron oxide	0·079	0·073	0·078	0·074
Lime	0·011	0·010	0·008	0·017
Phosphoric acid	0·012	0·012	0·021	0·693
Sulphuric acid	0·003	0·002	0·004	0·001
Magnesia	0·003	0·002	0·004	0·001
Silica	0·003	0·002	0·004	0·001

The inorganic salts form approximately 1 per cent. of the total blood constituents. They consist of sodium and potassium chlorides and phosphates, potassium sulphate, sodium carbonate, and calcium and magnesium phosphates. Sodium chloride is the most abundant constituent and the next abundant sodium carbonate, these two salts representing nine-tenths of the total salts present.

With regard to the amount of blood in the body, Colin gives the following figures, which he obtained by bleeding methods:

Percentage of blood in terms of body weight

3-month old calf	4·315	Dog	5·086
8-year old cow	4·654	Pig	3·720
2-year old ox	3·343	Fowl	3·795
Horse	5·435	Rabbit	3·292
Goat	4·170		

The specific gravity of the blood of the domestic animals is approximately 1·050. Blood is faintly alkaline to litmus solution, and both blood and living cells have the property of neutralising considerable quantities of acids or alkalis so as to maintain neutrality. This maintenance of neutrality of the body fluids is extremely important, since physiological reactions are easily affected by changes in acidity or alkalinity. In order to understand the mechanism whereby blood and tissue fluids maintain neutrality, a slight knowledge of physical chemistry is necessary. We are familiar with the expressions 'strong' and 'weak' acids, that a strong acid such as sulphuric acid will turn out a weaker acid such as hydrochloric acid from its salts such as, say, sodium chloride. We are also familiar with the fact that certain substances dissolved in a solution conduct electricity, whereas others do not. The first class of substances we call electrolytes. Now according to the theory of electrolytic dissociation originally propounded by Arrhenius, when an electrolyte such as sodium chloride is dissolved in water the sodium chloride molecules are partly 'active' in the sense that they exhibit electrolytic and chemical phenomena, and partly inactive. In concentrated solution, the proportion of inactive molecules to active molecules is high, but in dilute concentrations practically all the molecules are in an active state. The active molecules become dissociated into their respective constituents, at the same time carrying an electric charge. Thus an inactive molecule NaCl when dissociated in water becomes an atom of sodium with a positive charge, represented as Na· and an

atom of chlorine with a negative charge, represented as Cl′. Na·
is thus the symbol for a sodium ion and Cl′ the symbol for a
chlorine ion. Similarly, an acid such as hydrochloric acid when
dissociated in water forms hydrogen ions H· and chlorine ions
Cl′, and a base such as sodium hydroxide forms sodium ions
Na· and hydroxyl ions OH′. Now the common characteristic
of all acids in solution is the presence of hydrogen ions and of
all bases the presence of hydroxyl ions, so we can use the
amount of these ions present in a solution as a measure of its
acidity or alkalinity. The difference between a strong acid and a
weak acid has been shown to be associated with the degree to which
they respectively dissociate in solution, the strong acid possessing
a greater electrolytic conductivity than the weak acid. Since it
would be inconvenient to express acidity in terms of hydrogen ion
concentration and alkalinity in terms of hydroxyl ion concentration, it is usual to express both acidity and alkalinity in terms of
hydrogen ion concentration; this being possible owing to the fact
that the product of the hydrogen ion concentration and the
hydroxyl ion concentration is a constant, at any given temperature.
A solution can therefore be regarded as neutral when there are
equal numbers of molecules of H-ions and OH-ions present, acid
when the H-ions are in excess, and alkaline when the OH-ions are
in excess. Pure water is dissociated to only a slight but definite
extent. It has been estimated that at 22° C. only one molecule of
water out of every 555 millions present is dissociated. The hydrogen
ion concentration [cH'] of water at 22° C. is 0·0000001 gram ions
per litre, or expressed in the usual mathematical way, to avoid
writing so many noughts, 1×10^{-7}. A one-thousandth normal solution of HCl has a hydrogen ion concentration of $9·7 \times 10^{-4}$ and
a one-thousandth normal solution of acetic acid a hydrogen ion
concentration of $1·36 \times 10^{-4}$. It will be seen that the stronger
acid hydrochloric is much more dissociated than the weaker
acid acetic. In order to avoid the use of such expressions as
1×10^{-7}, $9·7 \times 10^{-4}$, and $1·36 \times 10^{-4}$, Sörensen suggested the
adoption of the negative exponent of 10 as a whole number,
calling it the hydrogen-ion-exponent or pH. Thus a cH of
1×10^{-7} becomes log cH of -7 or $-$ log cH $= 7$. The pH of
water is therefore 7·0. Similarly $9·7 \times 10^{-4}$ expressed logarith-
mically becomes $\overline{4} + $ log $9·7 = \overline{4} + 0·987 = - 3·013$. The pH of a
thousandth normal solution of HCl is therefore 3·013. The hydro-

gen ion concentration of blood at 38° C. is 0.4×10^{-7}, so that the pH value of blood is 7·398, which is just above neutrality, i.e. blood is slightly alkaline in reaction.

Since the physical and chemical changes that occur in cells are very easily disturbed by changes in the concentrations of hydrogen ions, and since we know that cell metabolism involves the production of acids and alkalis, it is important to ascertain the means whereby the neutrality of blood, lymph, and cell fluids is maintained. This neutrality is maintained chiefly by the phosphates and bicarbonates present in these fluids, and to a subordinate extent by the proteins, which are amphoteric, i.e. have the power of acting either as weak acids or weak bases according to circumstances. In the cells the phosphates play the important part in maintaining neutrality, in the fluids the bicarbonates. When the blood or lymph is brought into contact with acids, the acid reacts with the sodium bicarbonate present in these fluids with the production of the neutral sodium salt of the acid and the setting free of the CO_2 in the gaseous phase. This CO_2 is removed from the sphere of action owing to lung ventilation of the blood; and until all the sodium bicarbonate present in the blood is used up the hydrogen ion concentration remains unaltered. Similarly, if free alkali is brought into contact with the blood, it combines with the CO_2 present in the blood to form a bicarbonate, and again the reaction remains unaltered. In the case of the phosphates, the two phosphates concerned are monosodium dihydrogen phosphate (NaH_2PO_4) and disodium hydrogen phosphate (Na_2HPO_4). In a water solution of NaH_2PO_4 the hydrogen ions are in excess of the hydroxyl ions and the reaction is therefore acid. In a water solution of Na_2HPO_4 the hydroxyl ions are in slight excess, and the reaction is consequently alkaline. If an alkali such as sodium hydrate is added to a mixture of NaH_2PO_4 and Na_2HPO_4 the sodium hydrate reacts with the NaH_2PO_4 to form Na_2HPO_4; and until the whole of the NaH_2PO_4 is converted into Na_2HPO_4 the reaction is but slightly altered. Similarly, if free acid such as HCl is added to the mixture, the acid reacts with the Na_2HPO_4 to form NaH_2PO_4 and again the reaction is but slightly altered until all the Na_2HPO_4 present is converted into NaH_2PO_4. It is by means of such reactions that the neutrality of the fluids of the body is maintained.

CHAPTER X

THE RESPIRATORY ORGANS

In the act of inspiration the air passes in through the nostrils (or sometimes through the open mouth) and traverses, first, part of the pharynx, and then the larynx and trachea before entering the lungs. The narrow slit-like opening from the pharynx into the larynx is called the glottis. The larynx is the enlarged first portion of the trachea. The latter organ, which is commonly called the wind-pipe, is kept open for the free passage of air by a number of rings of cartilage which are not quite complete. After reaching the thorax the trachea divides into the two bronchi which are provided with similar cartilaginous rings, and these bronchi after entering the lungs divide into smaller air tubes each of which in turn divides further into a number of bronchioles. In addition to the cartilaginous rings the walls of the trachea and bronchi contain some muscular and connective tissue and are lined internally by a ciliated epithelium. The bronchioles widen out into the air sacs of the lungs, which are arranged around the ends of the bronchioles like bunches of grapes. The walls of the air sacs are very thin, and are in contact with innumerable capillaries which form a close

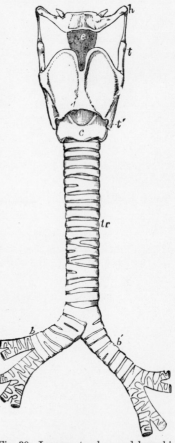

Fig. 39. Larynx, trachea and bronchi (after Allen Thomson, from Halliburton). *h*, hyoid bone; *e*, epiglottis; *t* and *t'*, thyroid cartilage; *c*, cricoid cartilage; *tr*, trachea; *b* and *b'*, bronchi.

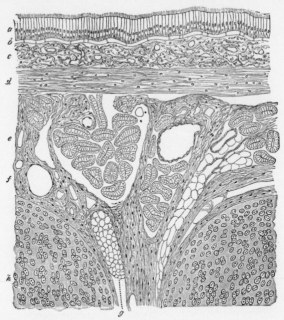

Fig. 40. Longitudinal section of trachea (after Klein, from Schafer). *a*, ciliated epithelium; *b*, basement membrane; *c* and *d*, mucous membrane; the superficial part with vessels and lymphoid tissue, the deeper part with elastic tissue; *e*, sub-mucous areolar tissue containing glands, fat, etc.; *f*, fibrous tissue; *g*, adipose tissue; *h*, cartilage.

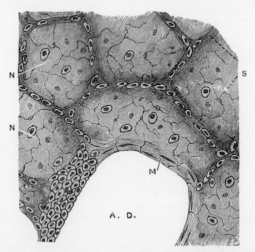

Fig. 41. Section through lung tissue (after Klein, etc., from Halliburton). *A.D.* alveolar duct; *M*, unstriated muscle; *N*, alveoli or air-sacs; *S*, septa.

meshwork. Thus these capillaries are separated from the air in the air sacs by the thinnest possible layer of protoplasm through which a gaseous exchange is effected. The result of the repeated branching and subdivision of the air tubes is to bring a very large surface of blood under the influence of the air in the air sacs of the lungs. In the human subject it is estimated that no less than 1500 square feet of blood surface is exposed to the air in this way.

In the act of expiration the air passes through the same passages as in inspiration but in the reverse direction.

Each lung is surrounded externally by a layer of fibrous tissue, and the wall of the thoracic cavity is lined by a similar layer. Normally these two layers or pleurae are separated by only a very small quantity of serous fluid which, however, increases in amount in the inflammatory condition known as pleurisy.

Inspiration is brought about by the expansion of the thorax, the surfaces of the lungs continuing in contact with the pleurae and the pleurae with the thoracic wall. In this way the lungs are caused to expand, and air is drawn into them through the trachea so as to fill up the spaces which would otherwise occur. The thoracic movement involved in inspiration is produced by the contraction and consequent recession of the diaphragm, and by the elevation of the ribs through the contraction of the intercostal muscles. In the reverse process of expiration the ribs are let fall to their former position and the diaphragm becomes extended again. Expiration requires little or no muscular effort.

The amount of air inspired in ordinary quiet breathing in man is about 500 c.c. (tidal air). By a forced inspiration another 1500 c.c. may be taken in (complemental air). Following upon an ordinary expiration an additional 1500 c.c. may be expelled by a forced expiration (supplemental air). The maximum amount of air which can be expelled after the deepest possible inspiration (i.e. tidal + complemental + supplemental air) is defined as the vital capacity. In man this quantity is on an average about 3500 c.c. (or from 3 to 3·8 litres). In the horse the vital capacity is from 25 to 30 litres. The air which remains in the lungs after a forced expiration (residual air) is about 1·5 litres for a man, or from 7 to 17 litres in a horse.

The number of respirations or breaths per minute varies in different animals, and as a general rule the smaller the animal the greater is the frequency. The following are average numbers for man and the domestic animals in a state of rest:

Man	14 to 18 per minute	Pig	10 to 15 per minute
Horse	8 to 10 ,,	Dog	15 to 20 ,,
Ox	12 to 15 ,,	Fowl about 60 ,,
Sheep	12 to 20 ,,		

The Respiratory Quotient. Carbon dioxide contains its own volume of oxygen. Thus if carbon is burnt in air the volume of gas remains unchanged. Carbohydrates (e.g. $C_6H_{10}O_5)_n$ contain sufficient oxygen to oxidise their hydrogen. Proteins, on the other hand, do not, and still less do fats. Consequently when proteins or fats are consumed in metabolism the carbon dioxide produced is less than the oxygen used; that is to say, oxygen has been employed to oxidise the hydrogen as well as the carbon. The following are the exact figures:

In the case of carbohydrate 1 vol. of O_2 produces 1 vol. of CO_2.
In the case of protein 1 vol. of O_2 produces 0·83 of CO_2.
In the case of fat 1 vol. of O_2 produces 0·71 of CO_2.

The ratio $\dfrac{CO_2 \text{ produced}}{O_2 \text{ consumed}}$ is called the respiratory quotient. This in a man on an ordinary mixed diet is 0·9 or somewhat less. It can be raised by increasing the relative amount of carbohydrate in the food, and lowered by protein or by fat. Thus the respiratory quotient is higher in herbivorous animals than in carnivorous ones. If a herbivorous animal be kept on carbohydrate diet its respiratory quotient may be raised to unity, but only for a short time, since it very soon begins to consume its own stored up proteins and fats.

The Chemistry of Respiration.

The daily amount of air respired by domestic animals is considerable. Taking the amount of air breathed by a man in twenty-four hours (10,000 litres) as unity, the amounts of air breathed by the various domestic animals are, according to Colin:

Horse	9·6	Pig	3·4	Cat	0·14
Cow	7·9	Sheep	2·0	Rabbit	0·13
Ass	3·1	Dog	0·8	Fowl	0·05

Analysis of the relative compositions of the inspired and expired air reveals the fact that the chief changes that the respired air undergoes in the lungs are loss of oxygen and gain of carbon dioxide. It has already been stated that the surface of blood exposed to the influence of the air of the air sacs of the lungs in man is no less than 1500 square feet. In other words, the blood coming from the pulmonary arteries is spread out into the equivalent of a film one blood cell thick with an area equivalent to the floor space of a room 75 feet long by 20 feet wide and is then gathered up again into the pulmonary veins. The conditions for interchange of gases between the alveolar air and the blood pulsating through the lungs are consequently ideal, and it would be a natural inference to assume that the blood gains oxygen and loses carbon dioxide during its passage through the lungs. Experiments have shown this to be actually the case. By subjecting a measured volume of blood to a vacuum it is possible to remove and collect the gases contained in it. A sample of blood gases so obtained is found to consist of oxygen, nitrogen and carbon dioxide, and 100 vols. of blood yield approximately 60 vols. of mixed gases measured at N.T.P. (the normal temperature and pressure, 0° C. and 760 mm. pressure of mercury). The relative proportion of carbon dioxide, oxygen, and nitrogen present can then be ascertained by exposing the blood gas sample first to caustic potash to absorb the carbon dioxide, and then to alkaline pyrogallol to absorb the oxygen. The gas remaining is nitrogen. By means such as these 100 vols. of blood from the pulmonary artery and vein have been found to yield 60 vols. of gas having the following approximate composition:

From the pulmonary artery		From the pulmonary vein	
O	12 vols.	O	20 vols.
CO_2	46 ,,	CO_2	38 ,,
N	2 ,,	N	2 ,,

These figures clearly show that in its passage through the lungs the blood absorbs oxygen from the alveolar air and yields up carbon dioxide to it.

Internal Respiration. Analysis of the gases of blood going to a tissue or organ and that proceeding from it shows quite clearly that oxygen is taken up from the blood by the tissue or organ concerned and that carbon dioxide is yielded up to it. Thus 100 vols. of venous or arterial blood will yield approximately 60 vols. of blood gases having the following composition:

Arterial blood		Venous blood	
O	20 vols.	O	12 vols.
CO_2	38 ,,	CO_2	46 ,,
N	2 ,,	N	2 ,,

The actual amount of oxygen present in venous blood will vary from 8 to 12 vols. according to the activity of the tissue from which it is derived and the rate of flow of the blood through it.

From the facts already given, it is clear that a series of oxidation processes are constantly taking place in the tissues, and that the oxygen required for these processes and the carbon dioxide produced by them is conveyed to and taken away from the tissues concerned through the medium of the blood stream. The venous blood thus charged with carbon dioxide and depleted of oxygen, after returning to the right ventricle, re-circulates through the lungs, and by means of the lung ventilation loses a proportion of its carbon dioxide and becomes re-charged with oxygen. It becomes of interest to ascertain the precise functioning of the mechanisms governing these gaseous interchanges.

The first point of interest is the state of combination of the blood gases in the blood, namely, whether the gases are present in the blood in a state of true solution, or whether they are chemically combined with one or other of the constituents of the blood itself. If a gas is in contact with a liquid, the liquid will absorb a certain volume of the gas; the number of c.c. of that gas (measured at $0°$ C. and 760 mm. pressure) that dissolve in 1 c.c. of the liquid being called the absorption coefficient at 760 mm. pressure of that liquid for the gas in question. The absorption coefficient of a gas diminishes as the temperature rises. Thus the absorption coefficients of oxygen, carbon dioxide and nitrogen, which are $0\cdot0489$, $1\cdot713$ and $0\cdot0239$ respectively at $0°$ C., become $0\cdot0231$, $0\cdot530$ and $0\cdot0118$ at $40°$ C. Furthermore, since the actual volume dissolved is a constant at any given temperature, *whatever the pressure*, the amount of gas dissolved will vary with the pressure. Thus 1 c.c. of water at $0°$ C. and 760 mm. pressure will dissolve $0\cdot0489$ c.c. oxygen measured at N.T.P., whereas at $0°$ C. and 1520 mm. pressure it will dissolve $0\cdot0978$ c.c. oxygen measured at N.T.P. Moreover, in a mixture of gases, each gas exerts its own pressure independently of the other gases present, so the total pressure exerted by a mixture of gases is the sum of the partial pressures exerted by each component gas. Thus, the pressure exerted by the atmosphere is the sum of the partial pressures exerted by the nitrogen and oxygen present. Since these gases are present in the proportion of 79 to 21 by volume, the pressure exerted by the nitrogen is $\frac{79}{100} \times 760$ mm. $= 600\cdot4$ mm. and that exerted by the oxygen is

$\frac{21}{100} \times 760$ mm. $= 159.6$ mm., when the atmospheric pressure is 760 mm.

The oxygen, carbon dioxide, and nitrogen in the air present in the air sacs or alveoli of the lungs are distributed as follows, per 100 vols. of alveolar air:

Oxygen	Carbon dioxide	Nitrogen
14·5	5·5	80

Owing to the fact that the alveolar air is saturated with water vapour, the pressure exerted by these gases is not 760 mm. but $760 - 50$ mm., i.e. 710 mm., since the water vapour at 37° C. exerts itself a pressure of 50 mm. The approximate pressures exerted by the oxygen, carbon dioxide and nitrogen will therefore be $\frac{14.5}{100} \times 710, \frac{5.5}{100} \times 710$, and $\frac{80}{100} \times 710$ respectively. The oxygen pressure of the alveolar air thus becomes 103 mm., the carbon dioxide pressure 39 mm., and the nitrogen pressure 568 mm. We have already seen that the absorption coefficients of water at 40° C. for oxygen, carbon dioxide and nitrogen are 0·0231, 0·530 and 0·0118, but Bohr has shown that the presence of proteins and salts in water depresses the solvent power of water for gases. The *simple solution* absorption coefficients of blood for oxygen, carbon dioxide and nitrogen at normal body temperature are 0·022, 0·511 and 0·011 respectively. The amounts of these gases due to simple solution in arterial blood can therefore be calculated per 100 vols. of blood as follows:

Oxygen $\frac{103}{710} \times 2.2$ $= 0.3$ c.c.

Carbon dioxide $\frac{39}{710} \times 51.1 = 2.7$ c.c.

Nitrogen $\frac{568}{710} \times 1.1$ $= 0.88$ c.c.

Since 100 c.c. of arterial blood contain approximately 12 c.c. of O_2, 46 c.c. of CO_2 and 2 c.c. of N, it is obvious that the oxygen and carbon dioxide must both be present in the blood in chemical combination with some of its constituents. The nitrogen alone yields a figure at all approximate to that possible on a true simple solution hypothesis.

It has been shown that, so far as the oxygen is concerned, the chief constituent of the blood with which it combines is the haemoglobin of the red blood corpuscles. Under suitable pressure conditions, haemoglobin combines with oxygen to form oxy-haemoglobin, 1 g. of haemoglobin absorbing no less than 1·34 c.c.

of oxygen. The relationship existing between the oxygen pressure and the formation of oxyhaemoglobin from haemoglobin has been exhaustively studied by Barcroft and others (see diagram). If a solution of oxyhaemoglobin be subjected to a gradually diminishing pressure, little gas is evolved until the partial pressure of the oxygen reaches 30 mm., when copious quantities of oxygen are given off. As will be seen from the diagram (Fig. 42), the loss of oxygen goes on

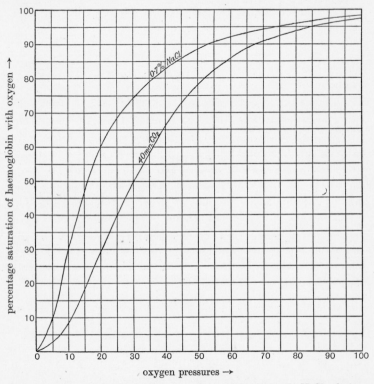

Fig. 42. Diagram of dissociation of oxyhaemoglobin, in 1·7% NaCl solution, and under 40 mm. pressure of CO_2.

until, at a pressure of 0 mm., the oxyhaemoglobin has been entirely converted into haemoglobin. If the process be reversed, oxygen will be readily absorbed by haemoglobin until at a partial oxygen pressure of 30 mm. the haemoglobin becomes 75 per cent. saturated with oxygen. Barcroft has shown that the dissociation curve of haemoglobin in a fluid is affected by the presence of salts and also by the reaction of the fluid. Acidity, as represented by the presence of CO_2 in the blood, or by lactic acid, increases the ease with which oxyhaemoglobin yields up its oxygen. Salts such as sodium chloride and potassium chloride have a like effect, and Barcroft and Cairns have shown that the differences in the dissociation curves of bloods of different animals are associated with the differences in saline content and not with specific differences of the haemoglobin itself.

The reason why blood yields up oxygen to the tissues and absorbs oxygen from the alveoli can now be explained. The active cell elements are constantly using up any oxygen that is available, so that the oxygen pressure in the tissue itself is zero. The oxygen in the arterial blood has been absorbed at a partial pressure of 103 mm. There will consequently be a difference of pressure between the oxyhaemoglobin of the red blood corpuscles and the active tissue cell of 103 mm. Oxygen will therefore readily flow from the haemoglobin to the tissue cell *via* the blood plasma, capillary cell wall and lymph. If the blood remained stationary, this process would go on until all the oxygen had been used up (as actually happens in asphyxia), but owing to the fact that the blood is in movement, it is removed from the sphere of action before complete depletion takes place. As we have already seen, venous blood still contains 8–12 vols. per cent. of oxygen, and this represents a pressure of 37·6 mm. On reaching the lung capillaries, this blood is subjected to the partial pressure of 103 mm. oxygen existing in the alveoli. Oxygen will consequently flow from the alveolar air to the blood corpuscles *via* the intervening tissues.

With regard to carbon dioxide, the position is by no means clear. It has already been shown that arterial blood contains 38 vols. per cent. of carbon dioxide, and that only 2·7 vols. of this are due to simple solution. The remainder therefore must be in a state of chemical combination. The carbon dioxide exists in the blood in three forms: in simple solution, as sodium bicarbonate, and in organic combination. Calculating from data given by Loewy, approximately 50 per cent. of the carbon dioxide in the combined form is present as bicarbonate and 50 per cent. in organic combination. The plasma contains 62 per cent. of this amount and the corpuscles 38 per cent. The portion held in organic combination is much more easily dissociated than that held as bicarbonate, and it is therefore highly probable that it is the organically combined carbon dioxide that plays the important rôle in the transference of carbon dioxide from the seat of its formation, the tissues, to the place of its elimination, the lungs. Such evidence as is available indicates that haemoglobin plays a preponderant part in this process. Setschenov in 1879, and Bohr in 1891, showed that haemoglobin has the power of taking up and releasing carbon dioxide, but it was not until Buckmaster (1917) re-investigated the subject that it was realised that haemoglobin provided the necessary mechanism for the transport of carbon dioxide from the tissues to the lungs. At the carbon dioxide tension that exists in the lungs (40 mm. Hg) sodium bicarbonate does not yield up its carbon dioxide, so that this product can be ruled out as an important factor in the transport of the carbon dioxide released from the blood to the alveolar air. 100 vols. of blood in the absence of oxygen at a carbon dioxide tension of 40 mm. Hg absorbs approximately 58 vols. of carbon dioxide, and in the presence of oxygen absorbs 52 vols., and at the carbon dioxide tension existing in the tissues (approx. 63 mm.) blood in the absence of oxygen absorbs 67 vols. of carbon dioxide, and in the presence of oxygen 62 vols. The conditions that exist with regard to the oxygenation of the blood consequently favour the absorption of CO_2 by blood from the tissues and its release in the lungs. As we have already seen, the blood circulating through the tissues becomes deoxygenated, its capacity for absorption of carbon dioxide therefore increases, and the carbon dioxide produced in the tissues is consequently linked up with the haemoglobin in organic combination. On arrival at the lungs, the reverse change takes place. The deoxygenated blood becomes saturated with oxygen, its capacity for holding carbon dioxide decreases, with the result that the haemoglobin yields up to the alveolar air the carbon dioxide that has been absorbed during its passage through the tissues.

The Mechanisms involved in the Control of Respiration. The actual amount of oxygen used up, and the carbon dioxide produced, by an individual, obviously varies according to the activity of the tissue elements. The rate at which oxygen is absorbed by the blood and carbon dioxide released will depend upon the number and depth of the respiratory movements, since it is in the lungs that the interchange of blood gases occurs with the external air. In conditions where large quantities of oxygen are being used up by the tissues with the consequent production of large quantities of carbon dioxide, such as in physical exertion, we find that the respiratory movements are quickened and deepened, whereas in conditions of reduced tissue activity, such as during sleep, the respiratory movements become slower and shallower in character. The ventilation of the alveoli brought about by the respiratory movements is largely automatic in character, and it becomes of interest to ascertain the nature of the mechanisms involved in this physiological process.

As we have already stated, the enlargement of the thorax is brought about either by elevation of the ribs or by contraction of the diaphragm. Two types of respiration are recognised, a costal type, in which respiration is mainly brought about by the movements of the ribs, and an abdominal type, in which respiration is induced by movements of the diaphragm. The muscles involved in these movements are many, but the two chief groups of muscles responsible are the intercostal muscles, innervated by the intercostal nerves, and the muscles of the diaphragm supplied by the phrenic nerves. Efferent impulses passing along the intercostal or phrenic nerves cause contraction of the muscles they innervate, thus leading to a respiratory movement, and while such movements are under the control of the will, in that they can be temporarily stopped or increased by voluntary effort, under normal conditions they are largely automatic, the co-ordination of these movements being brought about by a respiratory centre situated in the medulla. Since rhythmic respiratory movements continue even when afferent impulses to this centre are prevented by surgical interference, it is evident that the centre is truly automatic in character and not merely reflex, i.e. the efferent impulses originate in the centre itself and are not called into being only as a response to afferent sensory impulses received by the centre.

Nevertheless, the rhythm and character of the respiratory movements are to a large extent influenced by the nature of sensory impulses reaching the respiratory centre. Stimulation of any sensory nerve trunk containing cutaneous fibres either gives rise to quicker and stronger respirations or has the reverse effect, according to whether the sensory fibres concerned are augmentor or depressor in character. Of special significance in connection with the normal rhythm of respiration are the sensory fibres distributed along the respiratory passages themselves. Those in the lungs themselves are derived from the vagus, and those in the larynx from a branch of the vagus known as the superior laryngeal nerve. Section of the vagi in the region of the neck leads to a slowing and deepening of the respiratory movements. Stimulation of the superior laryngeal nerve causes a slowing or even cessation of the respiratory movements; stimulation of the vagus below the exit of the superior laryngeal nerve causes a quickening of the respiratory movements. The nature of the respiratory responses to the cutting and subsequent stimulation of the vagi show that the sensory fibres of the lung tissue act like the governor of a steam engine in regulating the normal rhythm of respiration. The normal mechanism involved in the control of the respiratory movements is essentially nervous in character, but the rate and rhythm of the respiratory movements, and thereby the ventilation of the lungs themselves, are to a large extent controlled by the chemical composition of the blood passing through the respiratory centre itself.

If the normal ventilation of the lungs be mechanically interfered with, such as by simple closure of the main air passages as in strangling, a series of characteristic changes occur in the nature of the respiratory movements. The normal movements quickly give place to laboured breathing (dyspnoea) in which the respiratory movements quicken and deepen. Towards the latter end of dyspnoea the movements become convulsive in character, and the expiratory movements particularly become very pronounced. If, when this stage is reached, cessation of ventilation be still continued, exhaustion supervenes, and the violent convulsive movements give way to asphyxia, a stage of comparative quiescence characterised by a series of long drawn out inspiratory movements growing feebler and longer in intervals until death supervenes.

On the other hand, if the ventilation of the lungs be increased beyond normal, as, for instance, by taking several deep respirations in quick succession, cessation of respiration will occur for many seconds owing to lack of stimulation of the respiratory centre. This condition is known as apnoea.

The above-mentioned changes in the respiratory movements have been shown to be due to the sensitivity of the respiratory centre to changes in the gases of the blood passing through it. During suffocation, the oxygen content of the blood rapidly decreases, and the carbon dioxide content increases. In apnoea, the reverse occurs. The natural inference from these facts is that either the CO_2 or the O_2, or both, in the blood passing through the respiratory centre provide the stimulus whereby the afferent impulses are set up which control the respiratory movements

Haldane has shown that this is indeed the case, and that lack of oxygen or excess of CO_2 in the blood passing through the respiratory centre excites it, but that, under normal conditions, the excitatory factor is the CO_2 rather than the oxygen. The determining factor appears to be not the percentage of carbon dioxide in the alveolar air but the tension of CO_2. As the carbon dioxide in the atmosphere is increased by artificial means or by natural means such as keeping an individual in a badly ventilated room, the depth and frequency of the respiratory movements rapidly increase, thus increasing the ventilation of the alveolar air. What actually happens is that the increased partial pressure exerted by the extra CO_2 present in the respired air tends to prevent the exchange of CO_2 between the blood and the alveoli, with the result that the CO_2 in the blood, and thus the hydrogen ion concentration, is temporarily increased. This stimulates the respiratory centre to activity, lung ventilation is thus stimulated, and the alveolar CO_2 tension is again reduced to normal, resulting in bringing about favourable conditions for the evolution of CO_2 from the blood, thus again reducing the CO_2 tension to normality. The response of the respiratory centre to the slightest increase in CO_2 tension in the blood circulating through it is extraordinarily rapid and effective. The response of the centre to oxygen lack is, however, by no means so rapid, and the oxygen content of the respired air may be lowered from 20 per cent. to 13 per cent. without effecting the ventilation of the lungs. If the percentage of oxygen present in the lungs is reduced below this figure, however, increased lung ventilation takes place. Haldane demonstrated this differential response of the respiratory centre to carbon dioxide and oxygen in a very striking manner by allowing an individual to breathe air from a closed bag, in one case absorbing the carbon dioxide produced, by means of soda lime, and in the other case allowing the carbon dioxide produced to remain. In the first case, the oxygen content of the bag became reduced to 8 per cent. before the patient began to show signs of distress, but in the latter case, when the carbon dioxide was allowed to accumulate, signs of distress were quickly noted, and when the experiment was discontinued owing to the obvious distress of the patient, the gas analysis of the contents of the bag showed that the carbon dioxide had been raised to a level of 5·6 per cent. from the original ·04 per cent., whereas the oxygen was still 14·8 per cent.

CHAPTER XI

THE EXCRETORY ORGANS

When protein substances undergo decomposition or combustion they ordinarily yield ammonia together with sulphides or sulphates. But ammonia, being a poisonous substance, is not permitted to circulate freely in the body in any considerable quantity. The ammonia, therefore, which is produced as a result of the oxidation of proteins is converted into other substances which are less toxic. The principal of these is urea, which is one of the principal constituents of normal urine. It is probably produced in the organism from ammonium carbonate, which is itself formed from ammonia, carbon dioxide and water:

$$2NH_3 + CO_2 + H_2O = (NH_4)_2CO_3$$

and $$(NH_4)_2CO_3 = 2H_2O + CO(NH_2)_2.$$

Urine, the composition of which is described below, is excreted by the kidneys. These organs are of the nature of compound tubular glands and are situated dorsally on each side of the lumbar region of the vertebral column, the right kidney being placed in front or headwards of the left. The ureter or kidney duct issues from about the centre of the inner or concave surface of the kidney and conveys the urine to the bladder into the posterior side of which the two ducts open side by side not far from the opening of the bladder into the common urogenital passage. The latter communicates with the exterior in the male by the penis and in the female by the common vaginal opening.

To the naked eye the kidney (as seen in longitudinal section) appears to be formed of a cortical portion on the outside, and a medullary portion on the inside. The medullary portion surrounds the cavity or pelvis which is the dilated end of the ureter. Into the pelvis one or more conical processes project. These are called the papillae, and they contain the openings of excretory tubules into the pelvis. Each papilla really represents the apical part of a pyramid, for the medulla of the kidney in most animals is divided into a number of pyramidal portions, the bases of which are surrounded by cortex. Both medulla and cortex are largely composed of uriniferous tubules, but the cortex contains more blood vessels and is consequently darker in appearance.

The tubules begin as Malpighian capsules and these are confined to the cortex. Each capsule has projecting into it a bunch of coiled capillaries called a glomerulus, and the blood enters these capillaries by a small artery and leaves them by a small vein.

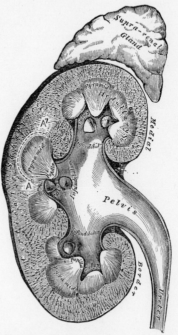

Each tubule as it leaves its dilated end or Malpighian capsule becomes convoluted, passing through the medulla in the direction of the apex of the pyramid, and then back again to the cortex. The loop which is thereby constituted is known as the loop of Henle. In the cortex the tubule again becomes convoluted and then after uniting with other tubules passes straight to the papilla. The tubules are lined throughout by an epithelium which varies in character in their different parts. The cells lining the convoluted tubules and those of the ascending limb of the loop of Henle are

Fig. 43. Vertical section of kidney (from Gray).

granular and striated and generally large, while those of the collecting tubules and the descending limb of the loop of Henle are cubical and free from granules.

The Mechanism of Renal Secretion. There appear to be two main factors in the secretion of urine, (1) the supply of blood, and (2) the composition of the blood flowing through the kidney. There are no secretory nerves going to the kidney.

That the secretion of urine is affected by the blood supply to the kidney is rendered obvious when we consider the result of different degrees of temperature upon the skin. Cold causes a constriction of the vessels in the skin and consequently lessens the supply of blood to the skin, while the supply going to the kidney is correspondingly increased. Conversely when the skin is hot and flushed, and when evaporation of moisture from the skin is considerable, the quantity of urine secreted is diminished. Just as the vessels in the skin are under the influence of vaso-constrictor nerve fibres which react to external cold, so also the vessels supplying the kidneys are controlled by nerve fibres which regulate the supply of blood and the consequent secretion of urine. Thus, if the renal nerves are cut, the renal arteries dilate, and the flow of urine

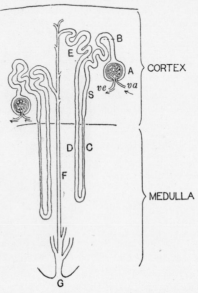

Fig. 44. Diagrammatic view of the course of the tubules in the kidney. *A*, Malpighian capsule containing a glomerulus; *B*, first convoluted portion of tubule; *C*, descending limb of loop of Henle; *D*, ascending limb of loop of Henle; *E*, second convoluted portion; *F*, collecting tubule; *G*, apex of pyramid; *S*, spiral tubule; *va* represents a small branch of the renal artery, which breaks up into a bunch of looped capillaries, the glomerulus finally joining up again to form the vein *ve*.

increases. On the other hand, if the renal nerves are stimulated the vessels are constricted, and urinary secretion is diminished.

It is believed that the glomeruli act somewhat after the manner of a filter and allow the water and salts of the blood plasma to pass through. At the same time the cells of the kidney have the definite property of picking out certain substances from the blood and permitting these to be excreted while other substances (e.g. the proteins in solution in the blood) are not normally allowed to pass through. Further, it has been established that certain substances (e.g. pigments such as indigo carmine, and probably some of the substances present in normal urine) are excreted by the epithelial cells lining the convoluted tubules and not by the glomeruli.

Certain substances known as diuretics promote urinary secretion within a very short time after they are taken into the system, probably through their action on the nerve fibres supplying the renal vessels. Thus it is well known that alcohol and various drugs have such an action, and that tea, coffee, etc. contain diuretic substances.

The urine is driven along the ureters into the bladder largely as the result of pressure by gravity. The ureters are lined by a stratified epithelium surrounded by unstriated muscle which assists in the passage of the urine into the bladder. The walls of the latter organ also contain an abundant supply of unstriated muscle (lined internally by a transitional stratified epithelium). Around the neck of the bladder is a sphincter which is kept contracted excepting during micturition or the evacuation of urine. During micturition the sphincter relaxes, while the walls of the bladder contract. The abdominal muscles also contract, and in the male the perineal muscles. Normally in animals micturition is a reflex act presided over by a centre in the lumbar part of the spinal cord, the accumulation of urine in the bladder being the necessary stimulus for inducing the reflex. In man, however, and to some extent in animals, micturition (like defaecation) may be a voluntary act, that is to say, it is possible to inhibit the reflex which would otherwise occur.

A horse during micturition stands with its hind-legs extended, its fore-legs generally advanced, and its tail raised upwards. After micturition the mare erects the clitoris, but why this should happen is not obvious. Horses as a rule can only micturate when standing upright. They cannot do so while lying down, or while at work or trotting, but an oestrous mare can discharge urine while cantering. In the ox micturition can occur while walking. The cow raises her back and brings her hind limbs forward, at the same time lifting her tail.

The following are the daily amounts of urine discharged in man and the domestic animals under normal conditions:

Man	1·5 litres		Sheep	1 to 5 litres
Horse	5 to 8 litres		Pig	1·5 to 8 ,,
Ox	10 to 25 ,,		Dog	0·5 to 3 ,,

It will be seen that the amounts given for any one species show a wide range of variation. This is due partly to differences in the size of the animal, but to a greater extent to the influence of temperature variation and the factors referred to above.

Composition of Urine. Normal urine may contain the following substances:

(1) Water.

(2) Nitrogenous end products (urea, uric acid, hippuric acid, creatine, creatinine).

(3) Aromatic compounds (benzoic acid, ethereal sulphates of indol, etc.).

(4) Mucus.

(5) Colouring matter.

(6) Inorganic salts (chlorides, sulphates and phosphates of sodium, potassium, calcium and magnesium).

(7) Gases (chiefly carbon dioxide, and traces of nitrogen and oxygen).

(8) Ammonia.

We may now consider these separately and then pass on to deal with certain features of special interest in the urine of the different domestic animals.

Urea. $CO{<}^{NH_2}_{NH_2}$ is a substance which readily crystallises into four-sided prisms or indefinitely shaped prisms. With nitric or oxalic acids it forms characteristic crystalline salts. It is soluble in water and alcohol and neutral in reaction. Under the influence of organised ferments (due to *Micrococcus ureae* or other bacteria) it takes up water and forms ammonium carbonate $(NH_4)_2CO_3$; hence the ammoniacal odour of putrid urine. The amount of urea present in a given sample of urine can be estimated by making use of the following equation:

$$CO(NH_2)_2 + 3NaBrO = CO_2 + N_2 + 2H_2O + 3NaBr.$$

The sodium hypobromite solution also contains caustic soda (if not some soda should be added) and this absorbs the whole of the carbon dioxide evolved. The nitrogen therefore is the only gas given off, and this on being measured gives a basis for estimating the original quantity of urea present. The urine of man and that of the horse contain about 3 per cent. of urea; that of the ox contains $1\frac{1}{2}$ per cent., whereas the pig's urine contains less than 1 per cent.

Urea is produced in the liver and not in the kidneys which merely excrete it. Thus after extirpation of the kidneys the quantity of urea in the circulation is greatly increased. If ammonium carbonate is given by the mouth the urea output is also increased. The portal vein which conveys blood to the liver contains more ammonia than the hepatic vein which drains the liver. If, however, the portal vein is ligatured or united artificially with the vena cava, the quantity of ammonia in the blood is raised. After removal of the liver in frogs urea formation almost ceases and ammonia is found in the urine instead. Moreover when the kidneys are diseased in a certain way urea is still formed in the body but cannot be excreted and we get the condition known as uraemia. On the other hand, when degenerative changes occur in the liver, urea formation is lessened, and in acute yellow atrophy may scarcely be produced at all.

Uric acid ($C_5H_4N_4O_3$ tri-oxypurine) crystallises in rectangular prisms. It does not occur free in urine but combined with bases (sodium and potassium) in the form of urates. The amount of uric acid in urine may be estimated by adding ammonium chloride; ammonium urate is produced and is dissolved in an alkaline solution. Hydrochloric acid is then added and uric acid is precipitated and can be weighed directly (Hopkins's method).

From a chemical standpoint, uric acid is a member of a group of bodies called purines, all of which are characterised by the presence of a ring compound called purine ($C_5H_4N_4$). The chief physiological compounds representative of this group are adenine and guanine, xanthine, hypoxanthine and uric acid. The active constituents of tea, coffee and cocoa are the methyl purines caffeine, theine and theobromine. Adenine and guanine are constituents of the nucleic acid contained in cell nuclei, and by means of ferments these bodies are oxidised to hypoxanthine ($C_5H_4N_4O$) and xanthine ($C_5H_4N_4O_2$). Further oxidation of hypoxanthine and xanthine gives rise to uric acid.

Uric acid is found only in small quantity in the urine of herbivorous animals, and in the healthy horse it is altogether absent. In Carnivora it is abundant and it is the principal nitrogenous constituent of the excretory products of birds and reptiles. In man it is present, and frequently to an extent which is pathological.

The amount depends on the diet, and meat eating always favours uric acid production. It is present in all young animals which are living on their mother's milk, and in herbivorous animals which are being starved or are in a state of fever, since these are for the time being living on their own tissue and are therefore temporarily carnivorous. Like urea, uric acid is not manufactured by the kidneys, since after the removal of these organs it is still produced. In birds uric acid is formed in the liver and ceases to be excreted if the liver is excised. In mammals, however, its origin is more complicated, but there can be little doubt that the liver and spleen are responsible for much of its formation. Certain kinds of food which contain a large quantity of nucleic material (e.g. liver and pancreas which possess many nuclei, and to a greater or less extent meat generally) are known to be very rich in purine bases, and these are converted into uric acid through the action of ferments. Such ferments, which are termed nucleases, are most abundant in the liver and spleen. It follows from what has been said that uric acid may be formed, partly as a result of eating food which is rich in nuclei or purine bases (exogenous formation), and partly in metabolism from the nuclei of the various organs and tissues (endogenous formation). The former mode of production is largely responsible for those disorders (e.g. gout) which are due to excess of uric acid, and such disorders may be palliated or cured by restricting the diet (as by avoiding meat which is especially rich in the purine base hypoxanthine, $C_5H_4N_4O$).

Hippuric acid ($C_6H_5CO.NH.CH_2.COOH$ benzoyl glycocoll) is especially characteristic of the urine of Herbivora in which it is present in the form of hippurates. It may be crystallised out from horse's urine by evaporating to a syrup and saturating with hydrochloric acid. As its formula suggests, it originates through the combination of benzoic acid ($C_6H_5.COOH$) and glycocoll ($CH_2(NH_2).COOH$) with the elimination of water. This synthesis occurs in the kidney itself, and is possibly due to the action of a ferment. This is rendered probable by the fact that benzoic acid and glycocoll can be made to unite to form hippuric acid in the presence of ground up kidney extract mixed with blood. There is a hippuric acid forming substance in hay, grass and grains.

Benzoic acid ($C_6H_5.COOH$) is said to be present in the urine of working horses, and, as has been stated, it is a precursor of hippuric acid. Benzoic acid is apparently derived from various aromatic substances which are present in plants and are absorbed in the food.

Creatine ($C_4H_9N_3O_2$ methylguanidine acetic acid) is a constituent of muscle and is not found in urine excepting during starvation, and in certain febrile and other pathological conditions.

Creatinine ($C_4H_7N_3O$), which is the anhydride of creatine, is present in normal urine and in generally constant amount. There is evidence that the liver is the chief seat of its formation. It is a product of protein metabolism, and according to Mellanby probably gives rise to the creatine of the muscles, any excess of creatinine which is not required for this purpose being excreted by the kidneys.

Indican. Of the ethereal sulphates occurring in the urine, phenyl sulphate of potassium and indoxyl sulphate of potassium are the chief. The latter is formed from indole and potassium hydrogen sulphate. Indole (C_8H_7N) is a product of intestinal disintegration produced from tryptophane by bacterial putrefaction. It is not normal in human urine, though it very frequently occurs, but it is always present in the urine of the horse and many other Herbivora. It may be made to yield indigo.

Mucus. The urine of the horse is generally more or less mucinous, the amount of mucus depending upon diet, the occurrence of oestrus, etc. On a diet of oats without hay the quantity may be considerable. Mucus in small amounts is often present in the urine of other animals.

Pigments. The chief colouring matter of urine is urochrome, an oxidation product (on exposure to air) of urobilin which is a derivative of bile-pigment.

Salts. These are derived partly from the salts of the food, but to a greater extent are metabolic products of the tissues. They are always present in considerable quantity, but vary in kind according to diet and according to the species of animal.

Gases. The gases in urine only occur in insignificant quantities.

Ammonia. Urine always contains a small quantity of ammonia, since blood containing this substance traverses the kidney before reaching the liver where it is converted into urea.

Pathological constituents of urine. Protein is present in human urine in cases of Bright's disease (albuminuria) and in certain other pathological conditions, especially when pus is formed through bacterial action. Protein occurs in horse's urine in cases of inflammation of the lungs and pleura. In cases of glycosuria, where the tissues are unable to utilise the sugar in the blood, glucose overflows into the urine. Such a condition may be produced experimentally by removing the pancreas (see p. 192), by puncturing the floor of the fourth ventricle of the brain, or by injecting adrenaline, phloridzin and certain other drugs. In lactating animals lactose may occur in the urine. Sugar is rarely or never present in horse's urine. Bile occurs in urine in cases of jaundice, rendering the fluid a dark brown colour. Blood appears in the urine when haemorrhage in any of the urinary passages takes place. Further, a blood pigment (methaemoglobin) is found in cases of haemoglobinuria, which is due to a disintegration of corpuscles in the circulating blood. In cattle with 'black water fever' (a disease of Tropical Africa) this pigment may also occur in urine associated with oxyhaemoglobin. Amino-acids, such as tyrosine, are occasionally found in urine after a disintegration of protein tissue (as in atrophy of the liver).

The urine of the horse has normally a specific gravity of about 1·036 (that of man being about 1·020). In colour horses' urine is yellowish-brown, rapidly becoming brown on standing. It is always turbid (owing to suspended calcium and magnesium carbonates). Its odour is due to aromatic substances. Indican and hippuric acid are well-marked constituents, the latter taking the place of uric acid. Phosphates are absent or only present in small amounts. The quantity secreted depends upon the season, the diet, and the amount of work done. On a nitrogenous diet the amount of water in the urine is greater; on a diet of oats and no hay the mucinous substances are more numerous and may be so much so that the urine has the consistency of egg albumen. In winter, owing to the effect of cold on the skin, the quantity of urine is greater than in summer. For a similar kind of reason horses at work secrete less than horses at rest. The urine of mares during oestrus may have the consistency of oil.

The urine of the ox has a specific gravity of about 1·015, being less than that of the horse owing to the greater amount of water secreted. The nitrogenous content consists chiefly of urea and hippuric acid but there is less of the latter than in the horse. Straw of cereals produces a large amount of hippuric acid, and when this is so the amount of urea is correspondingly less. Calves while sucking yield a urine in which phosphates and uric acid are abundant, such animals resembling Carnivora.

The urine of the sheep has a specific gravity of about 1·010. Hippuric acid is abundant, being produced especially by a diet of new meadow hay.

The urine of the pig has a specific gravity of about 1·015. Its composition varies with the diet, pigs being, comparatively speaking, omnivorous. Uric and hippuric acids are both important constituents, and there is also much urea.

The urine of the dog has a specific gravity of about 1·030, but it varies within wide limits. Uric acid is present typically, but is absent on a herbivorous diet. On a normal flesh diet the reaction is very acid (owing to acid sodium phosphate resulting from oxidation of the phosphorus of proteins in the meat). Indican is usually present.

CHAPTER XII

THE FUNCTIONS OF THE SKIN

The skin is composed of two main parts, the epidermis and derm. The epidermis is subdivided into the cuticle or stratum corneum and the rete mucosum or Malpighian layer. Neither part of the epidermis contains any blood vessels.

The cuticular part consists of a stratified epithelium which is being continually given off in flakes. It is hard and horny. The rete mucosum is soft and protoplasmic, its cells frequently containing pigment (as in the coloured races of mankind). Intercellular channels conveying lymph are found in both parts of the epidermis but especially in the rete mucosum.

The derm or cutis vera is a dense connective tissue containing numerous blood vessels. Its surface adjoining the epidermis is raised into little more or less rounded elevations called the papillae. These often contain sensory end organs (tactile corpuscles). Adipose tissue, sweat glands, and the roots of the hair are also present in the derm in greater or less profusion.

The hair. A hair consists of horny epithelial cells. The part of it below the surface of the skin is enclosed in a kind of sac or follicle. At the bottom of this sac is the vascular papilla in which the newest portion of the hair develops. The shaft of the hair is developed by the epidermal cells surrounding the papilla becoming converted into horn. The cornified hair cells formed in this way are continually pushed outwards by fresh cells developed from below and the shaft of the hair consequently comes to protrude from the surface. When the hair is fully grown a new hair may arise by budding from the old papilla and sac. The walls of the sac or follicle form the root-sheaths and are composed of epidermal and dermal cells which dip down from the surface, so as to enclose the hair root. The follicle, papilla and root-sheath are provided with nerve fibres, especially well developed in large tactile hairs (whiskers). The hair shaft (i.e. the hair itself) is composed of a medulla or pith of loose texture and frequently containing air spaces, and a cortex which surrounds the medullary portion, and generally contains pigment giving the hair its peculiar colour. With the advance of

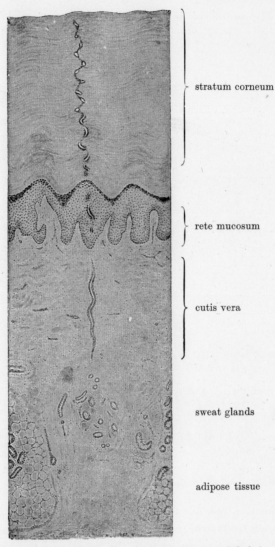

stratum corneum

rete mucosum

cutis vera

sweat glands

adipose tissue

Fig. 45. Vertical section through skin of sole of foot (from Schafer).

age this pigment is often removed by the action of phagocytes. Outside of the cortex is a thin cuticle formed of flat horny plate-like structures.

The use of hair is to assist in heat retention. For this reason

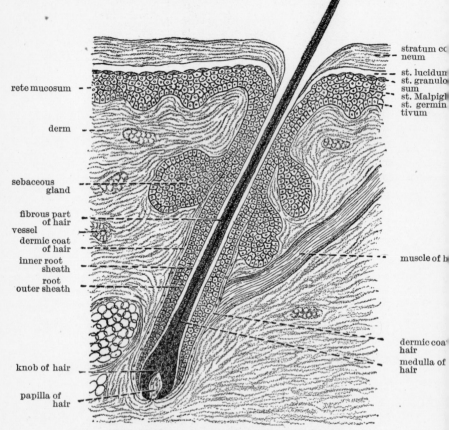

rete mucosum

stratum corneum
st. lucidum
st. granulosum
st. Malpighi
st. germinativum

derm

sebaceous gland

fibrous part of hair
vessel
dermic coat of hair
inner root sheath
root outer sheath

muscle of h

knob of hair

dermic coat hair
medulla of hair

papilla of hair

Fig. 46. Section of epidermis and derm (from Gray).

animals which are subjected to severe climatic conditions have thicker coats than those in warm countries. With horses the thickness of the hair varies with the breed, and the better bred the animal the finer the coat. There are about 4300 hairs to a square inch excepting on the muzzle and lips, the inside of the ears, the inside of the thigh, the mammary glands and the external genera-

tive organs where there are very few hairs. The coat is changed
twice a year, being alternately fine and thick. Generally speaking,

Fig. 47. Icelandic pony showing 'tail-lock' (from Ewart).

this change is related to the temperature of the air, and is not
simply seasonal. Thus horses in a heated atmosphere (such as a
horse deck on board ship) may shed their winter coat in a few days
although the outside temperature may be below freezing; similarly

if taken to a cold locality from a warm climate the hair responds by growing longer. There are, however, temporary exceptions to this rule, for horses after crossing the Equator may take a year before adjusting the length of their coat to the changed conditions. There are some hairs which grow permanently, not being shed at recurrent periods. Such are the hairs of the mane and tail (with some exceptions), the eyelashes, and the long tactile hairs on the muzzle. The comparatively short hairs of the upper part of the tail (i.e. those forming the tail-lock) in Icelandic ponies and other ponies of the Celtic type are shed at the beginning of summer and regrown at the commencement of the following cold season. These hairs, as Ewart has pointed out, serve the purpose of protecting the anal region from snow which collects upon the upper surface of the tail-lock. It is well known that clipping or cutting has a stimulating effect upon hairs, causing them to grow longer. In some animals there are muscles attached to the hair roots, the function of which is to ruffle the hairs and so diminish the conduction of heat. Similar muscles are connected with the feathers of birds.

The hairs of various kinds of animals present considerable differences. Thus the hairs in deer are composed almost entirely of medulla; those in pigs consist largely of horny substance; while hair which has the property of mutual cohesion or 'felting', depending upon a rough scaly surface and a disposition to curl, is characteristic of the sheep, being commonly called 'wool'.

Nails and claws, like hairs, are formed from the corneous cells of the epidermis which, instead of being thrown off as flakes, are consolidated to form horny structures. Underneath the nail is the vascular nail bed which is a modified part of the derm thrown up into parallel ridges. The hoofs of ungulates (described below in the chapter dealing with the organs of locomotion) have a similar origin to nails, being developed from horny epidermal elements fitting on to a modified derm. The horns of cattle and sheep consist of bony processes ensheathed in a case of true horn which, like the structures mentioned above, is of epidermal origin.

Sweat glands. Over most parts of the epidermis in man and in the horse, but confined to more or less restricted areas in certain other animals (see p. 141), are numerous pores which represent the openings of the ducts of the sweat glands. These ducts convey the secretions of the glands to the surface of the skin, and in so doing they traverse a portion of the derm and the whole of the epidermis. The actual glands are situated in the derm and consist of coiled tubes surrounded by a network of capillaries not unlike the glomeruli of the kidneys. The secretion (sweat or perspiration) contains protein, fat, salts and water and is alkaline in reaction.

Sebaceous glands. Sebum is the greasy material secreted by the sebaceous glands. These lie alongside of the hairs and communicate by short ducts with the hair follicles. The secretion lubricates the hairs, and in horses gives gloss to the groomed coat. It also helps to keep off wet.

Dandruff, which is the material removed in grooming a horse, consists of epithelial scales, fat, sebum, etc.

The functions of the skin are five in number:

(1) Protective.
(2) Sensory.
(3) Respiratory.
(4) Absorptive.
(5) Heat-regulating.

(1) The skin supplies a strong elastic coating for the body. It is thickest at places where liability to injury is most frequent.

(2) The skin is an organ of touch, being highly endowed with sensory nerve endings, especially in certain parts (e.g. the region of the external generative organs).

(3) The respiratory function is practically negligible in mammals and birds, but in some lower Vertebrata it is well developed. Thus frogs can live by breathing through their skin after the complete removal of the lungs.

(4) The skin's capacity for absorption is very low in mammals though it definitely exists. Colin kept the lumbar region of a horse wet with a solution of potassium ferrocyanide and found traces of the salt in the urine after $4\frac{1}{2}$ hours. The ill-effects of varnish on the skin are not owing to absorption, but are due to the fact that the varnish causes the capillaries to dilate and so produces an undue loss of heat.

(5) The heat-regulating mechanism possessed by the skin of all 'warm-blooded' animals is of very great importance. It is well known that in mammals and birds the temperature of the body is generally higher than that of the surrounding air. Moreover, under normal conditions it keeps approximately constant, not-

withstanding the varying temperatures to which the animal is exposed. This fact is implied in the term homoiothermal, which is applied to such animals. On the other hand, in poikilothermal or so-called 'cold-blooded' animals (e.g. reptiles and amphibians) the temperature of the body is, roughly speaking, the same as that of the outside air and varies with it. In hibernating animals (e.g. hedgehogs) there is a marked fall in the body temperature during the period of hibernation when the animal is in a state of deep sleep and complete inactivity.

The average normal temperatures in man and the domestic animals are as follows:

Man	98·4° F.	Pig	103° F.
Horse	100·5° F.	Dog	101° F.
Ox	100–102° F.	Fowl	101–6° F.
Sheep	103° F.		

These are the temperatures at or near the surface. In the centre of the body the temperature is slightly higher.

It is evident that since heat production is always going on in the body there must be a corresponding heat loss if the temperature is to keep constant. It has been estimated that a horse produces sufficient heat during rest to raise its temperature to boiling point in less than two days. The heat loss which prevents such a rise of temperature is regulated by certain special mechanisms in the skin.

The muscles are the chief seat of heat production. They make up half or more than half of the body weight. During rest the oxidation processes which give rise to heat are always going on, and during activity the output of heat is still greater, as can be proved directly by observing that the temperature of a muscle rises as a consequence of contracting. Besides the muscles, however, heat production is associated with oxidation in all the organs, and the liver and other glands are sources of much bodily heat.

This continual heat production is compensated for by the loss of heat by evaporation, radiation and conduction which takes place over the surface of the skin. The warmer the surface the greater is the heat loss, and the more blood going to the surface, the greater the warmth of the surface. The quantity of blood going to the surface is regulated by the nervous system. Thus when the surrounding air is warm, or when the bodily heat is increased by muscular exertion, the skin becomes hot and the vessels are dilated. The converse happens when the temperature is cold and the body is at rest; then the surface vessels become constricted and the heat loss is greatly reduced.

If however the external temperature is very high or exercise is severe, no amount of dilatation of vessels is sufficient to produce the necessary heat loss, and then another regulating mechanism comes into play, and this is the secretion of sweat. The moisture generally evaporates quickly unless formed too fast. It is a means of losing bodily heat. The secretory process is essentially a nerve reflex, and as in the case of the salivary glands may be antagonised by administering atropine. Moreover, by stimulating certain nerves electrically, sweat secretion can be increased (e.g. by stimulating the sciatic nerve in the dog when the sweat glands of the foot-pad secrete profusely).

There is experimental evidence of the existence of a centre in the fore brain which presides over and co-ordinates all the functional activities concerned with both heat production and heat loss.

As already mentioned, there is a compensating action between sweating and the secretion of urine, these two processes being inversely proportional in their respective activities. Furthermore, the sweat glands, besides supplying a heat-regulating mechanism, are definite organs of excretion.

The horse is the only hairy animal which sweats easily from nearly every part of the body. A horse begins to perspire at the bases of the ears, the neck, chest and back follow, and finally the hindquarters. Sweating does not take place on the legs. With donkeys and mules sweating is confined chiefly to the bases of the ears. Oxen sweat mainly on the muzzle, and only with some difficulty elsewhere. Sheep also perspire very little, the number of sweat glands being relatively few. In pigs sweating only takes place on the snout. Dogs and cats can sweat profusely on the muzzle and foot-pads, but not on the general surface of the body. A dog when heated by exertion pants and throws out its tongue, thereby admitting of an increased rate of heat loss, but the glands inside the mouth are not sweat glands.

The fact that oxen and many other animals possess comparatively few sweat glands and do not perspire freely on the body explains the much greater range of body temperature which these animals normally possess. They cannot undergo prolonged exertion without getting into a condition of distress, whereas a horse can gallop for miles. This is a point of some importance when we consider one of the methods of applying the tuberculin test to cattle. Before injecting the tuberculin, the temperature of the animal is taken frequently on several successive days (but very often in practice on only one day). It is again taken after injecting, and a rise of 2·5° F. consequent upon it is regarded as denoting a reaction (that is to say, that the animal is affected with tuberculosis which augmented by the tuberculin injected causes a rise of temperature). It should be remembered, however, in the light of what has just been stated that the rise of temperature in animals so susceptible as cattle, may be due to other and quite different causes, such as excitement or the periodic occurrence of oestrus, and that a rise apparently associated with an injection may be a coincidence. Furthermore, the initial temperatures taken before an injection may be abnormally high owing to the same or similar causes, and a genuinely tuberculous condition may pass unnoticed owing to there being little appreciable rise of temperature following upon the injection.

It is well known that moisture present in cold air assists in heat conduction but that moisture in warm air hinders evaporation. This is why a hot dry climate is so much less trying than a hot moist one. In warm, moist, tropical climates it is difficult for the heat-regulating mechanisms to cope with the extreme conditions.

Clipping or shearing is liable to throw a severe strain on the heat-regulating apparatus, especially in cold moist weather. For this reason a shepherd cannot be too careful not to shear his sheep when the weather is unfavourable. On the other hand, in very woolly or fat animals the accumulation of heat may be such as to constitute a source of danger.

It is interesting to note that in the pig the fat in the derm is normally well developed, for the pig has few hairs to withstand the conduction of heat.

In addition to the heat-regulating mechanisms described above there is some evidence that heat production within the body is regulated by the outside temperature. Thus animals which are exposed to cold tend to eat more, and so a greater quantity of food is available for heat production. Starvation produces a lowering of the temperature of the body, and the absorption of food raises it. Cold is least well stood by small lean animals, since in them the surface of the body is greater relative to their weight than in larger animals.

The rise of temperature which occurs during fevers is due partly to a defective dissipation of heat, the regulating mechanisms of the skin being deranged. Thus the skin surface is unusually dry and hot. Nevertheless, there is frequently also a great increase in the amount of heat actually produced during fevers, since the quantity dissipated may largely exceed the normal.

Cold perspiration is a pathological phenomenon and is apparently due to derangement of the nerves supplying the glands. It is unaccompanied by dilatation of the vessels. Disordered sweating is often associated with nervous affections.

CHAPTER XIII

THE NERVOUS SYSTEM

Every 'nerve' or nerve-trunk is composed of a number of fibres arranged in bundles and separated by connective tissue. The functional part of the nerve fibre is called the axon, and this in medullated nerves is surrounded by an insulated jacket composed of phosphorised fat and called the medulla or myelin. The medulla is broken at certain intervals to admit of the passage of nutriment

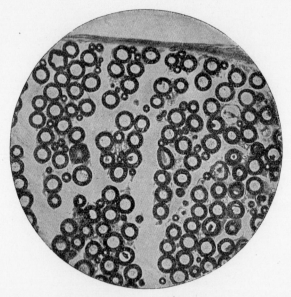

Fig. 48. Section through sciatic nerve of cat showing constituent fibres of different sizes (from Schafer).

to the axon from the tissue outside. The axons are extensions of nerve cells, and a nerve cell may have a number of such extensions. The name 'neuron' is given to a nerve cell together with all its extending axons, and the whole of the nervous system is composed of vast numbers of neurons.

The function of an axon is to convey a nerve impulse. The precise nature of such an impulse is still very obscure, but it appears to be a reversible physico-chemical process unassociated, so far as is known, with any but the very slightest metabolic change. It is accompanied, however, by the evolution of minute quantities of heat, and very small quantities of oxygen are absorbed and carbon dioxide given out. It is suggested that the surface of the nerve is the seat of the process which is of the nature of a local change in surface tension.

An impulse may be started artificially (as by stimulating with an electric current) at any part of a neuron, and if this is done it travels to every other part of the neuron. In normal life the impulse is started at one end of the neuron (being transmitted from the adjoining neuron), and travels to the other end, but in the case of accidents it may start at any point. Some slight expenditure of energy is required to set it up at the stimulated spot, but when once this is done, if the stimulus is sufficiently strong, it causes a propagated disturbance without being attended by any marked consumption or evolution of energy.

It is known that a nerve impulse is accompanied by an electrical change in the neuron concerned, and by taking advantage of this fact the rate of transmission of an impulse can be measured. A stimulus is applied at one end of a long nerve, and the electrical condition of the nerve is recorded by a galvanometer at the other end. In this way it has been found that an impulse travels at the rate of twenty feet per second.

When an axon is cut the part still connected with the cell survives, the severed portion alone undergoing degenerative changes, the subsequent observation of which may serve as a guide to the destination of particular fibres.

The nervous system is composed of (1) the brain and spinal cord (together constituting the central nervous system), and (2) all the other nerves of the body, these forming collectively the peripheral nervous system. Impulses are of two principal kinds, those passing into the central nervous system(or afferent impulses) and those passing out (or efferent impulses). These two chief kinds of impulses are never transmitted along the same neurons.

An afferent or sensory impulse starts at some special sense organ and is conveyed along a neuron, whose nerve cell is small and placed in a ganglion (a collection of nerve cells) outside of but not far from the brain or spinal cord. The particular impulses differ from one another in that each starts from a different position and is carried to its own special destination in the central nervous system. The skin is full of such end organs, and an impulse started in any one of them is different (though it may be only very slightly different) from an impulse started in any of the others.

The sensory end organs, the more important of which are described in the next chapter, may here be tabulated:

(1) End organs in the skin setting up impulses either on the application of pressure, or on being warmed or cooled.

(2) End organs in muscles, tendons, and ligaments, starting impulses when these are extended or contracted.

(3) The eye.

(4) The ear.

(5) The semicircular canals of the ear, which serve the purpose of balancing organs, owing to their containing fluid capable of running in three directions in a system of tubes, according to the position in which the head is held.

(6) The nasal organ (organ of smell).

(7) The mouth (taste organs).

(8) End organs which start impulses when neighbouring tissue is destroyed, the impulses conveying the sensation of pain which must be regarded as a warning of the existence of danger.

(9) Special end organs starting sensations peculiar to themselves (e.g. in the rectum, when full of faeces and calling for the act of defaecation).

The impulses which enter the central nervous system pass up and down through many neurons, the direction that they take being determined partly by congenital tendency and partly as a result of previous impulses which have acted on the nerve cells through which they passed; that is to say, the direction of a nerve impulse may be effected both by heredity and by education or training, and a nerve reflex may be established in either of these ways.

An impulse can pass from one neuron to the next in one direction only. This is because the synapse or region where two neurons join has a valve-like effect.

The efferent nerves by which the impulses leave the central nervous system are of two kinds. First, there are axons which innervate voluntary or striated muscles (the movement of which is under the control of the will). Such nerve fibres pass directly to the muscle without interruption, and the nerve cell from which the axons arise is situated within the central nervous system. Secondly, there are efferent nerve channels which, instead of going directly to the organ to be supplied, terminate at a nerve cell located in a ganglion. Such fibres are called 'pre-ganglionic'. The nervous message is then transmitted through another nerve fibre, which is therefore post-ganglionic and innervates the organ or part concerned, in this case either a secreting gland or involuntary unstriated muscle.

Examples of secreting glands which are thus innervated by post-ganglionic fibres are the salivary glands, the gastric and intestinal glands, the sweat glands and the lachrymal or tear glands. Examples of involuntary muscle innervated in the same kind of way are the muscles of the stomach and intestine, those of the uterus and bladder, as well as the muscles of the heart and blood vessels. All these muscles are uncontrolled by the will, and act in a purely automatic way.

The autonomic system which supplies involuntary muscle and secreting glands may be divided into cranial, thoracic and sacral nerves, according to the region of the central nervous system from which they take origin. The thoracic autonomic system is frequently designated the sympathetic nervous system owing to an idea which formerly prevailed regarding its nature. It has already been shown in previous chapters that many organs have two sources of autonomic nerve supply, the functions of which are different or even antagonistic. Thus the heart is excited to beat faster by stimuating the sympathetic supply, and slowed down by stimulating the vagus or cranial autonomic fibres, the vagus nerves having been described as the 'reins of the heart'. Similarly the arteries receive vaso-constrictor and vaso-dilator fibres which arise from different regions of the central nervous system, but the constrictor nerve fibres are always thoracic autonomic (i.e. sympathetic) in origin, and it is these fibres which are acted on so powerfully by adrenaline, which is the active substance of the secretion of the suprarenal body.

THE CENTRAL NERVOUS SYSTEM

The body wall of the cranium and of the vertebral canal is lined internally by a fibrous membrane called the dura mater. The central nervous system throughout is lined by another membrane termed the pia mater which is very vascular. In between these membranes and loosely attached to them is a third membrane called the arachnoid membrane. All these membranes are composed of connective tissue.

Both brain and spinal cord contain grey matter and white matter. The grey matter consists of nerve cells together with their

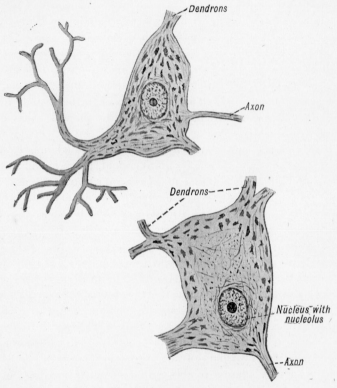

Fig. 49. Nerve cells from spinal cord of ox.

smaller processes and a framework of supporting cells called neuroglia. The white matter consists entirely of nerve fibres representing axons of cells in the grey matter and tending to run in parallel strands along the length of the cord. It is soft and pulpy and contains very little connective tissue.

The Brain. The different parts of the brain are described in every text-book on anatomy, and it will suffice here to give a very

brief description of the principal of these parts with some reference
to their more important functions.

The cerebrum, which occupies a large part of the cranium, is
divided into the two hemispheres. The surfaces of these are convoluted, the extent of the convolutions varying considerably in
different species of animals. The grey matter is external to the
white matter. The cerebral hemispheres are especially well developed in man, being the seat of the intelligence. An animal
without the cerebrum is incapable of conscious sensation and can
perform no voluntary movement. It can respond appropriately
to every kind of stimulus from outside, but it cannot originate,
and it cannot associate its sensations. It is quite devoid of all

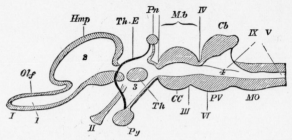

Fig. 50. Diagrammatic longitudinal section through brain (after Huxley, from
Halliburton). *Olf*, olfactory lobe; *Hmp*, hemisphere; *Th.E*, thalamencephalon;
Pn, pineal body; *Py*, pituitary body; *Th*, optic thalamus; *M.b*, midbrain; *CC*,
crura cerebri; *Cb*, cerebellum; *PV*, Pons Varolii; *MO*, medulla oblongata;
I–IX, cranial nerves; 1–4, cavities or ventricles.

reasoning power. A frog deprived of its cerebral hemispheres will
swim to land if put into water but once it has reached a position
of rest it will remain in that position until interfered with by any
fresh stimulus. A dog so deprived will eat and perform all its
essential bodily functions, but it will never recognise its master,
nor carry out any act implying intelligence. The hemispheres
contain certain areas associated with particular functions and any
injury to these areas destroys or deleteriously affects the discharge
of the function in question. Thus there is a visual and an auditory
area, and areas for taste and smell, as well as for tactile and muscular sensibility, for speech, for the association of ideas, and
various other functions.

The two hemispheres are connected by a transverse commissure
called the corpus callosum. The hemispheres are connected with
the medulla or hind brain by two large bands of nerve fibres called

the crura cerebri. The olfactory lobes project forward from beneath the front end of the hemispheres.

The thalamencephalon is the vesicle of the fore brain from which the hemispheres arise in development as hollow outgrowths. It comes to be completely obscured by the hemispheres. Here all the afferent nerves of true sensation meet and then extend to the hemispheres.

The corpora quadrigemina or optic lobes are also almost com-

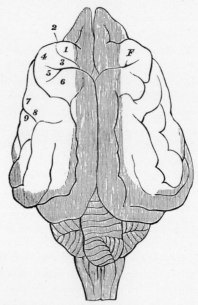

Fig. 51. Brain of dog (after Dalton, from Halliburton). *F*, frontal fissure; 1–9, motor areas (1 and 2 for head, 3–6 limbs, 7–9 facial muscles).

pletely covered by the hemispheres. They contain centres for the adjustment of the pupil of the eye for light, for sneezing, and for various other movements.

The cerebellum lies behind the hemispheres. Its surface is folded, and it has grey matter outside and white matter within. It is in reality a paired expansion of the pons, just as the cerebrum is a paired expansion of the extreme anterior end of the central nervous system. The cerebellum receives afferent nerves from the semi-circular canals of the ear, and from many joints, muscles, and tendons concerned with bodily movement. Nerve fibres pass from this part of the brain to other parts of the central nervous system and especially to the spinal cord. Injury to the cerebellum is followed by lack of co-ordination in muscular movement.

The pons Varolii is a stout band of nerve fibres passing transversely across and in front of the medulla oblongata. It connects together the two sides of the cerebellum. It contains the centre for closing the eyelids in the presence of strong illumination.

The medulla oblongata or hind brain is a continuation of the spinal cord within the cranial cavity. It differs from the cord in having white matter penetrating the internal grey matter. In the medulla large strands of white fibres in passing back from the cerebral hemispheres cross over one another to the opposite side, and it is for this reason that injury (as in an apoplectic fit) affecting one side of the fore brain produces a condition of paralysis, not on the same side, but on the opposite side of the body. The medulla contains numerous centres presiding over particular functions, some of which have been referred to in previous chapters. Thus the centres regulating the respiratory movements, the beating of the heart, the secretion of saliva and gastric juice, and the movements of the oesophagus, stomach and intestines are situated in the medulla.

The cavities of the cerebral hemispheres are termed the lateral ventricles, that of the thalamencephalon is the third ventricle, and that of the medulla is the fourth ventricle.

The cranial nerves with their points of origin may here be enumerated, but for detailed accounts of their respective courses the reader is referred to text-books on anatomy. The nerves arise in pairs and are as follows:

1. Olfactory, or nerves of smell, arising from the front of each cerebral hemisphere.

2. Optic, or nerves of sight, arising from the thalamencephalon.

3. Ocular-motor innervating some of the muscles of the eyeball and arising from the region of the corpora quadrigemina.

4. Trochlear, motor nerves supplying the superior oblique muscle of the eyeball, and arising from the same region as the 3rd nerves.

5. Trigeminal, so-called because on each side they divide into three; they contain sensory fibres for the mouth and tongue, and motor fibres for the muscles used in mastication; they arise from the pons.

6. Abducens, motor nerves supplying the external rectus of the eyeball, and arising just behind the pons from the medulla.

7. Facial, motor nerves supplying the muscles of expression (in face, mouth and lips) and arising immediately behind the trigeminals.

8. Auditory, or nerves of hearing, arising from the sides of the medulla.

9. Glossopharyngeal, partly sensory and partly motor nerves, supplying the tongue and muscles of the pharynx, and arising from the side of the medulla.

10. Vagus, or pneumogastric, partly motor and partly sensory, passing from the sides of the medulla and running down the neck and thorax to the abdomen, and giving branches to the larynx, lungs, heart, oesophagus, stomach, intestines, and liver.

11. Spinal accessory, motor nerves, arising by ten rootlets from the medulla and spinal cord, and supplying certain muscles in the neck.

12. Hypoglossal, arising from the ventral surface of the medulla and supplying the muscles of the tongue.

The *spinal cord* is continuous with the medulla and passes backwards through the spinal canal inside the vertebral column as far as the lumbar region. Like the brain it is composed of both grey and white matter, but the grey matter in the cord is always

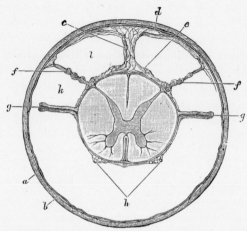

Fig. 52. Section through spinal cord within its membranes (after Key and Retzius, from Schafer). *f*, bundles of posterior root; *h*, bundles of anterior root; *a–g*, membranes, trabeculae etc.; *k*, *l*, spaces.

centrally placed and gives off symmetrically on each side a dorsal and a ventral horn, and in some regions a lateral horn. The dorsal and ventral horns are clearly shown in any transverse section through the cord. There is a deep dorsal fissure almost joining a shallower and more open ventral fissure, and these fissures divide the cord into two lateral halves excepting for the median portion between them in the middle of which is the central canal. The fissures are partly filled with connective tissue which contains vessels and passes into the substance of the cord supplying it with blood.

The white matter which lies on the outside of the grey matter contains fibres connecting together the different parts of the central nervous system. These fibres convey impulses up and down the cord, and one well-marked tract of white matter coming from the cerebral hemispheres is believed to be concerned with the co-ordination of skilled movements.

The spinal nerves are given off in pairs at regular intervals from the cord. Each nerve arises by two roots, one dorsal and one ventral. The dorsal root contains only afferent fibres, and each has its ganglion containing the nerve cells of the fibres. The ventral root contains efferent fibres. The two roots join one another a short distance from the cord, and form a mixed nerve trunk containing both sensory and motor fibres, the ganglia of the dorsal roots being situated a short distance away from the cord and near the place where the two sets of fibres merge to form a single trunk containing mixed fibres. If the dorsal root is destroyed, the sensations which

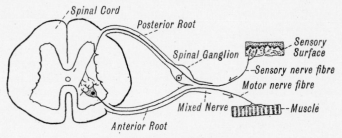

Fig. 53. The simple reflex arc.

the nerve fibres normally convey can no longer be felt. Similarly if the efferent fibres of the ventral root are destroyed, although the sensations conveyed by the fibres of the dorsal root are felt, the muscles in the part of the body concerned (e.g. those of an injured limb) are paralysed and can no longer respond to stimuli by appropriate movements.

If the spinal cord is transected as by an animal breaking its back the portion of the cord posterior to the break will be cut off from the higher centres of the brain, and all those parts of the body which are innervated from the isolated region of the cord will be devoid of feeling. Nevertheless, reflex action can still occur in those parts, since afferent impulses can enter the cord and efferent impulses pass out although unaccompanied by sensation. Thus a frog whose brain has been destroyed, if its foot is pinched or irritated by an acid, will withdraw its leg or attempt to rub away the source of irritation with its other leg, but it is incapable of sensation and unconscious of its actions.

As has been shown already, the spinal cord contains numerous centres which preside over certain necessary functions of the body (e.g. defaecation, micturition, seminal ejaculation, penile erection, and parturition) and admit of the appropriate reflexes being carried out. But in the normal uninjured animal it is also the function of the cord to transmit sensory impulses to the higher centres of the brain, and so to bring the consequent motor impulses under the control of the volition.

Inhibition and Sleep. Certain efferent nerve fibres passing to glands or muscles are not excitatory but inhibitory in function, and if stimulated will prevent the continuance of the active process which otherwise would have gone on. Thus, according to Pavlov, the vagus contains fibres which are inhibitory for pancreatic secretion. The vagus also contains fibres which may be inhibitory to the heart's action, and can transmit impulses which produce increased resistance to transmission from auricle to ventricle. Moreover, certain parts of the brain can exert an inhibitory influence over centres situated posteriorly. Thus Sherrington found that after cutting through the crura cerebri, centres for certain groups of muscles were greatly increased in excitability. The centres in question are situated between the crura cerebri and the medulla, and normally their activity is partially inhibited by the cerebral cortex.

Bayliss has suggested that sleep is a condition of inactivity (displayed by the parts of the brain associated with consciousness) which follows on inhibition if no further excitatory stimuli occur. The inhibition may be brought about by a stimulus as in the case of a child who is soothed to sleep by a lullaby. After all excitatory stimuli have been removed, the inhibition itself disappears and sleep continues as a zero state, excitation and inhibition both being absent. It is well known that hypnotic sleep in man is caused by stimuli from without, and these stimuli must be supposed to produce a state of inhibition in nerve centres in the brain.

The unconscious state characteristic of sleep can be brought to an end by excitatory stimuli of relatively great intensity. Taking advantage of this fact, deepness of sleep may be measured by the intensity of the stimuli necessary to awaken the sleeper. Thus it has been ascertained in man that sleep is most intense during the first hour and a half (after the first few minutes) and then becomes rapidly less. Thus sounds which fail to wake the sleeper during the early hours of the night, will bring sleep to an end at any time from the beginning of the third hour onwards.

Apart from loss of consciousness, certain other physiological phenomena characterise sleep. The respirations and the heart beats become slower. Secretory activity, such as that of the kidney, or of the mucous glands is diminished. It is believed, however, that the digestive organs are little if at all less active during sleep, provided that there is food in the stomach or intestines. The supply of blood to the brain is said to be diminished during sleep, and this according to some is one of the main factors inducing sleep. On the other hand, according to Howell, the diminished supply of blood is of the nature of a result, the cause being fatigue on the part of the vaso-motor centre in the medulla. As a result of constant activity in the daytime this centre is supposed to become so fatigued that it is no longer able to maintain a sufficient flow of blood through the brain, and unconsciousness or sleep is the result.

Sleep is the period of rest and recuperation when the constructive or anabolic side of animal activity dominates over the destructive or katabolic side. Want of sleep is even more damaging than starvation, for dogs deprived of food for three weeks may yet undergo recovery, whereas after five days without sleep they die. But why the state of sleep should recur normally with such rhythmical regularity and what are the precise factors in metabolism which govern this recurrence, are questions which on the evidence available admit only of very imperfect solutions. That night is the time for sleep, both with man and with most animals, is known to all, and it is obvious that the setting in of darkness is its immediate cause, while the daylight which comes at dawn is the stimulus for awakening.

CHAPTER XIV

THE ORGANS OF SPECIAL SENSE

The organs of special sense have been alluded to in the preceding chapter. It will suffice here to give a short description of the eye, the ear, and the organs of taste and smell.

The Eye. The eye is an organ specially adapted to receive and retain visual impressions. It is a globular structure, consisting for the greater part of a tough white fibrous coat, the *sclerotic* coat,

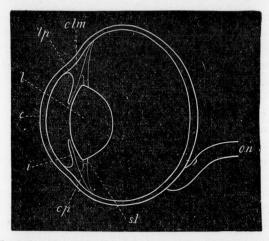

Fig. 54. Vertical section of the eye of the horse, natural size. *c*, cornea; *l*, lens; *i*, iris; *cp*, ciliary process; *lp*, ligamentum pectinatum; *clm*, position of ciliary muscle; *sl*, suspensory ligament of lens; *on*, optic nerve, showing its curve. Note its attachment to the lower part of the globe. (From Smith, Messrs Baillière, Tindall and Cox.)

bounded in front by a transparent watch-glass-like structure called the *cornea*. Inserted into the sclerotic coat towards the front portion of the eyeball are six muscles, the superior and inferior oblique muscles, the superior and inferior rectus muscles, and the internal and external rectus muscles. These muscles, which all find their origin in the rear of the bony orbit or eye socket, by their action control and facilitate the movement of the eyeball in any desired direction. Together they play an extremely important part in the case of man in ensuring that the images received by the two eyes give rise to a single visual impression.

The accessory structures, the eyelids, eyelashes, and the lachrymal glands, together with the conjunctiva, a delicate membrane lining the inner surface of the eyelids and continued over the front surface of the eyeball, protect the eye from the liability to injury from dust and other foreign bodies. The watery secretion from the lachrymal glands continually floods across the surface of the conjunctiva to the inner angle of the eyes, whence it drains away through the lachrymal duct to the nasal cavity, carrying with it any dust particles which may have lodged on the surface of the conjunctiva.

The internal structure of the eye. A longitudinal section through the eyeball demonstrates that the eye is divided into two compartments by a delicate, elastic, transparent, lenticular-shaped body, the crystalline lens, which is doubly convex, and is held in place by a strong membranous frame called the suspensory ligament, which in turn is itself inserted into the inner or choroid coat of the eye-ball. The front compartment, bounded externally by the cornea and internally by the crystalline lens, is filled with a semi-fluid, transparent substance called the aqueous humour. The posterior compartment is also filled with a clear jelly-like substance called the vitreous humour, and these humours by their action cause the eye to preserve its globular shape. Lying in front of the crystalline lens is a pigmented, curtain-like structure called the iris which is pierced in the centre by an aperture, the *pupil*, through which the light rays penetrate into the interior of the eye. The shape of the pupil varies in the domestic animals, in man and the dog it is circular, in the horse, sheep and ox it is elliptical, the long axis of the ellipse being horizontal. The iris itself is pigmented, is opaque to light, and contains circular and longitudinal unstriated muscular fibres, which by their action cause the pupil to dilate or contract and thus regulate the amount of light which is allowed to pass through the crystalline lens.

Action of the crystalline lens. Light rays passing from a near or distant object and falling on the surface of the eye are refracted or bent in passing through the crystalline lens and are brought to a focus on the hinder part of the inner surface of the eye, so forming an inverted image of the object in a way similar to that in which the lens of a camera, when properly focused, throws an image on the ground glass focusing screen. By the contraction or relaxation of a muscle, called the ciliary muscle, the convexity of the crystalline lens is varied so that a sharp image of the object looked at is thrown on the back interior surface of the eyeball. Inability to focus the image sharply gives rise to the defects of vision known as longsightedness (hypermetropia) and shortsightedness (myopia). Stretching over the posterior two-thirds of the inner surface of the eyeball is a delicate nervous curtain, the *retina*, and it is on this curtain that the image is thrown and focused. The retina, which is partially formed from the continuation of the fibres of the *optic* nerve, is a very complex structure and contains the sense end-

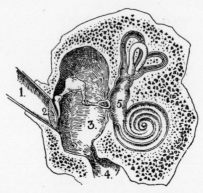

Fig. 55. Diagrammatic section of the horse's ear. 1, External auditory canal; 2, the tympanum; 3, chain of bones across the middle ear; 4, the Eustachian tube; 5, the internal ear; the number is on the vestibule, above which may be seen the semicircular canals, while below is the cochlea. (From Smith, Messrs Baillière, Tindall and Cox.)

organs, the stimulation of which by the action of light give rise to the sense of perception in the brain.

The Ear. The auditory apparatus consists of three parts—the external ear, the middle ear, and the internal ear. The internal ear contains the essential mechanism which converts the external waves of sound into a condition suitable for transmission into the brain, the middle and external ear acting as agents for the collection and transmission of sound to the internal ear.

The *external ear* is made up of the pinna and the external auditory meatus. The pinna, which is varied in shape, is composed chiefly of elastic fibro-cartilage, invested with a thin closely adherent skin. In the domestic animals muscles are present which

enable the animal to move the pinnae in the direction of the source
of sound. The pinnae by their shape serve to collect and intensify
the sound waves transmitted through the air in the direction of
the animal. From the central hollow or concha of the pinna passes
a canal, the external auditory meatus, along which the sound waves
pass. The external auditory meatus consists partly of cartilage
and partly of bone and at its termination in the bony part of the
skull is bounded by a parchment-like membrane called the tympanic membrane, or drum of the ear.

The *middle ear* consists essentially of a cavity in the temporal
bone of the skull, is lined for the most part with ciliated mucous
membrane, and communicates with the cavity of the mouth by
means of the cylindriform canal called the Eustachian tube, the
external opening of which occurs in the pharynx. The function of
the Eustachian tube is to allow the passage of air from the exterior
to the middle ear, thus allowing for variations of pressure of the
atmosphere and ensuring equality of pressure on both sides of the
tympanic membrane.

The walls of the middle ear are bony except where interrupted
by small apertures covered with membrane, as at the fenestra
rotunda and fenestra ovalis, and in the outer part, the tympanic
membrane. The tympanic membrane is tightly stretched in an
oblique direction across the end of the external auditory meatus,
forming a division between this canal and the middle ear. Stretching from the tympanic membrane across the cavity of the middle
ear to the fenestra ovalis is a chain of three small bones, the auditory
ossicles, called by reason of their shapes the malleus, incus and
stapes. The malleus is attached to the tympanic membrane and the
foot of the stapes (or stirrup bone) is attached to the fenestra ovalis,
the incus articulating between these two bones.

The tympanic membrane and the fenestra ovalis are also
provided with small but relatively strong muscles which by their
action vary the tension of these two membranes as required.

The *internal* ear, or ear proper, consists of a membranous bag
(the membranous labyrinth) filled with a fluid called the endolymph, and this bag is lodged in cavities of the petrosal portion of
the temporal bone specially hollowed to receive it. Between the
membranous labyrinth and the investing bony or osseous labyrinth
is a fluid called the perilymph.

The osseous labyrinth consists of three portions, the vestibule, the cochlea and the semicircular canals (fig. 55). The vestibule, or middle cavity, presents several apertures through which penetrate divisions of the auditory nerve. The portion of the membranous bag or labyrinth lying within the vestibule forms two communicating compartments, the utricle and the saccule. Into the utricle open the semicircular canals, while the saccule communicates with the canal of the cochlea by a small canal called the canalis reuniens. The cochlear portion of the osseous labyrinth resembles in shape a snailshell, the circular coil consisting of two and a half turns, closed at its upper termination, but presenting openings at the base for the fenestra ovalis, the fenestra rotunda and the canalis reuniens. A section through one of the coils reveals the fact that the coil is separated into three portions, the scala media or canal of the cochlea, the scala vestibuli and the scala tympani. The division of the cochlea into the scala vestibuli and scala tympani is effected by a flat sill-like projection of bone from the internal surface of the coil (the lamina spiralis), the outer edge of this spiral being continued to the outer border of the coil by a membrane called the basilar membrane. On this membrane rests the canal of the cochlea. The scala vestibuli is closed at its basal portion by the *fenestra ovalis* and communicates with the scala tympani at its apical end by a small aperture called the *helicotrema*. The scala tympani in its turn is closed at its basal portion by the fenestra rotunda.

Nerve distribution. The auditory nerve divides into two branches, one of which supplies the utricle, saccule, and the semicircular canals, the other or cochlear branch, running up the centre of the cochlea, giving off branches through the lamina spiralis, these branches terminating in fine filaments which form special end sense organs in the canal of the cochlea. These sense end organs have a complicated structure and are known collectively as the organ of Corti. The semicircular canals are balancing organs (see p. 146).

Physiology of hearing. The transmission of sound waves to the brain takes the following course. The wave-like concussions caused by the vibration of air particles against the tympanic membrane make this tightly stretched membrane vibrate rapidly. These vibrations are communicated to the bony ossicles, which undergo varied movements. The stapes, which, as we have already seen, is attached to the fenestra ovalis, causes this membrane to vibrate and so sets up a series of vibratory waves in the perilymph which fills the scala vestibuli. These waves travel up the cochlea, pass through the helicotrema, travel down the scala tympani and end against the fenestra rotunda which in turn is set in vibration. During their passage through the cochlea these vibration waves impinge on the membranes enclosing the canal of the cochlea setting up a sympathetic series of vibrations in the endolymph of the canal of the cochlea and so act on the delicate nerve endings in the organ of Corti. The stimuli thus received are conveyed to the brain and give rise to the sensation of hearing.

The Sense of Taste. The sense of taste is associated with the presence of certain well defined groups of cells, called gustatory cells, which are found in the characteristic papillae of the mucous membrane of the tongue and are restricted to well-defined areas. According to their shape, these papillae or projections are called filiform, fungiform and circumvallate papillae, and the fungiform and circumvallate papillae are specially associated with the sense of taste. The gustatory cells are found in bud-like groups and are called taste buds. In the ox, the fungiform papillae are numerous and distinct and are found scattered over the dorsum and edges of the free part of the tongue. The circumvallate papillae number 8 to 17 on each side, forming a narrow group on either edge of the base of the tongue. In the horse the fungiform papillae are large and easily seen and occur principally on the lateral part of the tongue. The circumvallate papillae are two or three in number, the two constant ones being $\frac{1}{4}$ in. or more in diameter and are found on the upper surface of the base of the tongue, one on each side of the middle line about an inch apart. Foliate or leaf-like papillae are also present on the anterior pillars of the soft palate and contain taste buds.

Each gustatory cell is long and very thin, has a large nucleus at its middle point, and ends in a delicate process which projects like a stiff hair through the open mouth of the taste bud. The papillae are supplied with branches from two nerves, the glosso-pharyngeal nerve, and the gustatory nerve which is a branch of the 5th cranial nerve. There is evidence for the belief that different taste sensations are supplied by these two nerves. In the case of man, we find that tastes may be classified under four chief heads: sweet, bitter, sour or acid, and salt. In order to taste a substance it must first be dissolved, in order to act upon the gustatory cells.

The Sense of Smell. The sense of smell is very well developed in animals and plays a large part in their normal life and habits. The organ of smell consists of a well-defined area of mucous membrane lining part of the nasal cavities, and characterised by the absence of cilia. This olfactory region, as it is called, is well supplied with branches of the olfactory nerve, together with a few fibres from the 5th cranial nerve. The olfactory mucous membrane contains cells of two kinds, those associated with the production of the sense of smell, numerous, long slender rod-shaped cells, and others whose chief function is to support the true olfactory cells with which they are intermixed. The sensation of smell arises through the stimulus of minute quantities of odoriferous matter exciting the olfactory cells, the stimulus thus created being carried back through the olfactory nerve to the brain.

CHAPTER XV

THE ORGANS OF LOCOMOTION

The muscular tissues of an animal have the special function of altering the positions of various parts of the body relative to one another. By means of this function, which is due to the contractility of the tissue and its capacity to respond to nervous impulses, locomotion is effected. The principal kinds of muscle have been already sufficiently described. It has also been mentioned that whereas the muscles of the heart and blood vessels and the unstriated muscles generally are involuntary, those of the limbs, which are striated, are under the control of the will.

The contraction of a particular muscle (e.g. the gastrocnemius of the calf of the frog's leg) can be induced experimentally by stimulating electrically the nerve which supplies it (e.g. the sciatic), and if the stimuli are made to succeed one another at a rate such that the muscle has not begun to relax before the next stimulus reaches it, it is driven into a condition of continuous contraction or 'tetanus'.

The process of contraction in muscle is associated with the splitting off of lactic acid, but at first there is no evolution of carbon dioxide. This takes place in the second stage which succeeds the contraction stage. Fats or carbohydrates are then oxidised, and the lactic acid is restored to the muscle. Energy is set free equivalent to the heat evolved and the work done, the former being utilised to keep up the temperature of the body.

It is well known that exercise increases muscular efficiency. This is due partly to the direct effect of exercise in developing the muscles, and partly to the fact that with repeated usage the muscles work more economically, those which are superfluous remaining at rest. It is only after repeated trials that the nervous impulses become properly distributed to the necessary muscles.

The composition of muscular tissue varies within considerable limits owing to the inconstant quantities of fat or connective tissue present. The following represents the approximate average composition after removal of the more obvious fat:

Protein	18	per cent.	Salts	2·1	per cent.
Fat and gelatin	4	,,	Water	75	,,
Glycogen, etc.	0·9	,,			

The muscles of motion and locomotion act in virtue of their property of contraction. They are attached to bones by tendons, one tendon being attached to one bone and the other tendon to a separate bone, the muscular fibres in between passing over one or more joints. The attachment to the more stationary bone is usually referred to as the origin of the muscle, while the attachment to the more movable bone is generally called the insertion. Muscles can contract to about two-thirds of their normal length.

We may now consider very briefly some of the chief muscles in the fore and hind limbs of the horse, and then pass on to the mechanical laws under which these muscles work.

The Muscles of the Fore Limb. The shoulder blade is connected to the trunk by a very strong muscle (the serratus magnus) which is attached to the last five cervical vertebrae, to the first eight ribs and, in the middle, to the inside of the shoulder blade. When the front portion of the muscle contracts, the shoulder is drawn forwards. When the rear contracts it is drawn backwards.

The upper part of the shoulder blade is connected to the trunk by a muscle attached to the inner extremity of the former, and having one branch (the dorsal trapezius) going to the withers and the other (the cervical trapezius) going to the suspensory ligament of the neck. When the latter branch contracts it draws the shoulder blade forwards. When the dorsal trapezius contracts it has the reverse effect.

The fore limb is drawn forwards chiefly, however, by a muscle attached at one end to the head and top of the neck and at the other end to the middle of the humerus. The fore limb is drawn backwards by the action of two muscles. The first of these is attached to the sternum at one end, and to the humerus and shoulder blade at the other. It pulls the limb backwards and downwards. The second muscle is attached to the dorsal and lumbar vertebrae and to the humerus. It pulls the limb backwards and upwards.

When the fore limb is advanced, the shoulder blade is extended and the elbow flexed. This action is due to the contraction of a muscle (the flexor brachii) attached at one end to the front of the shoulder blade and at the other end to the front of the radius just below the elbow joint.

The chief muscle that extends the 'knee' or wrist (the extensor metacarpi magnus) has its origin in the front part of the humerus;

it runs down the forearm, its tendon passing over the 'knee' and being inserted on the head of the cannon bone.

The three muscles that bend the knee take origin on the back of the humerus just above the elbow and are inserted on the splint bones (internus, medius and externus metacarpi flexor).

The two muscles which extend the fetlock, pastern and coffin joints run down the front of the forearm. One has its origin on the head of the radius and is inserted on the front of the large pastern bone (extensor metacarpi). The other starts on the humerus above the elbow and passes to the front part of the coffin bone (extensor pedis).

The muscles that flex the fetlock, pastern, and coffin joints, and also aid in bending the knee, take their origin just above the elbow joint at the back of the humerus, and proceed down the posterior side of the forearm. A little above the 'knee' they become joined to their tendons. These are attached one to the base of the coffin bone (the flexor pedis perforans tendon) and the other to the small pastern or coronet (the flexor pedis perforatus tendon).

The Flight Muscles of Birds. The fore limb of most birds is specially adapted for flight, and the muscular arrangements involved form an interesting study. In flight a considerable number of muscles are involved, but those chiefly concerned in the up-and-down movements of the wings are the pectoral muscles. These are three in number. By far the largest of these is the pectoralis major, the fleshy origin of which is attached to the outer marginal third of the keel of the sternum, to part of the lateral wing of the sternum, and to the clavicle along its length. The broad tendinous insertion is attached to the proximal third of the humerus. Contraction of the pectoralis major exerts a powerful pull on the humerus, thus resulting in a downward movement of the wing. The pectoralis major is aided in its action by a small muscle, the pectoralis tertius, which arises from the body of the sternum and the lower outer third of the coracoid, and is attached to the humerus by a strong flattened tendinous insertion.

The elevation of the wing is brought about by the contraction of the pectoralis minor. This muscle, which underlies the pectoralis major, arises from the coracoid, keel and wing of the sternum, and is relatively small in size compared with the pectoralis major. The body of the muscle tapers to a long tendon which passes outwards and upwards round the coracoid, then passes backwards through a small canal (foramen triosseum) formed by the junction of the clavicle, the scapular and the coracoid, finally becoming inserted in the head of the humerus on its upper side. The pull of the pectoralis minor is thus reversed in direction and its contraction leads to the elevation of the wing.

The Muscles of the Hind Limb. The hip of the horse is extended by the croup (gluteal) muscles, and also by some muscles which lie at the back of the femur. It is flexed by muscles which have their origin on the under surface of the lumbar vertebrae and are inserted on to the femur.

The stifle (true knee) is extended by a muscle (triceps extensor) which has its origin on the under surface of the pelvis joint in front of the hip joint, and is inserted on the patella or knee cap. It is flexed by a muscle attached to the portion of the pelvis behind the hip joint, and to the tibia.

The hock is extended by the gastrocnemius which has its origin on the lower end of the femur, and is inserted by tendons on the point of the hock. One of the tendons (the one passing underneath) terminates at the hock, but the other (the flexor pedis perforatus) passes to the small pastern, and is the flexor of the fetlock. Thus the hock cannot be extended without the fetlock being flexed. The flexor metatarsi bends the hock.

The joints below the hock are extended by muscles which take origin near the stifle, run down the front of the limb, are continued as tendons down the front part of the cannon bone, and finally are inserted on the pastern and coffin bones. They are flexed by a muscle originating at the back of the upper portion of the tibia behind which it runs down to the hock joint where it is continued as a tendon (flexor perforans), and terminates, as in the fore limb, at the bottom of the coffin bone.

The Mechanics of Locomotion. The principal kinds of movements which the limbs may be made to undergo by the contraction and expansion of their muscles may be classified naturally under four heads: (1) Flexion or bending, (2) Extension or straightening out, (3) Abduction or drawing away from the middle line, and (4) Adduction or bringing to the middle line. To these may be added (5) Rotation, when a limb is made to turn on its own axis, and (6) Circumduction, when it is made to describe a conical surface by rotation around an imaginary axis.

Now in a large number of these movements a joint is involved, and the bone of the part which moves acts as a lever, and turns about that portion of itself which forms part of the joint concerned and acts as a relatively fixed point or fulcrum. We may now consider the three kinds of levers, and then proceed to give examples of these levers as shown by the movements of certain of the limb muscles which have been already described.

In the first kind of lever the fulcrum is between the weight and the power. It is the lever of power and in the body it is the lever of extension. Thus in extending the hind leg, the centre of the hock joint is the fulcrum, the gastrocnemius is the power, the distance from the summit of the calcaneum to the centre of the hock joint is the power arm, the leg below the hock is the weight and the length of the metatarsus is the weight arm.

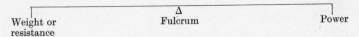

In the second kind of lever the fulcrum is at one end and is nearer to the weight than to the power. This lever is not common in the body. It occurs when the leg is fixed on the ground and the body is passing over it. The ground is the fulcrum, the gastrocnemius is the power, and the body through the elbow or hock joints is the weight.

In the third kind of lever the fulcrum is at one end but is nearer to the power than to the weight.

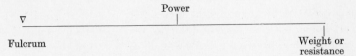

In the body it is the lever of flexion, and the nearer the power to the fulcrum the greater is the degree of flexion obtained for the same expenditure of muscular force. It is the lever of speed and what is gained in speed is lost in power. In one sense therefore it is a wasteful lever. In the horse it is commoner than the other two levers, since in the animal the movements of the limbs are directed principally towards carrying a comparatively light weight a considerable distance and in a short time. The following are examples. In the flexion of the elbow the weight is the leg below the elbow, the power is the flexor brachii muscle (which is inserted on the radius) and the fulcrum is the elbow joint. In the flexion of the hock the weight is the limb below the hock, the power is the flexor metatarsi, and the fulcrum is the hock joint.

In the three classes of lever as drawn above the power and weight are represented as working at right angles to the lever. In the actual levers of the body this is not the case. But the nearer the force is to being at right angles to the lever the greater is the mechanical advantage.

Thus if AP in the diagram represents the line of action of the force exerted by a muscle attached to a bone FA at A and causing by its contraction movement of the bone round the joint at F, the mechanical advantage may be represented by $P \times FA$ where FA is at right angles to the line of action of P. If however the bone is not at right angles to AP but is, say, in the position FA' or FC the mechanical advantage is not measured by

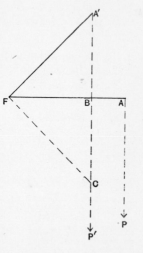

$$P' (= P) \times FA' \text{ or } P' \times FC$$

but by $P' \times FB$ where FB is at right angles to the line of action of P' or P. FB is greatest when it is equal to FA; that is, the mechanical advantage is greatest when the force exerted by the muscular contraction acting at its attachment is at right angles to the bone. Acting on this principle the cart horse, with a view to obtaining the utmost mechanical advantage when drawing a load, will endeavour to move the levers of its limbs in such a way that the power is in each case as nearly as possible at right angles to the lever. Thus the best results will be obtained by only slightly bending the joints and consequently taking short steps. On the other hand a horse when galloping will require the power of straightening out its limbs to their utmost capacity, and thus will obtain speed at a lavish expenditure of muscular exertion.

It was formerly believed that the muscular attachment of the fore limb to the trunk showed that the body was simply slung between the fore legs which acted as props while the hind legs did the work. Photography however has shown that this view is quite erroneous, and that the fore legs as well as the hind act as propellers to the body. This is especially well shown in photographs of horses galloping when the fore leg may propel the animal 10 feet forward, and in so doing raise it four inches vertically from the ground.

Joints. Where two bones with moving surfaces come in contact joints occur. There are three chief kinds of joints: (1) ball-and-socket joints (as in the hip), (2) hinge-like joints (as in the hock), and (3) sliding joints (as in the carpo-metacarpal joint of the knee). All these are covered with cartilage which is much more yielding than bone. The cartilage is covered by the synovial membranes which secrete the synovia or 'joint-oil'. This lubricates the joints and so facilitates easy and rapid movements.

We may now consider the joints in the horse's limbs.

Hind limbs

The hock joint. The principal movement of the hock takes place between the tibia and astragalus (a tarsal bone). Here the movement is simple and its range is great, but it is only in galloping and jumping that the angle formed by the tibia and cannon bone is much reduced. The movement between the tarsal bones is small and limited. It is in places of the nature of a rotation, as is shown by the presence of grooves on certain of the bones. The greatest amount of pressure comes on the anterior or inner surface of the bones, and it is here that we get the greatest damage in disease. The pressure is removed by flexing the hock which thereby rests the leg. Thus horses kept standing for a considerable time do not usually rest for long on both hind legs equally, but bend the hock of first one leg and then the other in order to escape the effects of the continuously exerted pressure.

The stifle joint. This is the largest joint in the horse's body, and it has considerable scope for movement. In reality, it consists of two joints, the femoro-patellar and the femoro-tibial. Owing to the presence of oblique (instead of vertical) ridges on the astragalus a rotation or screw action is produced, not on the hock, but on the stifle. This is turned outwards during flexion of the leg so that it moves clear of the abdominal wall. When the foot is at rest and on the ground the muscles of the stifle (i.e. those passing from the femur to the patella) contract, and thus the leg is maintained in a state of rigidity.

The hip joint. This is a ball-and-socket joint. Its range of outward movement in the horse is restricted by ligaments inserted, not into the middle, but into the head of the femur, and on the inner side. This arrangement makes it difficult for a horse to 'cow-kick'.

Fore limbs

The shoulder joint. The humerus has a great range of movement against the scapula, and thus the joint has very free play.

The elbow joint. This is a hinge joint. The articulating surface is provided with ridges which help to keep the knees in position.

The knee (or wrist) joint. Here there are three main joints and several lesser ones. The upper of these joints possesses great scope for movements; the lowest one is much restricted. The 'brushing' of the legs together in faulty movement is apparently due partly to the imperfect shape of the articular surfaces between the radius and the proximal row of carpals in horses which are so affected.

Hind and fore limbs

The fetlock joint. Here we have a yielding articulation due to the two sesamoid bones. These bones help to bear the animal's weight in a state of rest, and provide an anti-concussion mechanism, saving the limb from jar when it comes to the ground.

The pastern joint. This a joint of the hinge type, with very limited movements.

The coffin joint. This is a hinge joint, formed by the junction of three bones, the coronet, the coffin and the navicular.

POSTURES AND MOVEMENTS OF THE HORSE

When a horse is at rest the centre of gravity is stable; when it is in motion the centre oscillates backwards and forwards. If we draw a vertical line passing through a point six inches behind the shoulder and a horizontal line passing a little below the shoulder, the centre of gravity is approximately where these lines intersect. Thus the centre is nearer to the elbow than to the stifle. When pulling a load the centre is in front of the point in question; when backing a load it is behind it. In jumping the centre is behind this point when the hind legs leave the ground; it moves forward as the fore legs come to the ground. And similarly with the other motions.

It follows from the normal position of the centre of gravity that the fore legs bear a greater proportion of the total weight of the body than the hind legs, and it has been calculated that when carrying a rider, the fore legs bear two-thirds of the rider's weight and the hind legs one-third. It has been shown also that the amount of weight carried by the fore and hind legs respectively varies with the position of the horse's head. If the head is held well up, the fore legs carry less of its weight than if the head is drooping. It is important therefore to keep a stumbling horse in hand, and not to give him his head too much.

Standing. As already described, the fore legs are connected with the body by the great serratus muscles. The hind legs have no such muscular attachments, but simple ball-and-socket joints. The horse is enabled to rest in a standing position, and thus to sleep while standing by the help of the suspensory and check ligaments. The suspensory ligament arises by two heads from the carpus and upper part of the cannon bone; it divides into two, a branch being attached to each sesamoid bone and continued downwards and forwards, finally joining the extensor tendon. Its function is to support the fetlock. Further, in order that the muscles attached to the humerus may be relieved of strain, both their flexor and their extensor tendons are provided with ligamentous branches to the radius, carpus, and metacarpals. These are the check ligaments. In the hind limb we meet with the same sort of arrangement. As already remarked, a horse while standing does not normally keep its hind legs together, but flexes each one of them alternately so as to relieve the strain. On the other hand a horse almost invariably keeps its fore feet together while standing.

Lying down. A horse in coming to lie down brings all its legs under its body; it bends its knees and hocks, the former together with its chest coming into contact with the ground before the hindquarters. When actually lying down a horse either rests on one side of its chest with two legs (a fore and a hind) underneath and the other two outside his body, or else it lies on its side stretched out. A cow can rest vertically on the ventral ridge of the sternum, but this attitude is impossible in a horse owing to the sharpness of the edge of that bone.

Rising. A horse in getting up off the ground stretches out both its fore feet in front, pressing upwards its hindquarters by fixing its hoofs firmly on the ground. The fore part of the body is the first to rise, not as in the cow or sheep where the hindquarters rise first.

Fig. 56. The walk (after Ellenberger, from instantaneous photographs by Ottomar Anschütz; from Smith, Messrs Baillière, Tindall and Cox).

Rearing. In rearing a horse brings its hind legs some distance under its body, and at the same time throws up its head, and all the legs are then used to raise the body upwards. A great strain is thrown upon the hocks, and the ligaments of this joint may become injured and curbs* induced.

Kicking. When a horse kicks the head is lowered and the croup is raised, and the hind legs are thrust suddenly and forcibly

---

* Curb is the name given to the swelling on the straight ligament of the hock. It may result from any kind of strain on the hock, and is very common in cab-horses or any horses which are much used for driving on hard paved streets.

backwards. In 'cow-kicking', which is fortunately unusual in horses, one hind leg is brought rapidly forward, after the manner of kicking in cattle.

Walking. There are four stages:

(1) The body is balanced on 3 legs.

(2)   ,,   ,,   ,,   2 diagonal legs.

(3)   ,,   ,,   ,,   3 legs.

(4)   ,,   ,,   ,,   2 lateral legs (1 fore and 1 hind).

The next position is like the first only that the three legs employed are different. Considering the four movements more closely, we find: in (1) the horse puts one fore leg (e.g. the off fore) forward;

in (2) the near hind leg is lifted, the horse standing on the near fore and off hind (i.e. on diagonal legs);

in (3) the horse is balanced on both fore and the off hind leg;

in (4) the near fore and near hind are both put forward, the latter being advanced over the track of the near fore.

If a leg is not properly straightened by the extensor muscles the toe of the hoof comes to the ground first, and the horse stumbles.

Trotting. There are three stages:

(1) The body is balanced on two diagonal legs.

(2) All the legs are off the ground.

(3) The body is balanced on the other two diagonal legs.

The animal is propelled off the ground by the two pairs of diagonal legs (one fore and one hind) acting alternately.

If a horse falls while trotting, this is due to its knee not being properly flexed before extending its leg, or else it is due to the imperfect extension of the leg which is thereby insufficient to carry the weight.

Ambling. Lateral (and not diagonal) legs are on or off the ground at the same time (e.g. the off fore and off hind legs are lifted simultaneously, and not the off fore and near hind as in the trot). The amble is a very comfortable motion for the rider.

The canter. There are six stages:

(1) The body is propelled upward and forward by one fore leg e.g. by the off fore, the other three legs being off the ground.

(2) All the legs are off but near the ground.

(3) The near hind leg is on the ground.

(4) The off hind and near fore legs come to the ground, so that three legs (both hind and near fore) are on the ground.

(5) The off fore leg touches the ground, and simultaneously the near hind leaves the ground, so that three legs (now, both fore and the off hind) are on the ground.

(6) The near fore and off hind legs leave the ground, the horse being balanced on the off fore leg only.

The leading leg (in the case just described, the off fore) gives the body its final propulsion, and this causes it to become fatigued sooner than the others.

Fig. 57. The trot (after Ellenberger, from instantaneous photographs by Ottomar Anschütz; from Smith, Messrs Baillière, Tindall and Cox).

The gallop. This occurs in seven stages:

(1) The horse is in the air.

(2) One hind leg (e.g. the off hind) comes to the ground near the centre of gravity.

(3) The near hind leg comes to the ground (so that there are two legs in contact with the ground).

(4) The off fore leg comes to the ground, and the off hind is extended simultaneously.

(5) The near hind leg leaves the ground, the horse being balanced on the off fore leg only.

(6) The near fore leg comes to the ground, and the off fore leg leaves it, the body being balanced on the near fore leg only.

Fig. 58. The canter (after Ellenberger, from instantaneous photographs by Ottomar Anschütz; from Smith, Messrs Baillière, Tindall and Cox).

(7) The body passes over the near fore leg, and is then lifted off the ground as in the first stage.

The fore leg in propulsion rotates over the foot, the limb being extended in a straight line from the elbow to the ground. In the case of the hind leg propulsion is obtained partly by the foot being placed on the ground against which it presses, and partly by the

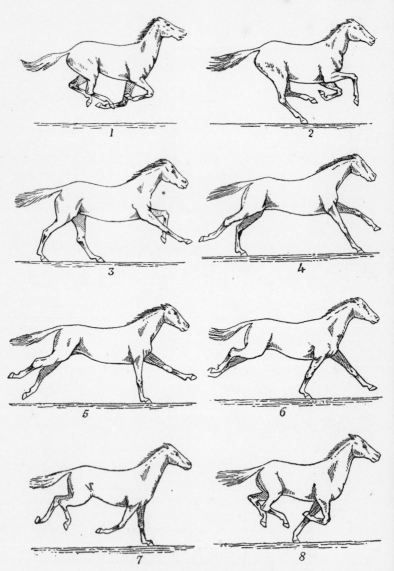

Fig. 59. The gallop (after Stanford, Muybridge and Stillman; from Smith,
Messrs Baillière, Tindall and Cox).

straightening of the hock. It is estimated that the hock performs twice the work done by the knee, and this, as will be seen again later, is one of the reasons why the hock is more liable to injury than the knee.

THE HORSE'S FOOT

The wall of the 'foot' or hoof is composed essentially and developmentally of two layers, (1) the horny part representing modified epidermis, and (2) the internal vascular part representing the derm.

The front part of the foot is called the toe; the hind part the heel; between are the two quarters.

The wall is the part of the hoof which is visible when the foot is resting on the ground. The sole is the part which is in contact with the ground. The foot-pad or 'frog' is the pyramidal-shaped part of the hoof filling the space left by the inflection of the walls in the hind part of the hoof. The bars are the inflected portion of the wall running forwards under the foot so as to form an acute angle, within which the frog lies.

The fore and hind feet are in a general way similar, but the hind feet are narrower and rather more upright.

The periople is the epithelial varnish covering the external surface of the wall, and thickest at the top of the wall where it forms the perioplic ring.

Inside the wall, which consists of horny laminae, are the sensitive laminae.

The coronary cushion is a prominent ring arranged round the edge of the hoof. It is lodged in a special groove in the horn, termed the cutigeral groove. The coronary cushion is continuous with the keratogenous membrane, a highly vascular structure (like the cushion). This membrane is directly inside the sensitive laminae of the hoof.

The plantar cushion is a fibro-elastic pad containing fatty tissue and few vessels. It is continuous with the coronary cushion. It is sometimes called the 'sensitive frog' and rests upon the frog or foot-pad. The sensitive sole is the part above the horny sole.

The principal functions of the foot are three, (1) wear and tear, (2) supporting weight, and (3) warding off concussion. The plantar cushion is especially constructed for the last of these functions, but in common with the vascular part generally it produces the horn which goes to form the hoof.

The foot contains three bones, the os pedis or coffin bone, the navicular which rests slightly on the os pedis and is held in position by ligamentous tissue, and the os coronae, which only partly belongs to the foot. Above the os coronae, is the os suffraginis which articulates with the cannon bone, but neither of these bones belongs to the foot. The pedal bone does not occupy the whole of the interior of the hoof but its place is taken on either side by a plate of lateral cartilage. The two lateral cartilages which reach high above the level of the hoof are attached to the pedal bone.

The navicular supplies a yielding articulation to the os coronae, since the latter bone rests partly on the navicular and only partly on the pedal bone. A direct concussion of the pedal joint is thereby avoided or at any rate reduced, for although the force of the body weight is partly transferred to the pedal bone on which the navicular rests, the latter bone yields under pressure, as does also the pedal bone.

The chief support of the navicular is the perforans tendon which passes beneath it, and so admits of the yielding articulation just mentioned. There is a synovial apparatus* attached which serves the purpose of reducing the friction. Nevertheless the navicular bone, owing to the important part it plays and its exposure to compression, is very liable to disease, and any inflammatory condition set up is likely to spread to the perforans tendon and other adjoining parts.

We may now consider more closely the structure and functions of the hoof- and the horn-producing tissues, and the relation of these parts to one another.

The keratogenous membrane has upon its outer surface a large number of leaves which constitute the sensitive laminae. These leaves are longer at the toe than at the heel where they are short and turned in to form the 'sensitive bars'. The keratogenous membrane is devoted to leaf formation excepting on its inner surface which encloses the pedal bone.

The coronary substance extends all round the coronet. The periople is secreted from that part of it which occupies the cutigeral

---

* This is commonly called the navicular bursa, but its function appears to be to lubricate the bone and parts concerned, and not merely to act as a cushion, like the bursae over which the extensor pedis and other tendons pass. These are little closed sacs and are so placed as to protect the parts from injury.

groove between the upper margin of the hoof and the skin. On its lower edge the coronary substance fuses with the fibres from the sensitive laminae, being continuous with the keratogenous membrane, as already stated.

The insensitive foot or hoof covers the sensitive part completely. The foot is covered by the periople which is a varnishing substance secreted in the coronary region where it is thickest. It gradually gets thinner lower down the hoof. Its function is to cement the junction of the skin to the hoof and also to control evaporation from the hoof.

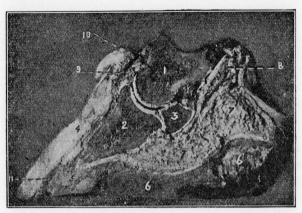

Fig. 60. Horse's foot (from Smith, Messrs Baillière, Tindall and Cox). 1, os coronae. 2, os pedis. 3, navicular. 4, wall. 5, sole. 6, frog. 7, plantar cushion. 8, perforans tendon. 9, wall-secreting substance. 10, extensor pedis tendon. 11, junction of wall and sole.

The colour of the wall is black or buff, the pigment being produced in the coronary substance.

The wall is thicker at the toe than at the heel, since at the toe, which is the final propelling part of the foot, the friction is greatest. The bars being in reality the inflected portion of the wall are, like the rest of the wall, intended to bear weight. The inflection admits of there being room for the elastic portion of the foot (the plantar cushion).

The sole is normally concave. As a practical matter it cannot be too thick. While the wall can go on growing indefinitely the sole cannot, since after a certain degree of growth the horn fibres become disintegrated and scales are shed. The junction of the sole and wall is marked by a white line where the horn is softer. The function of the horny sole is to provide protection for the sensitive structures within; its concave surface does not adapt it for carrying weight, excepting at the edge where it is connected with the wall.

The foot-pad or frog is moulded on the plantar cushion. The horn of which it is composed is markedly elastic and contains a relatively large amount of moisture. Like the sole it casts out scales. The frog serves as an anti-concussion mechanism, for the impacts it receives are transferred to the plantar cushion and thence to the lateral cartilages and wall of the foot which are stretched outwards. The frog normally comes into contact with the ground, and if this is not the case it is liable to disease. In hot dry climates the horny parts of the foot, especially of the frog, tend to become excessively hard and to cause lameness from bruising the underlying sensitive structures.

The structure of the horn. The horn of all parts of the hoof consists essentially of keratinised epithelial cells which are spindle-shaped, oblong, or irregular. They contain nuclei, granular matter, and very often pigment, and are united by a cement substance. The horn substance is soluble in caustic alkali, and consequently horses should not be allowed to stand in their own urine.

The horn structure in the progress of its development acquires canals or tubes which are used as a system of irrigation through which the hoof is supplied with the moisture necessary for preserving a proper elasticity. Without this moisture the horn substance crumbles. Evaporation from the substance is regulated by the periople as already mentioned, but nevertheless it is constantly taking place in some degree. In shoeing it is important to avoid injury to the periople as much as possible. The elasticity of the hoof is an essential quality, as without it the structure would no longer act as an anti-concussion mechanism.

The actual horny material is a protein of the following approximate composition:

C	51·41
H	6·96
N	17·46
O	19·49
S	4·23

Salts (chlorides, sulphates, and phosphates of sodium, magnesium, iron and silicon) are present in small amounts. The quantity of water is variable. The foot-pad contains the most and the wall the least.

The laminae of the hoof are attached at the antero-lateral part to bone, at the remaining parts to cartilage. The lateral cartilages supply a movable attachment to the sensitive laminae, and admit of their passing outwards. The lameness resulting from side-bone (or ossification of the lateral cartilages) is due to the sensitive structures within being squeezed between the pastern bone and the ossified cartilage.

The laminae of the hoof are much folded, and their entire surface if spread out has been estimated at from 8 to $10\frac{1}{2}$ feet.

Inflammation of the laminae occurs as a result of various causes. It may be due to overwork, or it may be due to a horse standing too long in one position when the laminae tend to become congested. Such a tendency may be overcome by exercise which relieves the congestion by causing the blood to circulate. This is one of the recognised modes of treatment for laminitis or founder. This disease frequently results in separation of the horny and sensitive laminae, and may be followed by descent of the coffin bone.

The chief anti-concussion mechanisms may now be summarised as follows: (1) the yielding articulation of the coffin bone, (2) the increase in the width of the foot when the heels come to the ground (the process being one of expansion), (3) the elastic foot-pad or frog, and (4) the slight up-and-down play between the pedal bone and the sublaminal tissue as the weight is removed from or comes on the foot. This latter movement is participated in also by the horny sole.

Shoeing. The following points have been emphasised by Smith in regard to 'physiological shoeing':

(1) Reduction of the wall to its right proportions such as would have occurred through friction had there been no shoe.

(2) Fitting the shoe accurately to the outline of the foot and avoiding rasping which destroys the periople, and so renders the horn brittle.

(3) Leaving the sole intact, since it cannot be too thick.

(4) Leaving the bars intact, since they are part of the wall and are intended to bear weight. (The shoe should rest on them.)

(5) Leaving the foot-pad intact. (This should be level with the ground surface of the shoe.)

(6) The pattern of the shoe is immaterial, so long as it has a true and level bearing and rests firmly upon the wall and bars.

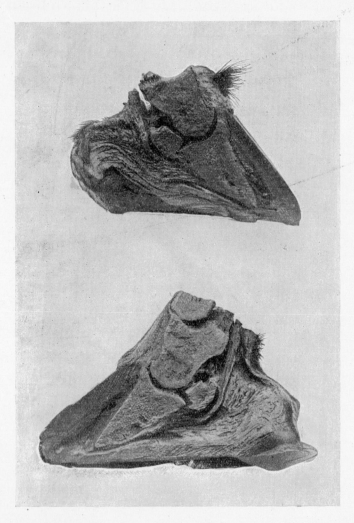

Fig. 61. Displacement of the coffin bone. (The lower figure represents the normal condition.)

(7) The shoe should be secured with as few nails as possible, so as to avoid any unnecessary destruction of the horn. Moreover the nails should not be driven in high up, as this is disastrous to the feet.

Chestnuts and ergots. The chestnuts (wrist and hock callosities)
are horny excrescences on the inside of the horse's forearms and
hocks. The wrist callosities are the biggest, but in horses belonging
to the heavy breeds the hind chestnuts are also large. In ponies of
the 'Celtic' type (e.g. Hebridean or Iceland ponies) the hind
chestnuts are generally absent. They are also absent in some Arabs

 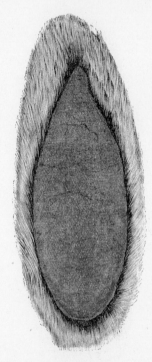

Fig. 62. Chestnut (hock callosity)
on right hind leg of pony of cart-
horse type (from Ridgeway).

Fig. 63. Chestnut in right fore leg
of Prejvalsky's horse—heavy type
(from Ridgeway).

and other 'well bred' horses (e.g. in North African horses and
occasionally in Thoroughbreds). The asses and zebras also have no
hind chestnuts.

The ergots are excrescences of a similar character and occur on
the back of the fetlock in nearly all equine animals. They are,
however, absent in Celtic ponies and sometimes in Arabs and
Thoroughbreds (i.e. in those breeds which tend to lack hock
callosities).

The hoof in ruminants and pigs. In the ox, the sheep, and pig, the hoof has the same essential structure as in the horse but has no frog and no lateral cartilages. It is, however, cleft into two portions corresponding to the two digits (the 3rd and 4th, the horse having only one digit, the 3rd). The cleft between is called the interdigital space.

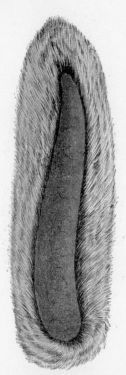

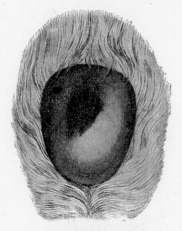

Fig. 65. Ergot on hind leg of ass (from Ridgeway).

Fig. 64. Chestnut (hock callosity) on right hind leg of Prejvalsky's horse (from Ridgeway).

Fig. 66. Ergot on right fore leg of Arab horse (from Ridgeway).

EXOSTOSES

When the fore leg of a horse descends upon the ground it is necessarily straight; otherwise the foot could not be put down flat, or heel first, as happens in fast pacers. Since the limb is rigid (the knee being quite straight) the force of concussion is greatest nearest the ground where the impact occurs, and gradually diminishes as it ascends the leg. As has been shown above, there are numerous devices present in the foot for reducing the shock caused by the impact, and not the least of these are the foot-pad or frog, the laminae of the hoof, and the yielding articulations of the foot and fetlock joints. In the case of the hind limb the shock of concussion is partly provided against by other means. Here, instead of the limb being straight, it is bent at the hock, and the impact is felt more especially at this point.

Fig. 67. Photograph of spavin.

Since these facts have a direct bearing on the causes of the various sorts of exostoses or pathological outgrowths of bone which are so common in horses under domestication, it is not out of place to give some account of them in dealing with the physiology of locomotion.

In view of the facts stated above it is not surprising that the hock is more frequently affected with disease than is the knee. In the case of bog spavin there is no bony outgrowth, but merely an enlarged condition due to the distention of the joint capsule by an abnormal quantity of synovial fluid which collects there in response to strain. It occurs most commonly in cart-horses, and especially in Clydesdales, whose hocks stand out far behind. It is generally the result of severe exertion or overstrain, but it does not as a rule cause lameness. In bone spavin or true spavin there is a genuine exostosis usually on the internal side of the hock joint. This growth of bone is the result of inflammation, but the precise point of origin of the inflammation (whether it is in the articular cartilage or in the

Fig. 68. Photograph of splint.

membrane covering the ends of the bones or elsewhere) is not clear. Spavin nearly always causes lameness. It is frequently followed by anchylosis* of one or more of the joints composing the hock. It is commoner in comparatively young than in old horses, and particularly in those having weak or ill-shaped hocks which are placed too far back or taper off too much towards the lower extremity. It

* Fusion of two or more bones which normally are capable of separate movement.

occurs as a result of high hock action on paved or hard roads, and in Hunters may be caused by the strain of jumping. When anchylosis has taken place lameness frequently ceases, so that the hastening of anchylosis should be the aim of all treatment.

Sometimes, however, the inflammatory action extends to the

Fig. 69. Photograph of ring-bone.

astragalus and damages the articular cartilage of the true joint. These cases are incurable.

Splints generally occur on the side of the cannon bone of the fore leg, or between the cannon and splint bones. They are much more common on the inside of the limb and are generally restricted to the upper third of the bone. They may occur so high as to involve the knee joint, causing lameness. They are not so common in the corresponding positions on the hind leg but may occasionally occur.

Like other exostoses they result from inflammation. They are sometimes brought about by external injuries, but are more frequently due to high knee action causing much concussion in horses driven or ridden on hard roads. Thus city horses are more

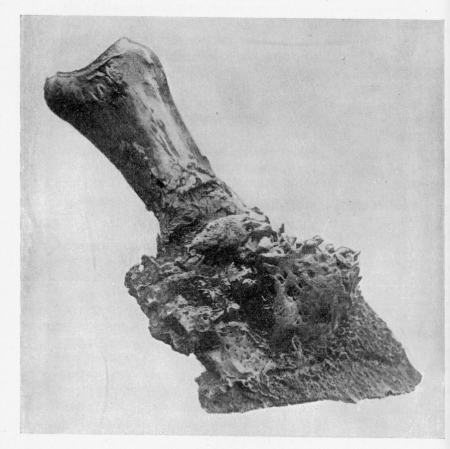

Fig. 70. Photograph of side-bone.

prone to splint than horses in the country. Splints do not necessarily cause lameness, but are more likely to do so when the inflammation is starting, and if the knee joint is affected.

Ring-bone is the name given to any exostosis occurring on the pastern or coffin bones; if involving either of these joints it is termed a true ring-bone; in other positions it is a false ring-bone.

It occurs more commonly on the front aspect of these bones and
may extend completely around them. It is commoner and more
liable to cause lameness on the fore limbs. It is often associated
with upright pasterns. Heavy horses are more disposed to it than
light ones. When we consider the amount of pressure which must
inevitably affect the pastern bones, it is easy to understand how
an inflammatory condition is liable to arise in this region. Ring-
bone often occurs in association with fractured pasterns, and may
result from such causes as galloping on a hard road or on an
irregular ground surface.

Side-bone or ossification of the lateral cartilage is common in
cart-horses with straight pasterns. It may result from hard work
or from going faster than the normal, as with heavy draught horses
when made to trot, or with light horses when over-driven. Side-
bone is frequently associated with ring-bone. The lameness which
results from side-bone is due to the sensitive structures being
squeezed between the fetlock bones and the ossified cartilage.

Besides the kinds of exostosis just described, osseous outgrowths may arise in other parts through inflammation induced
by injury, as by a horse falling or hitting 'timber' when hunting.

VOICE-PRODUCTION

Before concluding this chapter it may be well to consider briefly
the mechanism employed by animals in voice-production.

The larynx as described in an earlier chapter is a chamber with
cartilaginous walls and situated at the upper or anterior end of the
trachea, with an aperture (the glottis) communicating with the
mouth. It contains two elastic cords—the vocal cords—approxi-
mating to one another in a V-shape. The respiratory and vocal
movements necessitate the opening and closing of the angle within
the V, and this is effected by the muscles of the larynx. The walls
of the glottis are also moved by dilator (abductor) and constrictor
(or adductor) muscles, and these are used both in respiration and
in phonation. The muscles which relax the vocal cords or render
them tense are exclusively phonatory muscles. The chief changes
which the larynx undergoes in voice-production relate to the cords,
the mouth, pharynx, and nasal chambers participating in the sound
produced to a greater or less extent.

Neighing in a horse is an expiratory sound, and is produced

partly by the mouth and the nostrils. Braying in an ass is said to be partly inspiratory and partly expiratory. Bleating and bellowing (in sheep and cattle) are expiratory, the mouth participating. Yawning is a deep inspiration succeeded by an expiration. Coughing and sneezing are exclusively expiratory.

'Roaring' in a horse is a diseased condition due to the paralysis of one of the abductor muscles of the larynx, and almost invariably occurs on the left side only.

Voice-production in birds is brought about, not by the larynx, in which the vocal cords are missing, but by a special organ situated at the base of the trachea, the syrinx. The syrinx or song-box varies greatly in complexity, and in the least differentiated forms can only give rise to one or two notes. The capacity to produce a great variety of notes is not, however, necessarily associated with great complexity of structure.

The syrinx is formed by an enlargement of the base of the trachea and the first two or three rings of the bifurcating bronchi. It consists essentially of a main chamber with membranous walls, the tympanum, which in the fowl is compressed from side to side, with a corresponding increase in depth dorso-ventrally. By the aid of internal membranes (in the fowl chiefly two membranous folds known as membrana tympana interna) air passing through the syrinx is set up into a series of vibrations giving rise to the characteristic voice sounds. The membrane known as the membrana semi-lunaris, which plays an important part in the production of the varied notes in singing birds, is but poorly developed in the domestic fowl.

CHAPTER XVI

THE DUCTLESS GLANDS AND THE ORGANS
OF INTERNAL SECRETION

The idea that an organ may exert its influence upon the bodily characters or upon other organs by means of chemical substances secreted internally into the circulating blood seems seems to have been first definitely promulgated in 1849 by Berthold as a result of his experiments upon testicular transplantation in fowls. Berthold's work was, however, lost sight of, although his conclusions, as applied to the testis, were many years later completely confirmed (see p. 216). In the meantime Claude Bernard employed the term 'internal secretion' to describe the glycogenic function of the liver. This gland, as has already been recorded, stores up carbohydrate as glycogen and secretes it into the blood, as required, in the form of sugar. The liver, then, in addition to being an externally secreting gland (that is to say, a gland which elaborates substances, in this case bile, which are discharged outwards through a duct) is also an internally secreting gland. In one sense all the organs and tissues of the body are internally secreting organs since the substances which pass out from them into the circulating blood are different from the substances which pass in. But the term 'internal secretion' is usually restricted to those cases where the substances elaborated by the organs in question have a precise function and act upon other organs or tissues in the body in a definite way. The internally secreting or endocrine organs therefore are those which produce 'hormones' or chemical excitants which after being carried throughout the body in the blood stream promote the secretion of particular glands or the growth of particular tissues for which they have a specific action. Thus, the liver, although it is in a very literal sense an organ of internal secretion, is not ordinarily included in that category, since it does not elaborate any substances included under the term hormone.

We have already dealt with typical hormones in describing the mechanisms of pancreatic and gastric secretion, the chemical excitants in these cases being secreted by the wall of the duodenum and the pyloric end of the stomach respectively. We have seen also that the waste .product carbon dioxide is such that it may be regarded in a special sense as of the nature of a hormone, since when its tension in the blood reaches a certain point, it has a specific exciting action upon the respiratory centre in the medulla, thereby quickening the respiratory movements. It is possible that the other hormones of the body may have arisen in evolutionary development as waste products, and that the organs and tissues on which they now act may have only gradually learned to respond to their presence in the progress of phylogeny (i.e. the development of the race). However this may be, the functional correlation existing between certain often distantly situated organs has become very perfect, as the examples already given and described below sufficiently demonstrate.

The Pancreas. It has been shown by von Mering and Minkovsky that extirpation of the pancreas is followed by glycosuria, or the appearance of sugar in the urine, even though carbohydrate is excluded from the diet. This is because neither the liver nor the muscles can any longer store sugar (as glycogen) and the liver rapidly forms sugar from amino-acids and fats so that the proportion of sugar in the blood is increased. At the same time the quantity of urine excreted tends to increase, the percentage of urea is greater, acetone makes its appearance, there is an abnormal hunger and thirst, and these symptoms are associated or followed by emaciation ending in death. Retention of one-fourth or one-fifth of the total normal amount of gland tissue is sufficient to prevent glycosuria. Moreover, the connection of the pancreas with the duodenum may be cut off, and yet there is no glycosuria. It has been stated also that grafting of pancreatic tissue under the skin may stop these symptoms from appearing after the removal of the whole gland from the normal position. Ligature of the pancreatic duct does not cause glycosuria, though the gland, excepting for the islets of Langerhans, undergoes atrophy. A comparable condition to experimental glycosuria occurs in man as a result of disease of the islets (diabetes mellitus). It was concluded therefore that the pancreas elaborates an internal secretion, probably in the islets of Langerhans, which in some way regulates the glycogenic function of the liver, and that without this secretion the liver is no longer able to store up glycogen but discharges it as sugar into the blood whence it is excreted by the kidneys. In recent years this conclusion has been completely confirmed as a result of the work of Best and Banting, who have prepared an extract, the active principle of which is called insulin, from the islets of the pancreas, which extract, on being injected subcutaneously, causes a fall in the amount of glucose in the blood, and so takes the place of the normally produced hormone. In order to keep the patient free from a diabetic condition, the injection must be indefinitely repeated. In composition insulin is found to be a polypeptide which contains the amino-acid cystine.

The pancreas, therefore, is an example of an externally secreting gland (i.e. a gland provided with a duct) which is at the same time an organ of internal secretion, and this secretion is essential for the maintenance of life.

The Thyroid. The thyroid proper is represented by two oval bodies lying one on each side of the trachea at its junction with the larynx. It is composed of vesicles filled with a colloid substance and bounded by a cubical epithelium, the vesicles being separated by connective tissue containing vessels.

Schiff found that extirpation of the thyroid in dogs led to death in from one to four days. Previous to death the animals showed muscular tremors, convulsions and emaciation. Similar results occur in people afflicted with thyroid insufficiency. The diseases due to this cause are known as cretinism and myxoedema. The former of these occurs in children and is common in certain parts of Switzerland but is not very infrequent in other countries, including England. The individuals, who are known as cretins, suffer from greatly arrested growth and deficient mental development which may be very marked. Myxoedema, which affects persons of mature age, is a disease of a similar character. The symptoms are loss of hair, nervous and mental deterioration, and loss of memory which if not relieved by treatment are followed by premature death. The recognised treatment is feeding on raw thyroid gland or on extract, the glands being obtained from cattle or sheep. Thus the active substance of thyroid is presumably the same in all mammals, and it can be absorbed unaltered through the wall of the alimentary canal. Feeding on thyroid gland or the taking of the hormone thyroxine medicinally removes or greatly mitigates the symptoms due to cretinism, while myxoedema can often be completely cured. It is necessary, however, that the treatment should be continued permanently, otherwise the patient lapses into the state of disease, since the thyroid which is ad-

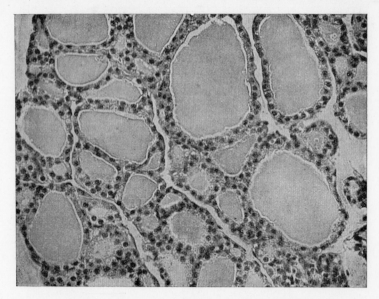

Fig. 71. Section through thyroid gland (from Schafer).

Fig. 72. Thyroidectomised or cretin sheep aged 14 months with normal sheep of same age (after Sutherland Simpson, from Schafer).

ministered merely takes the place of the secretion provided by a normal thyroid and has no influence in restoring the diseased organ to a healthy condition. Some animals do not appear to suffer any harmful effects from removal of the thyroid glands. Thus adult sheep seem to remain unaffected. If however the thyroids are extirpated from young lambs they become typical cretins and cease to grow. This has been shown by Sutherland Simpson. Thyroid grafts if successfully implanted may be as successful as feeding with extract, but if the graft does not become permanently 'established' the beneficial effect continues only so long as the transplanted tissue persists. The active principle of the thyroid which is called thyroxine has the empirical formula $C_{15} H_{11} O_4 N I_4$. Harington has prepared it synthetically from tyrosine. Accessory thyroid tissue is sometimes found posterior to the normal position of the thyroid, and this may hypertrophy and compensate for the extirpated glands.

The functions of the thyroids are not yet completely understood. They appear to exercise a profound influence on the nervous system and on the nutrition of the whole body. Moreover the thyroid is certainly an organ of growth. The age of the animal, however, is a factor in the results produced, and these are not the same for all species of animals.

The disease known as goitre is an enlargement of the thyroid and the condition produced may be one of either hypothyroidism or hyperthyroidism. In the case of endemic goitre, notwithstanding the enlargement of the gland the symptoms are those of hypothyroidism. In the case of exophthalmic goitre or Grave's disease, the condition is apparently the result of hypersecretion, for some of the symptoms can be induced by the excessive administration of thyroid extract. The most obvious symptom is the protrusion of the eye-ball, this being accompanied by rapid and irregular cardiac action, nervous excitation, and an increased metabolism.

The Parathyroids. Normally there are two parathyroid glands on each side; sometimes they are embedded in the thyroid tissue but more generally they are situated just outside. Accessory parathyroids are not uncommon. Unlike the thyroids proper the parathyroids are composed of solid masses of rounded cells and contain no vesicles. It is said however that after thyroidectomy the parathyroids may develop a vesicular structure and even take the place of the thyroids proper. Extirpation of the parathyroids without the thyroids induces tonic muscular contractions or tetany, and the injection of parathyroid extract relieves the condition. Moreover, parathyroidectomy is followed by a diminution of calcium ions in the blood. It is believed, therefore, that the parathyroids control calcium ion metabolism. It is believed also that they control guanidine metabolism, the hormone being supposed to counteract the toxic action of this substance by changing it into another substance which is disposed of in the urine.

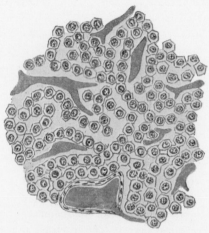

Fig. 73. Section of parathyroid, showing columns of granular epithelial cells with sinus-like capillaries.

It is suggested that many of the effects of thyroid removal may in reality be due to the extirpation of the parathyroids, since it is not easy to remove the former organs without destroying the latter ones.

The Suprarenal Bodies. These bodies are situated one on each side just in front of the kidney. Accessory suprarenals are not uncommon. Each gland has a capsule of connective tissue giving off strands into the interior, a yellow cortex consisting of parallel rows of cells, the long axis of each row or column being at right angles to the surface, and a dark red medulla consisting of a mass of irregularly arranged cells with blood vessels.

Brown-Séquard showed that removal of the suprarenals caused death in shorter time than removal of the thyroids. The symptoms preceding death were great muscular weakness, intense prostration, and loss of vascular tone. These are the symptoms of Addison's disease which is a disease of the suprarenals. Oliver and Schafer showed that extract of suprarenal medulla when injected into the circulation causes a very marked rise of blood pressure, produced by the contraction of the peripheral arteries. If the vagi are then

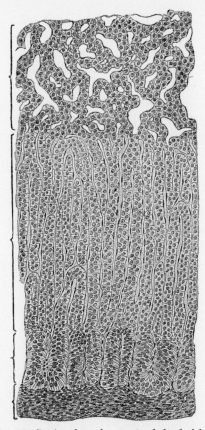

Fig. 74. Section through suprarenal gland of dog (after Böhn and Davidoff, from Schafer).

cut or paralysed, the heart's action is enormously accelerated and strengthened. Elliott and others have shown that the extract acts upon the sympathetic fibres of the vessels, and there is a special connection (developmental as well as functional) between the suprarenal medulla and the sympathetic system. The effect of suprarenal extract in constricting the arteries is taken advantage of by surgeons and others to stop bleeding or inflammation, but in the latter case the effect is transient and continues only so long as the active principle is present.

The active principle producing these effects is called adrenaline. It is formed only by the medulla, the function of the cortex being problematical. Adrenaline has the empirical chemical formula $C_9H_{13}NO_3$. It was first synthesised by Takamine and Aldrich. It is of the nature of a hormone and is necessary for the normal metabolism of the muscles on which it acts through the sympathetic nervous system. Absence of the secretion causes loss of muscular tone and vigour, as exhibited by the muscles of the heart and vessels and by the skeletal muscles.

The Pituitary Body. This small organ lies at the base of the third ventricle of the brain with which it is connected by a short hollow stalk, the infundibulum. The stalk is formed of nervous tissue, and enlarges in the interior of the pituitary body, becoming the pars nervosa. In front of the pars nervosa is an epithelial portion constituting the anterior lobe or pars anterior. It contains numerous vessels. Between this and the pars nervosa is another epithelial portion, the pars intermedium, which is only slightly vascular. The pars nervosa and the pars intermedium together form the posterior lobe. The pars nervosa is the least vascular part of the pituitary.

There has for long been evidence that the anterior lobe plays an important part in metabolism. Thus tumours growing on it are often associated with acromegaly (or overgrowth of the bones of the face) and gigantism (or overgrowth of the bones of the limbs, the epiphyses not ossifying). These diseases are thought to be the result of hyperpituitarism. Premature or increased sexuality may also be an associated condition. On the other hand, pituitary tumours may produce an atrophy of the gland and so be a cause of hypopituitarism. The symptoms of this condition are infantilism and delayed growth, delayed sexuality, and impaired mentality, sometimes associated with adiposity. It is now known that the anterior lobe produces two and probably three hormones. One of these stimulates growth, as is shown by injection of extract containing this hormone. A second hormone is essential for the development and functional activity of the reproductive organs and the onset of sexuality (see p. 257). A third is more problematical, but it is believed to exert a specific influence on the ovaries giving rise to luteal tissue (see p. 257).

Active extracts containing hormones have been obtained from the posterior lobe. Thus Howell found that there was a hormone which acted on the heart and vessels, causing a great rise of blood pressure, strengthening the heart beats and constricting the arteries. Sharpey-Schafer and Herring found that posterior lobe extract has a diuretic effect on the kidneys, but only on anaesthetised animals (since in normal animals it diminishes diuresis); Weed and Cushing ascertained that the extract has a stimulating action on the flow of the fluid of the cerebro-spinal canal; and Ott and Scott discovered the galactogogue effect of extract of posterior lobe (see p. 258). It is certain also that the active principle (pituitrin) has a specific influence on uterine muscle, and hence the posterior lobe is believed to play an important part in the process of parturition (see p. 247). Lastly, Hogben has shown that posterior lobe extract has an expanding action on the branched pigment cells (melanophores) of the frog and other amphibians. It would appear therefore that the organ produces several hormones each having its characteristic function, but none of these has been isolated.

The Pineal Body. This is a very small glandular organ situated on the dorsal surface of the third ventricle. Its functions have not been ascertained, but it has been found that injection of pineal extract has a slight galactogogue action.

The internal secretions of the generative glands are more conveniently dealt with in the chapters describing these organs.

The Inter-relation of the Organs of Internal Secretion. There is considerable evidence of a functional inter-relation of certain of the organs of internal secretion with one another, but the whole subject is very obscure. It has been ascertained that removal of the thyroid leads to hypertrophy of the pituitary, but it is not very apparent whether the growth is compensatory or whether the two organs are antagonistic. Colloid substances tend to arise in the pars anterior of the pituitary after thyroidectomy, and there is an increased activity in other portions of the gland. There is also some relation between the suprarenals and thyroids since thyroid secretion appears to promote suprarenal activity, while thyroidectomy diminishes the secretion of the suprarenals. Again, extracts of suprarenal medulla and pituitary posterior lobe seem mutually to facilitate each other's action on the vessels. The connection between the thyroids and parathyroids has already been remarked on, and the inter-relation of the ductless glands and the sexual organs will be touched upon in the succeeding chapters. Whether or not there is any true compensating mechanism between internally secreting organs of various kinds is a very open question, but it is abundantly clear that such relation exists between organs of the same kind. Thus, removal of one suprarenal may be followed by compensatory hypertrophy of the other (just as happens in the

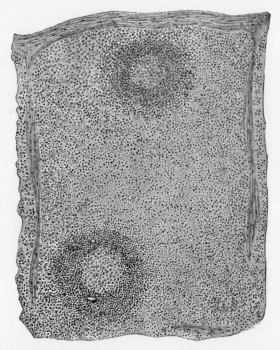

Fig. 75. Section through spleen showing Malpighian corpuscles (from Schafer).

case of the kidneys), and often after extirpation of the main internally secreting organs of a particular kind (e.g. the thyroids) accessory glands may hypertrophy and assume the functions of the glands removed.

In addition to the ductless glands described above, there are certain others which so far as known do not elaborate hormones. Of these the most noteworthy are the spleen and the thymus.

The Spleen. This organ is enclosed within a capsule which is partly fibrous and partly muscular, and some of the muscular tissue projects into the interior of the organ in the form of trabeculae. These trabeculae constitute a sort of framework in which the typical spleen tissues lie. The spleen is essentially a haemolymphatic gland, that is to say, a gland composed of lymphoid tissue but containing also a large number of erythrocytes, some of which are in a state of partial or complete disintegration. It differs from other haemolymphatic glands in possessing Malpighian corpuscles or nodules densely packed with lymphocytes, each nodule surrounding an arteriole. Apart from the vessels contained within the Malpighian corpuscles, all the arteries communicate directly with

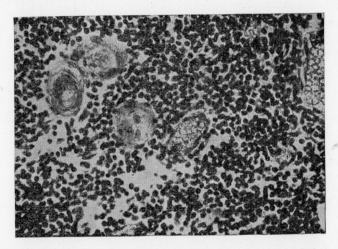

Fig. 76. Section of thymus showing Hassal's corpuscles (from Schafer).

the tissue elements of the spleen, and from this tissue the blood is gathered up anew so as to flow into the splenic vein.

The functions of the spleen are problematical. It can be removed without the animal appearing to incur any harm, but this may be due to other haemolymphatic glands (of which there are often many scattered about the alimentary region) taking on the splenic functions. It is known that the spleen is concerned to some extent with the destruction of red corpuscles, and that it contains a considerable amount of iron. It is also known that in common with other lymphatic glands the spleen produces leucocytes, and that uric acid is present in it in some quantity. During foetal life the spleen is a factory for red corpuscles and in post-natal life this function may be resumed after severe haemorrhage. Barcroft has recently shown that the spleen has an important storage function for the red corpuscles, acting somewhat after the manner of a sponge. During bodily rest the splenic muscles relax and the organ stores blood in considerable quantity. As a result of bodily exercise, on the other hand, the muscles contract, the red corpuscles entering the general circulation. Similarly during pregnancy, when an increased supply of blood is required by the enlarged uterus, the spleen is relatively contracted.

The Thymus. This organ is composed of lymphoid tissue closely packed in the cortex but less dense in the medulla. The latter contains the concentric corpuscles of Hassal which are epithelial cells arranged in rings and are specially characteristic of the thymus. Their significance is unknown. The organ is usually situated on the ventral surface of the great vessels communicating with the heart, but in some animals (e.g. guinea-pigs) the thymus bodies are placed much further forward in the neck. The thymus normally atrophies about the age of puberty. Its functions are very obscure, and its removal appears to be followed by no harmful results. It seems probable however that after extirpation the functions of the thymus are taken over by other lymphatic glands.

CHAPTER XVII

THE MALE GENERATIVE ORGANS

The spermatozoa or conjugating cells produced by the male are developed in the testicles which are therefore the essential reproductive organs in that sex, just as the ovaries which produce the ova are the essential reproductive organs in the female sex. The epididymis, vas deferens, urethra and penis which are instrumental in conveying the spermatozoa to the exterior, together with the various glandular structures which communicate with them, may be described as the accessory male generative organs.

The Testicle. In man and in all the domesticated animals the testes (or testicles) are a pair of glands lying outside of the body cavity in the scrotum which is situated posteriorly between the anus and the urogenital opening. The scrotum consists of a pair of pouch-like sacs communicating with the body cavity by the inguinal canals through which the spermatic cords and vasa deferentia pass. The spermatic cords contain the blood vessels and nerves which supply the testes, and the vasa deferentia are the ducts which convey the testicular secretion to the urethra or common urogenital canal.

In the lowest group of mammals (Monotremata) the testes remain in the body cavity always as they do in birds. In Insectivora (e.g. the mole) the testes descend periodically into temporary receptacles, and there is no true scrotum. In many rodents the testes after descending into the scrotum at the commencement of rut are withdrawn into the body cavity at the end of the period. In most other animals the testes after descending into the scrotum during early life (and generally before birth) remain there permanently, but it is noteworthy that in the ram after tupping the organs apparently become smaller and tend to be drawn upwards without, however, passing into the cavity of the abdomen. In most farm animals (including the ram), however, the male is capable of copulating and inseminating at any time of the year, though there may be some variation in sexual desire and in the number of spermatozoa produced.

Each testis is surrounded by a serous membrane (the tunica

vaginalis) within which is a fibrous capsule (the tunica albuginea). Posteriorly the fibrous capsule is prolonged into the interior of the gland to form the mediastinum testis. The greater part of the organ

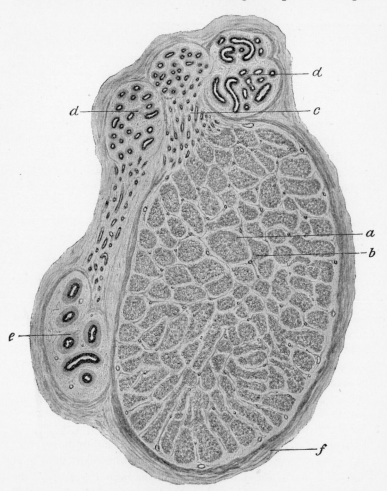

Fig. 77. Section through testis (from Marshall). *a*, seminiferous tubules; *b*, interstitial tissue; *c*, rete testis; *d*, vasa efferentia; *e*, vas deferens; *f*, tunica albuginea.

is composed of the seminiferous tubules which are separated from one another by epithelioid interstitial cells (fig. 79). The tubules contain several layers of epithelial cells supported externally by a basement membrane. On the internal surface of the basement membrane are the spermatogonia. Certain of the epithelial cells between the spermatogonia are enlarged and project among the more internal cells in association with developing spermatozoa. These are the cells of Sertoli. They are believed to have a nourishing and supporting function. On the inside of the spermatogonia are certain larger cells known as spermatocytes. They are the products of division of the spermatogonia. On the inside of the spermatocytes are the spermatids which are derived from the spermatocytes by cell division. The spermatids in many cases become elongated and converted into spermatozoa. A small quantity of fluid is secreted into the testicular lumina, but it does not appear to be certain as to what cells are especially concerned in this secretion.

A fully developed spermatozoon consists of an egg-shaped head which represents the cell nucleus, a short cylindrical body or middle piece, and 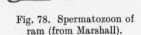 long delicate vibratile tail, by means of which the sperm is propelled forwards.

Fig. 78. Spermatozoon of ram (from Marshall).

In the process of spermatogenesis the quantity of nuclear material (as shown by the number of chromosomes or filaments which go to compose the nuclear material) in each final product of division (i.e. in each spermatozoon) is reduced to one-half of the normal amount characteristic of the cells in the species in question. Thus in the horse the normal number of chromosomes for all the cells of the body excepting the mature reproductive cells is 26, whereas the number of chromosomes in the spermatozoon of the horse is 13.* This is due to the fact that in the last cell division but one leading up to spermatogenesis the chromosomes do not undergo the splitting which universally characterises cell-division excepting in the reduction processes of the reproductive cells. In the final division the chromosomes split as usual. The nuclear material in the mature ovum is also reduced by half, so that in the act of fertilisation, when the ovum and spermatozoon unite, the number

* It is probable in reality that there are 25 chromosomes in the stallion and 26 in the mare, there being one fewer chromosome in the male than in the female in other species. There are probably also two kinds of spermatozoa in the horse, the 'male' spermatozoon having 12 chromosomes and the 'female' spermatozoon having 13. The ova all have 13 chromosomes (see p. 260). The sex of the future individual will then usually depend upon whether a 'male' or a 'female' spermatozoon conjugates with an ovum. A similar generalisation is believed to hold for other species of vertebrates and many invertebrates, only in birds there are two kinds of ova and one kind of spermatozoon.

of chromosomes becomes once more restored to the normal amount characteristic of the species.

The efferent ducts of the testis or vasa efferentia (about twelve in number) open into a single convoluted tube situated at the posterior

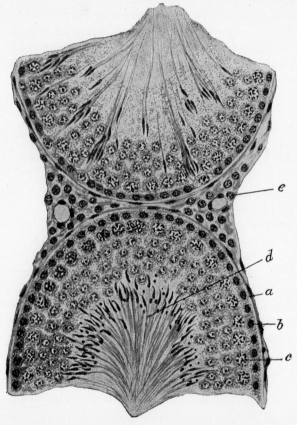

Fig. 79. Section through seminiferous tubules (from Marshall). *a*, basement membrane; *b*, spermatogonium; *c*, spermatocyte; *d*, spermatozoa in cavity of tubule; *e*, interstitial tissue containing blood vessels.

end of the testis. This is the *epididymis*. It is lined internally by a columnar, ciliated epithelium which is believed to have some secretory activity. The epididymis serves mainly as a storehouse for the spermatozoa prior to seminal ejaculation. Smooth muscle fibres are present in its walls as well as in those of the vasa efferentia.

The *vas deferens* is the duct conveying the seminal fluid in which the spermatozoa pass from the epididymis to the urethra. It is lined internally by a non-ciliated columnar epithelium, and its wall contains several layers of smooth muscle fibres.

The Accessory Glands. The semen or fluid discharged through the penis in an ejaculation is the secretory product of the testis, epididymis, vesiculae seminales and other accessory glands. Near the termination of the vas deferens there is a small sac, the *ampulla of Henle*, which also contains small secretory glands but according to Disselhorst its chief function is to act as a seminal reservoir. More recent work by Young *et al.* suggests that the lower part of the vas deferens including the ampulla is concerned with the absorption of non-ejaculated sperm.

The *vesiculae seminales* are situated at the ends of the vasa deferentia. They are provided with a glandular epithelium, outside of which are thin muscular layers. It was formerly supposed that they were of the nature of seminal reservoirs, but even in the hedgehog, in which these organs undergo a very great development at the breeding season, it has been impossible to find spermatozoa in the vesicular fluid. On the other hand, they contain a large quantity of glairy, milky fluid with much crystalloid material, which Hopkins has shown to consist of a phosphoprotein. The precise function of the vesiculae must still be regarded as undecided. It would seem probable that one of their functions is to dilute the semen and so assist in providing a medium for the transference of the spermatozoa.

The prostate is a tubular gland surrounding the urethra at the base of the bladder. It communicates with the urethra by numerous small ducts. Associated with the glandular tissue are a number of smooth muscle fibres, and there is an abundance of vessels supplying the gland. The prostatic secretion is viscid. It contains proteins and salts, and is sometimes very slightly acid in reaction. In old subjects concretions are frequently present in the gland. Concerning the function of the prostatic fluid nothing definite is known. It has been suggested that it assists in providing the spermatozoa with nutriment, and it is obvious that it contributes additional fluid to the semen. It is not improbable that one of its main functions is to cleanse the urethra of urine prior to the ejaculation of spermatozoa, for it has been ascertained that in a normal seminal ejaculation in the horse the first fluid to be discharged contains no sperms and is almost certainly chiefly of prostatic origin.

Cowper's glands are a pair of small tubulo-racemose glands situated near the anterior end of the urethra with which they communicate by two ducts. The glands are lined internally by a secretory epithelium. The significance of the viscous secretion which

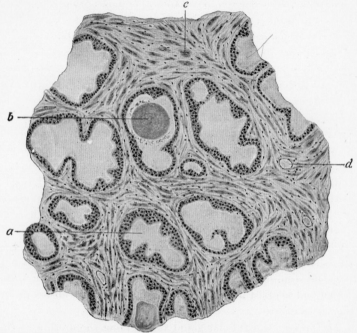

Fig. 80. Section through prostate (from Marshall). *a*, alveolus lined by epithelium; *b*, concretion (often found in old subjects); *c*, muscular fibres amid connective tissue; *d*, blood vessel.

the glands produce is obscure. Possibly they serve the same function as the prostate gland. The small glands of Littré which are present in most parts of the lining membrane of the urethra also contribute to the production of semen.

The Copulatory Organ. The penis is the intromittent organ of copulation. Besides serving to conduct the urine to the exterior through the channel of the urethra it has the further function of conveying the semen into the genital passages of the female. This latter function is made possible by the power of erection whereby the organ can be inserted into the vagina of the female.

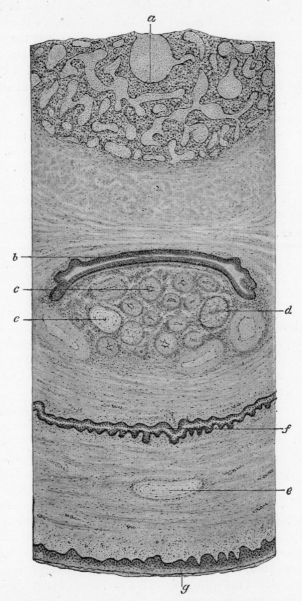

Fig. 81. Transverse section through penis of monkey (from Marshall). *a*, erectile tissue; *b*, urethra; *c*, artery; *d*, nerve; *e*, sensory end organ; *f*, fold of epithelium; *g*, surface epithelium.

The erectile tissue of the penis is contained chiefly in three tracts, the two corpora cavernosa which are situated one on each side and typically are united in the middle line, and the single corpus spongiosum which is placed inferiorly and surrounds the urethral channel. The corpora cavernosa are surrounded by an integument containing connective tissue and unstriated muscle fibres and giving off trabeculae which divide the structures into blood spaces or sinuses. These spaces become engorged with blood during the process of erection. The corpus spongiosum is similar in structure but its fibrous framework is less well developed. The wall of the urethral canal contains unstriated muscle fibres. At its distal end the spongy body becomes enlarged, forming the glans penis. At their proximal ends all the three bodies are swollen into bulbous enlargements, those of the cavernous bodies being surrounded by the ischio-cavernosus or erector penis muscles, and that of the spongy body by the bulbo-cavernosus muscle. The penis is supplied with blood by the pubic arteries and the dorsal arteries, and the blood is carried away by the dorsal veins and another set of veins communicating with the prostatic plexus. The integument of the penis is a loose fold of skin called the prepuce or foreskin which is especially thick in the bull. Sebaceous glands emitting an odoriferous secretion particularly during rut are present near the free margin of the prepuce. The penis is very sensitive to external stimulation, its surface being beset with numerous Pacinian corpuscles and other sensory end-organs.

The above description applies especially to the human penis, but in the domestic animals the structure of the organ is essentially similar. In the horse the end of the penis (the region of the glans) is rounded, and when inserted in a state of erection into the vagina of the female occupies the greater part of that passage. In the ram there is a peculiar filiform appendage attached to the left side of the penis, the distal end of which appears to have undergone some sort of torsion. The urethra opens to the exterior at the end of the appendage. This structure, like the main portion of the penis, is composed very largely of erectile tissue which surrounds the urethra and may be regarded as an extension of the corpus spongiosum. Outside of the erectile tissue is a well marked muscular layer which lies next to the integument. The appendage is supported by a pair of fibro-cartilage bodies placed one on each side of the urethra throughout the whole length of the process. As is shown below, there is evidence that the function of the filiform process is insertion into the external orifice of the cervix.

In the bull the filiform appendage is represented by a vestigial structure or papilla which is situated on the left side of the penis in the same position as the appendage in the ram, only in the bull the process does not project beyond the end of the organ. When erected the bull's penis does not increase in diameter to the same extent as in the horse, owing apparently to the thickness of the preputial folds.

The penis in the boar, like that of the horse, is not provided with a filiform prolongation or lateral papilla, and the urethral aperture is situated at the end of the organ and in the centre.

Fig. 82.　Penis of ram (from Marshall).

Erection, Ejaculation and Coition. The erection of the penis is brought about mainly by the dilatation of its vessels. First of all the proximal portion of the organ increases in size, and then the swelling extends throughout the corpora cavernosa, and eventually to the glans. The arterial pressure in the penis during erection has been found to rise from about one-half to three-fifths of that of the carotid. The erection is effected partly by the contraction of the ischio-cavernosus (or erector penis) and bulbo-cavernosus muscles which arrest the flow of blood along the efferent vessels, but it is believed also that the unstriated muscle fibres which are scattered through the framework of the corpora participate in the process. According to Kölliker, the action of these muscles is temporarily inhibited and the trabecular framework of the corpora is correspondingly relaxed. The whole process, which is essentially a reflex action, is presided over by a centre situated in the lumbo-sacral part of the spinal cord, and Eckhard and others have shown that the efferent nerves (called the nervi erigentes) arise from the 1st, 2nd and 3rd sacral nerves and are vaso-dilator in function. On stimulating the nervi erigentes electrically the penis can be made to erect.

Seminal ejaculation is brought about by a series of muscular contractions, which begin in the walls of the vasa efferentia and pass to the epididymis and thence along the vas deferens on either side. The vesiculae seminales contract simultaneously and the prostatic muscles also contract. The internal generative organs are supplied by nerves coming from the lumbar region, and Langley and Anderson found that stimulation of these nerves in the cat and rabbit produced a powerful contraction of the muscles of the vasa deferentia and related parts. Possibly more than one centre is concerned in the process of ejaculation, but it is evident that the one which presides over the muscular movements of the internal generative organs is situated in the lumbar portion of the cord.

The purpose of penile erection is to give the organ a sufficient rigidity to make it possible to insert the organ into the vagina of the female in the act of coition. In the stallion the erected penis almost fills the vagina of the mare and a considerable amount of friction occurs before seminal ejaculation is completed. In the bull the end of the penis is more or less pointed and it is believed that it is inserted into the orifice of the cervix. In the sheep the filiform appendage is probably normally projected into the os uteri. If the appendage is cut off the ram is generally rendered barren. This fact is sometimes taken advantage of by ram traders when wishing to discard tups for breeding purposes. The filiform appendage is removed before the ram is sent to market. Many novices have been deceived by this practice, which is called 'worming'; for such rams are bought by unscrupulous dealers for a butcher's price in open market and then sold at a profit as sound sires.

In the dog the process of coition is different from that of most mammals, and lasts for an unusually long time. This is due to the fact that after the penis has been introduced into the vagina the contraction of a sphincter in the female prevents the withdrawal of the organ until almost fully relaxed. In the ferret also coition lasts for a long time (sometimes an hour or more). In the pig coition lasts for ten to twenty minutes but in other farm animals it is of short duration.

The friction which is set up between the male and female organs during coition causes a reflex discharge of motor impulses in both sexes, the uterus undergoing a series of peristaltic contractions. Thus Heape has described a sucking action on the part of the uterus in the rabbit, the os uteri dipping down into the seminal fluid at the bottom of the vagina to be withdrawn again in correlation with a rhythmical contraction by the uterine muscles. According to

Walton, however, ascent of the spermatozoa in the female genital tract in the rabbit is effected by their own flagellar activity. The accessory sexual glands in the female (Bartholini's glands, etc.) emit a secretion which is added to the semen.

Artificial Insemination. Artificial insemination was first carried out by Spallanzani on a bitch, *circa* 1776, and was later repeated by Rossi at Pisa in 1782. This method has been practised with success on mares, cows and other domestic animals, in order to overcome certain forms of sterility in the female. It is only applicable in those species in which ovulation can take place spontaneously (that is irrespectively of the occurrence of coition, see p. 239), but this fortunately is the case normally with all farm animals. As Heape has pointed out, undue rigidity of the cervix uteri (see p. 219), constriction of the canal, occlusion of the os uteri, or other similar defects may prevent the passage of the spermatozoa into the uterus, while the presence of an abnormal acid secretion in the vagina may kill or deleteriously affect the spermatozoa before they can effect an entry. In such cases the defect may be overcome by inserting the end of a syringe or inseminator into the mouth of the uterus and so injecting the semen directly into the body of that organ. The semen can be obtained either from the vagina of the same mare (or other female animal in suitable cases) or from the vagina of another mare which has just been served, the method being to cause the fluid to collect in a little pocket or depression made by the finger tips and then to draw the semen into the syringe by relaxing the rubber bulb which is held in the hand at the other end of the inseminator and had been previously compressed. In our own experience a not uncommon cause of sterility in mares is evacuation of the semen immediately after service. In such cases the fluid can be caught in a beaker or other vessel on emission from the vagina and then injected. Another method of insemination is to collect the fluid in gelatine capsules which may be placed in the vagina before copulation, and then to remove them after they have been filled, close their lids and insert them into the uterus, either of the same or of another female, when the heat of the body melts the gelatine and sets free the spermatozoa. By this means a number of mares may be impregnated as a result of one service by a stallion. In Russia extensive use has been made of artificial insemination in horses, cattle and sheep. The most successful results have been obtained by injecting the semen into the cervical canal. The injection of semen in large quantities directly into the uterus is not so successful and may cause severe spasms of this organ.

The possibility of transporting semen from a distance and then utilising it for purposes of insemination is well worthy of consideration, but so far few experiments have been carried out. The spermatozoa of the rabbit retain their vitality within the male generative passages for at least ten days, and Walton has shown that outside the body at ordinary room temperature in sealed tubes they may be kept so as to retain their capacity for fertilisation for at least six days.

Castration and the Internal Testicular Secretion. The practice of castration or the removal of the testes has been carried out upon the domestic animals for economic purposes from the earliest times onwards. It is generally believed that the flesh of cattle, sheep, and pigs is much improved thereby, and that the animals fatten faster and more readily, but whether this effect is due directly to the removal of testicular influence upon the metabolism, or whether it is an indirect result of the greater lethargy and absence of excitement displayed by de-sexed animals is still an open question. Castration is practised on horses to make it possible for them to work in association with mares; moreover, geldings are in a general way more manageable and less excitable than entire animals.

It is usual to castrate colts or yearlings in the summer following birth. Calves are operated on at an age of six to twelve weeks. Lambs are castrated at any age between three weeks and three months; and young boars are 'cut' preferably when from six to eight weeks old.

The general effect of castration in all animals is to prevent the development of the secondary male characters, that is, of those characters which while correlated with the sex in question are not directly concerned with the reproductive processes. But this effect is usually only brought about provided that castration is performed prior to puberty or the age when sexual maturity is reached. Thus in man, early castration arrests the enlargement of the larynx and the consequent deepening of the voice; it likewise prevents the growth of hair on the face and the other parts of the body which are usually provided with hair in the adult, and consequently it produces a general appearance of femininity which is in reality a condition in which certain of the male characters are absent rather than one in which female characters have been acquired. In animals the effects are similar. For example, in those breeds of sheep which are horned in the male but hornless in the female (Herdwicks, Merinos, etc.) castration arrests the development of the horns, and it is noteworthy that this happens at whatever stage of growth the operation is performed, the horns ceasing to grow forthwith. It is clear therefore that the testicular stimulus is necessary not only for the initiation of horn growth but also for its continuance. In other breeds of sheep in which both sexes are horned (e.g. Dorset Horns, Scottish Black-faced and Lonks) the wethers have horns which are finer and less massive than those of the uncastrated males and so approximate towards horns of the female type. Early castration in deer prevents the development of the antlers. If the operation is performed late only clump or peruke antlers grow, and these tend to persist instead of falling off in the non-breeding season. If castration is done when the antlers have grown, these fall off, and next season are replaced by peruke antlers. The horn sheath, however, is not shed. In castrated cats the growth of the tissues of the cheek or jowl is partially arrested. In fowls the normal male plumage is generally assumed after caponisation or removal of the testes, but the comb, spurs, etc. do not develop to their full extent; there appears, however, to be some variation in these results.

Another result of early castration in both birds and mammals is the arrest in the ossification of the epiphyses, the consequence being that the limb bones grow larger and that there is a tendency towards giantism such as is associated also with pituitary disease. Again, the thymus gland which normally atrophies at or about puberty persists longer or even hypertrophies in individuals which have undergone castration.

Occasionally the testes do not descend into the scrotum but are retained in the abdomen at or near their primitive position in the embryo. Such animals are known as 'rigs' or cryptorchids. They usually have the external appearance of males, are often capable of service but are always sterile where retention of the testes is complete on both sides.

Castration is followed also by atrophy of the prostate and other accessory male glands, or if the operation is carried out before puberty these do not fully develop and sexual desire and penile erection do not occur, not even on stimulating the nervi erigentes artificially.

Transplantation of the testes or of portions of these organs to abnormal positions such as the ventral peritoneum or that of the gut (fowls, etc.) notwithstanding that the ordinary nervous connections of the testes are destroyed, does not arrest the growth of the secondary male characters. It would seem clear therefore that the testicular influence is chemical and not nervous, that is to say, that it acts by the internal secretion of substances into the blood, and that these substances are carried in the circulation to the various tissues influenced by them, growth and seasonal activity being thus brought about. It has been shown by Voronoff and others that the grafting of testicular tissue in the scrotum and on to the testes already present in senile animals may have a temporary rejuvenating effect and lead to a recrudescence of sexual desire.

The further question arises as to what part of the testis is concerned in elaborating this internal secretion or hormone. It has already been mentioned that in those animals in which testicular transplantation to abnormal positions had been carried out castration effects did not occur, and this is also true for animals in which the vasa deferentia had been cut. In such experiments, however, the spermatogenetic tissue underwent degeneration owing to the semen being unable to escape. The same effect is brought about by exposing the testes to the influence of Röntgen rays, as has been shown more especially by experiments on roe-deer by Tandler and Gross. On the other hand, the interstitial cells of the testis were not affected in any of these experiments, and the development of the secondary sexual characters (growth of horns, etc.) must be correlated with the persistence and functional activity of these cells. It must be concluded therefore that the interstitial cells are responsible for the secretion of the testicular hormone.

Further experiments have shown that unilateral castration in Herdwick rams does not affect the symmetry of horn growth, while, according to Ribbert, there is evidence that removal of one testis may be followed by compensatory hypertrophy on the part of the other.

Injection of testicular extract has been shown to induce growth in the comb and erectile structures about the head in castrated fowls and similar effects on the accessory generative organs have been obtained in castrated mammals. The testicular hormone is not specific for any one kind of vertebrate but preparations made from mammals' testes may be used effectively upon birds. The hormone has now been obtained in a crystalline form as an oxyketone of the formula $C_{16}H_{26}O_2$ (Butenandt, etc.) and is called *proviron*.

The correlation between the anterior lobe of the pituitary and the testis is briefly referred to in the next chapter, where the similar connection between the pituitary and the ovary is dealt with (p. 257).

The effects of feeding and general condition upon the reproductive functions are also briefly considered below (p. 249).

Note on the Male Organs of the Fowl. The testes of the fowl are two oval bodies, and are attached by a fold of peritoneum to the inner borders of the anterior lobes of the kidneys on the ventral surfaces of which they lie. Each testis is enclosed in a fibrous capsule, and histologically its structure resembles that of man and the domesticated animals (see p. 204). According to Boring and Pearl, interstitial cells are present in the testes of the chick but not in the adult.

Each vas deferens emerges from the inner side of the lower end of the testis and passes downward over the ventral surface of the kidney and on the outer side of the ureter, finally terminating in a small raised papilla in the cloaca. In the duck and the goose this papilla is developed to such an extent that it forms an erectile structure similar to the penis in mammals. Its presence in these latter birds may be used as a method of distinguishing the sexes shortly after hatching.

In the act of copulation, the male 'treads' the female and the cloacae are placed in close apposition, thus enabling the transference of the semen of the male to the oviduct of the female to take place.

CHAPTER XVIII

THE FEMALE GENERATIVE ORGANS AND THE MAMMARY GLANDS

The Ovaries are a pair of organs lying in the abdominal cavity to whose dorsal wall they are connected by the *broad ligament* which stretches across the body wall in this region. They are composed of a stroma or ground substance of connective tissue containing blood vessels and a number of vesicles of varying sizes

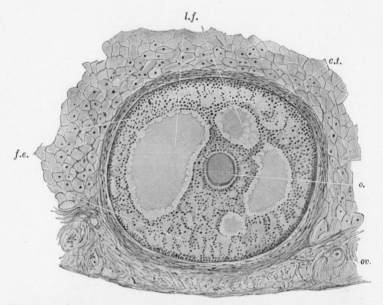

Fig. 83. Section through part of ovary of rabbit showing Graafian follicle (from Marshall). *c.t.* connective tissue wall of follicle; *f.e.* follicular epithelium; *l.f.* liquor folliculi; *o.* ovum; *ov.* primordial ovum.

called the *Graafian follicles*. The smallest of these—the primordial follicles—however, have no cavity, but consist merely of ova surrounded by a single row of epithelial cells; they lie just below the surface of the ovary. As the follicles increase in size they pass inwards towards the centre of the stroma, the epithelial cells multiply and a space is formed between those immediately covering the ova and the outer cells which are contiguous with the modified connective tissue which forms the outer wall of the follicle. This space is filled with a fluid containing protein substances, etc., the liquor folliculi, which is concerned in the nourishment of the ovum. The two portions of follicular epithelium, each of which is several cells deep, are connected by strands of similar cells. Each follicle contains one ovum (rarely two or more) and the largest or most mature follicles may occupy a considerable part of a section through an ovary; they may protrude visibly from the surface of that organ and in some animals (sow, etc.), at the approach of the 'heat' periods, the ovary presents almost the appearance of a bunch of small grapes. In addition to follicles the ovaries at certain seasons contain yellow pigmented bodies, or corpora lutea. These, as will be described presently, are formed from the ruptured follicles after the discharge of the ova. Epithelioid interstitial cells are also generally present in the stroma.

The Fallopian Tubes or **Oviducts**, whose function is to convey the discharged ova to the interior of the uterus, open internally into the body cavity close to each ovary. The ova pass into the fimbriated expansions at the ends of the tubes, which are provided with cilia to direct the passage of the ova. Internally the oviducts are lined by a ciliated epithelium outside of which are connective tissue and muscle. It is asserted that the fimbriated ends of the tubes erect at each ovulation. In some animals (dog, ferret) the ovaries are enclosed by a membranous covering which is continuous with the wall of the tubes, so as to ensure the discharged ova passing into the tubes and not being lost in the body cavity.*

The Uterus. The tubes which are attached to the broad ligament (or fold of peritoneum which connects the ovaries and uterus with the body wall) become expanded, passing backwards into the horns of the uterus (*cornua uteri*). These in many animals (mare, cow, ewe, sow, etc.) unite to form the body of the uterus (*corpus uteri*) which opens into the *vagina* or common urogenital passage of the female. The posterior end of the uterus is narrowed down to form the *cervix*, the actual uterine opening being called the *os uteri*. In the rabbit the uterine horns open separately but close together in the vagina. In man the uterine horns are so much reduced as to

---

* Vestigial structures called the parovarium and paroöphoron are found in some animals between the ovary and tube.

be almost unrepresented, the oviducts only expanding slightly for a short distance before opening into the body of the uterus.

The cavity of the uterus is lined by a ciliated cubical or columnar epithelium which together with the stroma beneath composes the uterine mucosa. This contains glands which open into the cavity

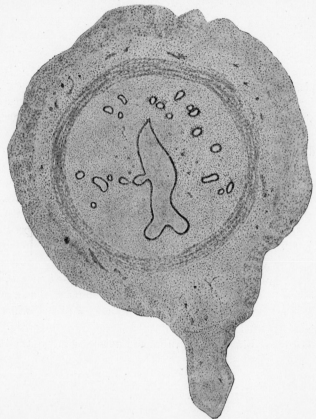

Fig. 84. Transverse section through uterine cornu of rat (from Marshall).

and have a secretory epithelium continuous with and similar to the epithelium bounding the cavity. The glands are sometimes very numerous, and vary in activity at different periods. The stroma is a primitive kind of connective tissue and contains vessels which increase in size and number at the approach of 'heat', as will be described later. The stroma is surrounded by unstriated muscular tissue which is arranged in two (or three) layers, the inner layer consisting of circular and the outer of longitudinal fibres. Connective tissue with good sized vessels is also present in the muscular layers. Outside of all is the serous or peritoneal coat.

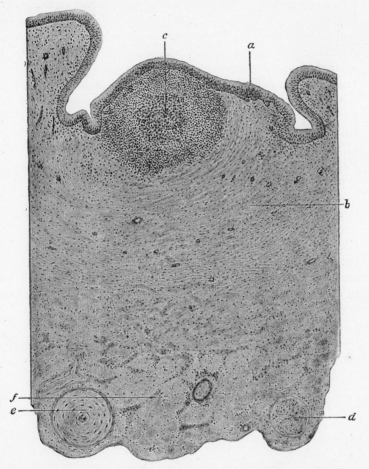

Fig. 85. Section through vagina of monkey (from Marshall). a, epithelium; b, submucous layer; c, lymphatic gland; d, nerve; e, sensory end-organ; f, fat cells.

The Vagina, into which the male organ penetrates during coitus, extends from the uterus to the exterior opening. Its walls contain longitudinal and circular muscle fibres, and internally it is lined by a stratified scaly epithelium. The female generative organs which are visible externally are known collectively as the vulva.

The clitoris is a small rod-like organ and represents the penis of the male, but, unlike the latter, is solid.

The Mammary Glands, the function of which is to provide a nutritive secretion for the newly born young, though rudimentary in the male are normally active only in the female. Their numbers and position vary in different species. In animals which possess a number of mammary glands, such as the pig, these are usually arranged in rows approximately parallel on the ventral side of the thorax and abdomen. In the cow the mammae are contained within a definite milk-bag or udder, which is surrounded by a fibrous envelope and suspended below the abdomen. This udder is provided with milk cisterns or galactophorous sinuses into which the ducts of the glands open and convey milk from the secretory alveoli. Each sinus communicates with the exterior by a teat, there being typically four teats in a cow, corresponding to the four mammary glands (and sinuses), commonly called the four 'quarters'. One quarter may run dry without the others but this does not happen normally. There is a fibrous division consisting of yellow elastic tissue between the two lateral halves of the cow's udder, but not between the anterior and posterior parts. Very frequently there are one, two, or even three extra teats which are placed posteriorly to or between the other teats, but are usually smaller than the normal; these supernumerary teats are associated with extra glands from which the milk constituents may be reabsorbed into the blood (the milk sugar sometimes appearing in the urine), since the secretion is not usually drawn off through the teats. In the sheep there are normally only two glands, sinuses and teats (occasionally four), and the mare is similar excepting that there may be two or even four sinuses opening into one teat.

The actual glandular tissue is divided into lobes, which are subdivided into lobules, containing secretory alveoli. These are bound together by connective tissue. The ducts through which the milk passes have walls containing areolar tissue and some unstriated muscle fibres, and are lined internally by columnar epithelial cells. In the secretory cells of the alveoli an active and a resting stage can be distinguished. In the latter the lumina are wide, and the cells of the lining epithelium form a single flat layer with centrally situated nuclei. In the active condition the epithelial cells are long and columnar and project into the cavity. In these cells granules (containing a protein material) and fat globules accumulate, and afterwards form the milk constituents which the cells discharge into the lumina of the alveoli. The so-called 'colostrum corpuscles' which occur in the milk in the first few days after parturition or shortly before are probably white corpuscles, since they have been

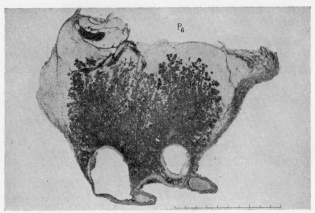

A. Udder of heifer: 7 months pregnant (fluids withdrawn).

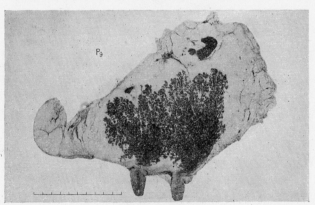

B. Udder of heifer: 8 months pregnant (fluids not withdrawn).
Fig. 86. Udders of heifers (after Hammond).

observed to undergo amoeboid movement. The milk constituents which are formed during lactation are discharged into the lumina of the alveoli without the cells which excrete them becoming detached or destroyed in the process. The milk thus produced passes from the alveoli into the ducts and sinuses, whence it is drawn off by the teat being sucked.

The development of the mammary glands during the first pregnancy in the cow has been studied by Hammond (see Figs. 86 and 87). It consists in the broadening out of the alveolar ducts near the milk cistern and the large ducts, alveoli being produced. This development is first apparent macroscopically about

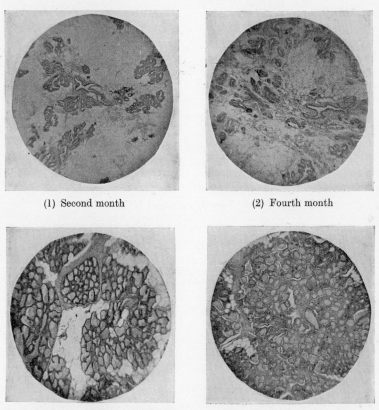

(1) Second month   (2) Fourth month

(3) Seventh month (fluids withdrawn)   (4) Eighth month (fluids not withdrawn
Fig. 87. Mammary gland during first pregnancy (after Hammond).

the fourth month of pregnancy. In later pregnancy this growth of alveoli increases, so that at the seventh and eighth months the gland has the typical macroscopical appearance shown in Fig. 86. In the first figure (A) the milk cisterns are well developed, this development being due to the fact that the fluids were withdrawn through the teats so that the heifer was actively secreting milk at this stage. In a normal heifer in the pregnant condition, the milk cisterns are undeveloped at the eighth month, as shown in Fig. 86 B. The histological appearance of the glands during the first pregnancy is shown in Fig. 87. During the second month of pregnancy the development of the alveoli is actively taking place, but, as will be seen from the section, the lobules are not yet distinct. In the fourth month, the lobules have become more distinct and the development of connective tissue in the region of the lobules is

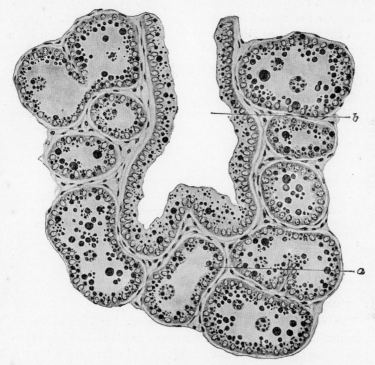

Fig. 88. Section of lactating gland (from Marshall). *a*, alveolus; *b*, duct.

more obvious. By the seventh and eighth months, the lobules are clearly defined, and have filled out, being separated from one another only by strands of connective tissue. Fluids are present in the alveoli, and the glands approximate in histological appearance to that of the typical lactating gland.

In the pig the tissue lining the ducts of the mammary glands may contain black or coloured pigment. This is clearly related to the pigment of the hair, since it is only present in the coloured breeds of pigs. It occurs usually only in unoperated sows, but occasionally also in the hog, in which rudimentary mammary glands (or at any rate ducts) may be found. When present in some quantity, as frequently happens, it gives rise to the condition known as 'seedy-cut', a term which implies that the bacon of the 'belly-piece' is discoloured. The pigment however is perfectly harmless, and unlike the black pigment in the uterus of the ewe (described below) is not blood pigment. The condition may be avoided by spaying or removing the ovaries from the young sow, since after this operation the mammary tissue in which the pigment is formed does not develop.

The Oestrous Cycle. The season of the year when an animal of any species or variety undergoes sexual intercourse has been called by Heape the *sexual season* for that animal. The actual periods at which copulation occurs are the oestrous periods. These may recur at rhythmical intervals within one sexual season as with the mare, the cow, the ewe and the sow (polyoestrous animals in Heape's terminology), or there may be only one oestrus to the sexual season as with the bitch (monoestrous animals).

A simple oestrous cycle in an animal of the latter kind (e.g. the bitch) has been divided into a number of periods as follows:

Anoestrum (period of rest),

Prooestrum (period of growth and congestion and period of destruction),

Oestrus (period of desire),

Pregnancy Pseudo-pregnancy.

The complete cycle in the monoestrous dog lasts about six months, there being two sexual seasons and 'heat' periods in one year, these occurring typically in spring and autumn, but there is some individual variation. In the smaller kinds of dogs the duration of the cycle may be less than six months, while in the larger varieties it may extend over a longer time.

The *anoestrum* in the absence of pregnancy lasts for about five months. The generative organs are in a state of quiescence. The ovarian follicles are probably undergoing a slow process of growth and ripening throughout the anoestrum, but they are not conspicuous upon the surface of the organs, at any rate until the approach of a new heat period. It follows that ovulation does not occur during the anoestrum and the ovaries do not contain corpora lutea. The uterus is relatively anaemic and the glands inactive. The mammary glands also are in a condition of rest unless lactation is going on as a result of recent pregnancy.

The *prooestrum*, which is the period of ' coming on heat', is marked by increased activity on the part of all the generative organs. The Graafian follicles, which at any earlier stage were situated more centrally within the ovary, increase in size so as to become easily visible on the surface from which they may protrude. The prooestrous uterine changes may be divided into two stages: (1) growth

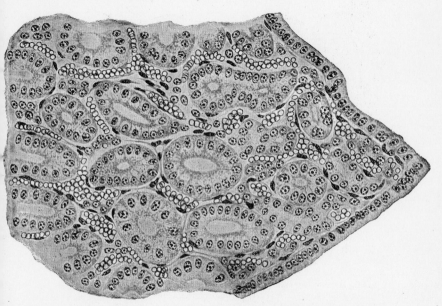

Fig. 89. Section through prooestrous uterine mucous membrane of dog showing congested blood vessels between the glands (from Marshall).

and congestion, and (2) destruction. In the first stage the uterine mucous membrane becomes thicker and more extensively vascularised, the capillaries being increased both in size and number and the glands becoming more active. In the second stage the walls of a certain number of capillaries break down and the blood corpuscles are extravasated in the stroma, and tend to become congregated just below the uterine epithelium; the latter ruptures in certain places and blood is poured out into the cavity of the uterus whence it passes down to the vagina and to the exterior.

Bleeding from the external vaginal opening in the prooestrous bitch may last for a week or even longer, and the entire prooestrum lasts for from ten to fourteen days. The whole process may be regarded as an act of preparation on the part of the uterus for the reception of a fertilised ovum, for at this period the superficial tissues of the mucous membrane undergo a process of partial renewal. The cornified layer of the epithelial wall of the vagina which is formed at the beginning of the period also becomes desquamated.

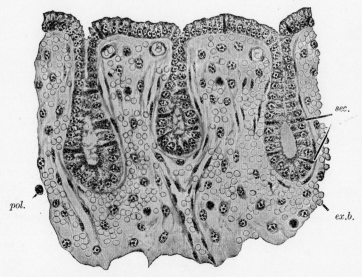

Fig. 90. Section through prooestrous uterine mucous membrane of dog showing extravasated blood (*ex. b.*); *pol.* polymorph leucocyte; *sec.* cells showing secretory activity (from Marshall).

Oestrus is the period of desire and sexual intercourse is ordinarily restricted to this period. In the bitch it lasts for about a week. Ovulation or the rupture of the Graafian follicles and the discharge of the ova occurs during this period, according to Evans and Cole near the beginning. The final maturation of the ova commences just prior to ovulation and is completed in the Fallopian tube. The process is similar to that which occurs in spermatogenesis (see p. 205) and results in the nuclear material of the mature ovum being reduced to one-half of what it was previously, that is to say, the number of chromosomes is one-half of the normal number characteristic of the cells of the body for the species in question (in the mare 26).*

The maturation of the ovum differs from the corresponding process in the spermatozoon in the unequal division of the cell. In the first division (which is the reduction division, the chromosomes not splitting longitudinally as they do in all other cell divisions) the first polar body is extruded. This consists of half the nuclear

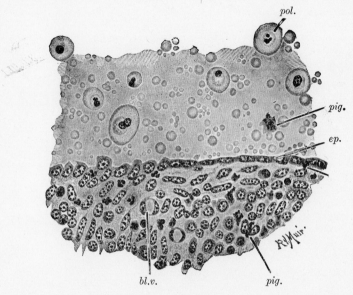

Fig. 91. Section through edge of mucous membrane of dog during early recuperation (from Marshall). *bl.v.* blood vessel; *ep.* epithelium in process of renewal; *pig.* pigment; *pol.* polymorph leucocyte.

material. The second division results in the formation of the mature ovum and the second polar body (the latter consisting, like the first polar, of nuclear material). The two polar bodies are extruded when the ovum is in the tube; sometimes the first polar body divides into two equal halves so that altogether there are three polar bodies; all of these die and disappear, the mature ovum with the reduced number of chromosomes alone remaining. The normal

* See footnote above, p. 205. In the mature ovum of the mare there are 13 chromosomes. In the human ovum there are 24 and in the human spermatozoon 23 or 24. In the cells of the human body there are 47 chromosomes in the male and 48 in the female.

number is restored by the union with a spermatozoon, this process usually occurring in the Fallopian tube.

During oestrus the mucous membrane of the uterus becomes recuperated and external bleeding from the vaginal opening ceases.

Oestrus in the bitch is followed either by pregnancy or by pseudo-pregnancy according to whether or not the ovum or ova become fertilised as a consequence of coitus. Under both conditions the uterus undergoes growth changes which relate chiefly to the blood vessels and glands in the mucosa. These increase in

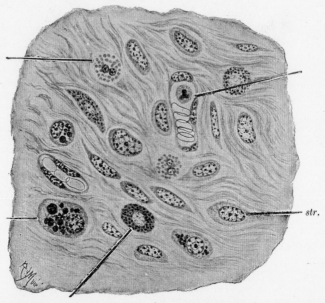

Fig. 92. Section through portion of uterine mucous membrane of dog during early recuperation showing different kinds of leucocytes (*l*) (from Marshall). *str.* stroma cell.

size, the whole organ assuming a histological appearance indicative of great activity. The secretion coming from the glands is a source of nutriment to the foetus in pregnancy and in some animals has been designated uterine milk; in pseudo-pregnancy a fluid is similarly secreted and as if intended for a foetus. Decidual cells (that is to say, large oval or polygonal epithelioid cells, formed by modification of the stroma cells, their development being correlated with the development of the foetal membranes and the nourishment of the unborn young) are not found normally except

in the presence of an embryo. Apart, however, from this difference
the changes undergone by the uterus of the bitch during pseudo-
pregnancy are in a general way similar to those which take place
in true pregnancy, but are less pronounced. The growth changes of
pseudo-pregnancy are succeeded after about four or five weeks by
degenerative changes when the glands become shrunken and blood
is extravasated into the tissue, but without leading to external

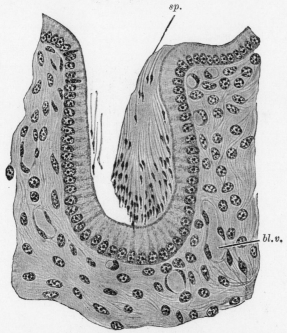

Fig. 93. Section through uterine gland of bitch after coition showing
spermatozoa (*sp.*) (from Marshall). *bl.v.* blood vessel.

bleeding. A somewhat similar condition occurs in the last stage of
pregnancy.

The ovarian changes also are identical under the two conditions,
at any rate in the earlier stages. At ovulation the egg, along with
some of the follicular epithelial cells and most of the liquor folliculi,
is discharged from the ovary. The remaining epithelial cells then
undergo a great and rapid hypertrophy, becoming converted into
the luteal cells of the fully formed corpus luteum. At the same time
strands of connective tissue grow inward from the wall of the

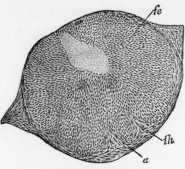

Fig. 94. Recently ruptured follicle of mouse (after Sobotta, from Schafer).
fe, follicular epithelium; *th*, connective tissue; *a*, ingrowth from same.

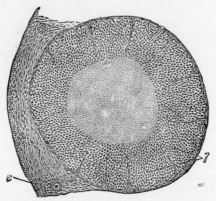

Fig. 95. Early stage in formation of corpus luteum of mouse (after Sobotta, from Schafer). *l*, developing luteal cells; *g*, germinal epithelium.

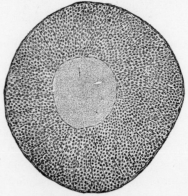

Fig. 96. Late stage in formation of corpus luteum of mouse (after Sobotta, from Schafer).

follicle carrying blood vessels along with them, so that the completely developed corpus luteum consists of large luteal cells partly separated by an anastomosis of connective tissue, the whole structure being highly vascularised. The remains of the central cavity of the original follicle is eventually filled in by a plug of connective tissue. The epithelial cells increase to about sixteen times their original cubical content and come to contain a yellow pigmented fat called lutein. The corpus luteum thus formed persists in the dog until the close of pseudo-pregnancy or pregnancy,

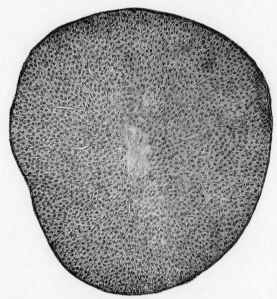

Fig. 97. Fully formed corpus luteum of mouse (after Sobotta from Schafer).

when the luteal cells become vacuolated and shrink. The corpus luteum eventually degenerates, leaving merely a scar.

Contemporaneously with the growth of the corpus luteum the mammary glands develop both during pregnancy and during pseudo-pregnancy, and milk secretion may occur at the end of each of these periods, but the growth of the glands, and their subsequent activity are less complete in the absence of true gestation.

The period of gestation in the dog is about 62 days, and pseudo-pregnancy may be said to last for about the same time or perhaps not quite so long. It does not terminate so abruptly as true pregnancy, and the uterus passes gradually back to the condition of quiescence which is characteristic of the anoestrum.* This period lasts for about three months and is succeeded by another prooestrum.

Polyoestrous animals differ from monoestrous ones in having short recurrent cycles within a single sexual season. Thus in the sheep the 'tupping time' may take place in autumn, and during this season the ewe will experience a succession of cycles, each

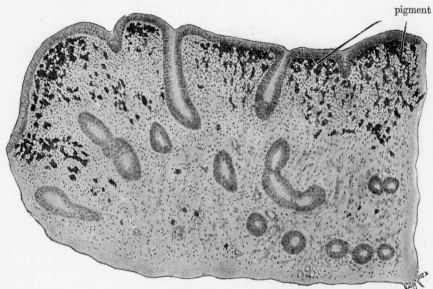

pigment

Fig. 98. Section through uterine mucous membrane of sheep showing pigment formed from extravasated blood (from Marshall).

lasting about 15 days, until pregnancy is induced or tupping is over; in the latter case the ewe passes into a state of prolonged sexual quiescence (anoestrum) which lasts until the next tupping season in the following autumn. The return of oestrus at short intervals during the sexual season is implied when the shepherds speak of the ewe as 'coming back' to the ram.

The short interval of superficial rest between the 'heat' periods is called by Heape the dioestrum and is characteristic of all

* It is noteworthy that at the end of pseudo-pregnancy a bitch may behave like one about to give birth and prepare a bed for pups. Hammond has noted similar phenomena with doe rabbits which (exceptionally) experience pseudo-pregnancy.

polyoestrous animals. In reality it is of the nature of a very abbreviated pseudo-pregnancy. In the sheep it lasts for about 12 or 13 days. It is followed by a brief prooestrum when the ewe's external generative organs become somewhat congested. There is however no external bleeding in the ewe, and the uterine blood which becomes extravasated during the prooestrum remains in the stroma, coming to lie just below the epithelium where it is converted into black pigment. After three or four heat periods this pigment may have accumulated in such quantity that almost the whole surface of the uterine mucosa is rendered jet black, the pigment only disappearing during subsequent pregnancy or during the anoestrum when it is said to be removed by leucocytes.

Oestrus in the ewe may last for a day or two days or for only a few hours, and the prooestrum and oestrus together do not occupy more than two or three days. Ovulation takes place during oestrus and the number of follicles which discharge is usually one or two, sometimes three, but rarely more than three.

The wild sheep (such as the Mouflon or the Barbary sheep) is said to be monoestrous and to experience only one sexual season annually. The Scottish Black-faced sheep in the Highlands is generally dioestrous, that is to say, it can have two 'heat' periods in the absence of the ram but not more than two, and the season for tupping is November. In the Lowlands, however, where the climate is less severe and food more abundant, there may be five or six dioestrous cycles if the ewe fails to become pregnant before anoestrum or prolonged quiescence is resumed. Amongst the English breeds the number of recurrent 'heat' periods is generally much greater and in Dorset Horns and Hampshire Downs the ewes may experience oestrus at almost any time of the year. The same is true of the Merino sheep amid favourable conditions, and in New South Wales the sexual season is said to embrace the whole year, there being in the absence of pregnancy an almost uninterrupted succession of dioestrous cycles. Amongst English varieties the Dorset Horns are almost alone in being able to have two crops of lambs in one year, but this practice is discouraged as it tends to cause too great a strain and thus deteriorate the ewe. The capacity to experience oestrus or the degree of polyoestrum is partly a racial characteristic, but it depends at least equally upon environment and nutrition which favour an increased fecundity.

The period of gestation in the sheep is 21 to 22 weeks or about five months, so that if lambing occurs twice in one year there is only about a month's interval between the end of one pregnancy and the beginning of the next.

In the goat the breeding season may extend from September to February (sometimes longer). Heat lasts about thirty hours and sometimes three days. As described by Asdell, the short cycle is about three weeks and the period of gestation on an average 151 days, but spring conceptions give slightly longer gestations than autumn conceptions.

The corpus luteum, which as we have seen is formed from the discharged follicle, develops very rapidly in the sheep. Its fate depends upon whether or not gestation supervenes as a result of coition, for in the pregnant animal the corpus luteum goes on increasing in size until about half way through the period and maintains its functional activity till at or near the time of parturition, whereas in the non-pregnant ewe after oestrus the organ continues to develop for only a few days before it becomes smaller. Mature (or almost mature) Graafian follicles are not associated with corpora lutea, and the latter organs when present appear to exercise a dominating influence upon the ovarian metabolism and to inhibit follicular growth or even to promote follicular atrophy. Consequently it is important in animals which come 'on heat' at short intervals that the corpus luteum should not persist for more than a short period, and this suppression of the corpus luteum in the non-occurrence of pregnancy is generally characteristic of polyoestrous mammals. In monoestrous animals between the heat periods and in all animals under a condition of pregnancy it is obviously not disadvantageous if ovulation or the ripening of the Graafian follicles is partially inhibited during these times when coitus does not occur. Correlated with the shortening in the period during which the corpus luteum persists (i.e. in polyoestrous animals), there is no pseudo-pregnant development of the uterus and mammary glands or only a very abbreviated one during the dioestrum. Even in polyoestrous animals, however, the corpus luteum may abnormally persist and cause sterility, and when this happens with cows the corpus luteum should be squeezed out from the ovary, for if this is done the oestrous cycle starts again forthwith, the cows very soon coming 'in use' after the operation of removal. Hammond has shown that by squeezing out the normal corpus luteum of the cow during the dioestrum this period may be shortened and heat be experienced after a briefer interval than the normal three weeks.

The cow, like the sheep, is polyoestrous, but the dioestrous cycle lasts for 21 days. The precise conditions which determine the duration of the sexual season are little understood, and investigation into this subject is urgently needed with the view of controlling the bulling times of heifers and cows so as to regulate the periods of calving and the supply of milk throughout the year. The prooestrous changes, like those of the ewe, are relatively slight and external bleeding from the vaginal opening does not usually occur. There is sometimes a mucous discharge but even this may be absent, and yet a normal oestrus may supervene. Owing to this circumstance some 'cowmen' will let a 'period' pass by, and so lose three weeks, and possibly the chance of getting an animal in calf for that season, simply because they failed to detect any of the signs of the onset of 'heat'. Dioestrous cycles (in the non-occurrence of pregnancy) may continue for the whole year but there is some individual variation. The period of gestation is nine months. Usually only one follicle is discharged at oestrus. Ovulation may, however, be postponed until a day or two after oestrus is over. Heat supervenes thirty to sixty days after parturition. Prooestrum and oestrus together only occupy two or three days.

In the sow the dioestrous cycle is also three weeks and pregnancy lasts four months. By weaning the young pigs early and giving the sow a plentiful supply of food it is possible to obtain five litters in two years, but the more usual practice is to have two litters annually. Heat may be experienced four weeks after farrowing and in the absence of the boar continue to recur at intervals of three weeks, each oestrous period lasting about a day. As a rule a sow which has been suckling does not come on heat until five or six days after the piglings are weaned or about six to eight weeks after farrowing. The indications of prooestrum are slight, there being generally no external bleeding, but the vulva is swollen. The ova are usually shed about thirty or thirty-five hours after the beginning of heat but the process may be postponed to as late as seventy hours.

In all the above-mentioned animals oestrus is a period of restlessness and excitement. The ewe on heat tends to follow the ram. The cow or heifer bellows and mounts other cows, and sometimes there is a slight rise of body temperature. The sow emits a peculiar grunting sound which is characteristic of oestrus and is not made at other times. But as compared with the bitch the symptoms of oestrus are slight and of brief duration.

The mare is polyoestrous, the normal dioestrous cycle being about three weeks and the oestrous period four or five days, though its actual length may vary by three or four days. Ovulation more usually takes place towards the end of oestrus and the occurrence of coition at too long an interval from ovulation may be a cause of sterility in mares. The sexual season in the absence of the stallion extends throughout the spring and early summer months, and is generally longest in the more domesticated breeds. Ewart has recorded a case of a pony imported from Timor (which is in the Southern Hemisphere), to Scotland, in which oestrus was experienced in the autumn, or at the same time as the spring in Timor. The period of gestation in the mare is eleven months, and 'heat' recurs from seven to eleven days after parturition. This is called the 'foal heat'. Certain mares are irregular in the recurrence of the 'heat' periods, and, in some, 'foal heat' does not occur until seventeen days after parturition instead of the usual time. In exceptional cases a mare, like a cow, may conceive at the 'foal heat' and yet take the horse three weeks later, just as though she had failed to become pregnant. Heape states that, very exceptionally, mares are monoestrous. Blood has been observed in the mare's prooestrous discharge, but it is not generally present. The external generative organs, however, are usually swollen and mucus is emitted. The clitoris and vulva often undergo a succession of spasmodic movements, preceded by the discharge of small quantities of urine and this fluid may have the consistency of oil. Suckling mares tend to fail in their milk supply, and the quality of the milk appears to undergo some kind of change, as it is frequently found that foals during the heat periods of their dams suffer from relaxation of the bowels or even acute diarrhoea. In mares which are not suckling the mammary gland becomes congested and increases in size during the heat. At the same time some mares develop great excitability, and kick and squeal, becoming dangerous to approach and impossible to drive. There is, however, great variation, for other animals may pass through the 'heat' period without exhibiting any well-marked signs of their condition which in a few instances can only be determined by the behaviour of the mare towards the stallion.

Of other domestic animals the cat is generally polyoestrous and has a dioestrous cycle of about 14 days and three sexual seasons annually, and the period of gestation is nine weeks. The ferret is monoestrous and has two or three sexual seasons which are, however, usually confined to spring and summer. Gestation lasts 40 days. The rat and other wild rodents are mostly polyoestrous.

In the mare, cow, ewe, sow and bitch ovulation takes place spontaneously, but in the rabbit and ferret and sometimes in the cat it requires the additional stimulus set up by coitus before it can occur. Presumably coition causes a nerve reflex, but there is evidence that the stimulus does not act directly on the ovaries but through the intermediation of the anterior pituitary gland (see p. 257). In the rabbit ovulation takes place from $9\frac{1}{2}$ to 10 hours after coitus. Maturation of the ovum also depends upon the occurrence of coitus and commences shortly afterwards, but is not completed until after ovulation. In such animals as the rabbit, which do not ovulate spontaneously, corpora lutea are not usually formed apart from pregnancy, and the pseudo-pregnant condition does not normally occur. Pseudo-pregnancy with growth and congestion of uterine mucosa and mammary development followed by milk secretion can, however, be induced in the female rabbit and ferret by permitting copulation with a sterile male. The male may be rendered sterile by severing the vasa deferentia (vasectomy). Pseudo-pregnancy may also be brought about in a female rendered sterile as by severing the Fallopian tubes. The rabbit and the ferret also resemble one another in that the female in the non-occurrence of coition may keep 'on heat' for weeks at a time during which period the follicles in the ovaries remain in a state ready for ovulation but without discharging until coition takes place. In the oestrous ferret the vulva remains swollen to about 100 times its anoestrous size but subsides in a few days if pregnancy supervenes. The function of the enlarged vulva is to facilitate coition.

Pregnancy. The ova are fertilised by the spermatozoa in the Fallopian tube. A spermatozoon after coming in contact with an ovum passes bodily through its wall; the head or nucleus of the spermatozoon fuses with the nucleus of the ovum thus restoring the amount of nuclear material or number of chromosomes to that characteristic of the species, while the tail of the spermatozoon breaks up and mingles with the external (or non-nuclear) proto-

plasm of the ovum. The fertilised ova then pass down the tube and
into the uterine cavity. Here they find a rich pabulum of nourishment provided by the prooestrous discharge. The ovum by a
process of division becomes converted into a mulberry-shaped
mass of cells, the morula, and this, through some of the cells within
becoming vacuolated, is converted into a hollow blastocyst. The
blastocyst elongates out within the horn of the uterus but there is
no attachment to the mucosa for some days (in the cow and sheep
not until the seventeenth day of pregnancy). The first attachment
is by means of the yolk sac, which is a little closed vesicle formed
within the blastocyst. Villous processes grow out from the yolk sac

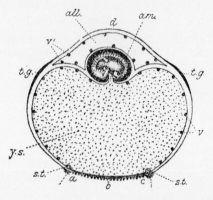

Fig. 99. Diagrammatic representation of 4 weeks' horse embryo and its foetal
appendages (after Ewart, from Smith, Messrs Baillière, Tindall and Cox). *am.*
amnion; *y.s.* yolk sac; *s.t.* and *v.* blood vessels; *d.* chorion; *t.g.* area of special
attachment to uterine wall; *all.* allantoic cavity; *a, b, c,* absorbing area of yolk
sac.

and anchor the embryo into which the blastocyst develops to the
wall of the uterus. The area of attachment is also an absorbing
area, nourishment being transmitted from the mother through the
villi of the yolk sac. Part of the cavity of the yolk sac is eventually
included in the embryo, becoming the alimentary canal, so that
the yolk sac opens widely into the embryonic gut. Meanwhile the
embryonic or foetal membranes grow outwards and form a bag
containing a watery fluid and enclosing the embryo, within. The
fluid serves as a protective covering for the embryo, keeping it
from the effects of jar or outside disturbance. The inner of the
membranes is called the amnion and the outer the chorion, and
this, like the yolk sac, also gives off villi which project as finger-like

processes into spaces in the maternal tissue of the uterus. The attachment by the yolk sac is then replaced by the attachment through the chorion. This occurs in the cow about the fourth or fifth week and in the mare about the sixth or seventh. This time is recognised as a critical period in the development of the foal which is then more liable to 'slip' than at other times.*

Meanwhile the uterus of the mother undergoes great changes, its muscle walls becoming enormously developed, while the outer

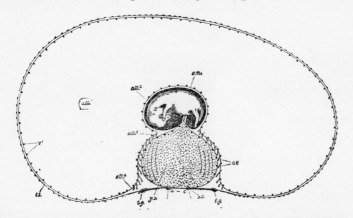

Fig. 100. Seven weeks' horse embryo (after Ewart from Smith, Messrs Baillière, Tindall and Cox). *all.* allantoic cavity; *all.*², *all.*³ and *all.*⁴ allantois; *am.* amnion; *c.v.* villous process between allantois and yolk sac; *y.s.* yolk sac; *v'* and *tt''*, vascular villi; *a—c*, absorbing area of yolk sac; *t.g.* area of special attachment.

portion of the connective tissue of the stroma gives rise to spindle-shaped decidual cells and at the same time becomes very greatly vascularised. This tissue forms the maternal placenta and contains large blood sinuses into some of which the chorionic villi project. In the mean time, from a point within the embryo, an outgrowth called the allantois arises, and the outer wall of this outgrowth blends with the chorion to form the foetal placenta. The inner wall of the allantois lies alongside the amnion and there is a large cavity between the outer and inner allantoic walls (the allantoic cavity). The portion of the allantois remaining within the foetus

* In most marsupials (kangaroos, etc.) the yolk sac represents the sole method of embryonic attachment, the young being born in a very immature condition and transferred to the pouch. The tendency for the embryonic foal to 'slip' or be aborted after losing its attachment through the yolk sac and before the new method of attachment has become consolidated may be regarded as a reversionary one towards a condition existing in a marsupial ancestor.

eventually becomes the bladder, and the point from which the
allantois passes out remains after birth as the navel. The chorionic
villi contain blood vessels connected with the circulatory system
of the developing foetus so that the foetal and maternal circulation
are brought into very intimate relation, being only separated by

Fig. 101. Foetal circulation, advanced period (after Colin, from Fleming, Messrs
Baillière, Tindall and Cox). *A*, cotyledons; *B*, umbilical vein which communicates
with *C* and *D*, venae portae (in liver) and with ductus venosus opening into *F*,
posterior vena cava; *G*, right ventricle; *H*, pulmonary artery; *I*, ductus anteriosus
(uniting *H* and *J*); *J*, aorta; *L*, umbilical arteries.

a very thin wall of protoplasm, but there is no direct communication between them. Nutritive materials—protein, fat and carbohydrate as well as oxygen—transfuse through this thin layer, from
the mother to the young, while excretory products and carbon
dioxide pass in the opposite direction from the foetal to the
maternal circulation. In this way the placenta acts as a foetal
alimentary canal, lung and kidney, but there is never any actual
contact between the maternal and foetal blood. In later embryonic

life the foetus retains its connection with the chorion and so with
the maternal placenta, by the umbilical cord which is formed partly
from the allantois where it passes out, and contains the umbilical
arteries and vein.

The form and mode of attachment of the placenta are different
in the various orders of mammals. The chorionic villi may be so
interlocked with the maternal tissue that in parturition some of
the uterine mucosa is torn away from the remainder, leaving a raw
surface. This is what happens in man and in the dog, as well as in
many other mammals. In the horse and other Ungulata, however,
this does not happen. In the Carnivora the villi are confined to a
zone or belt, in ruminants they occur in clumps or cotyledons
corresponding to the cotyledonary papillae which in these animals
protrude from the uterine mucous membrane, while in the horse
and pig the villi are scattered.

The highly developed uterine glands supply a secretion (called
in ruminants the uterine milk) which helps to nourish the developing
foetus.

The beginning of gestation is marked by a change in the
character of the mother. The pregnant cow and sheep 'settle' or
tend to fatten in the early months, and graziers take advantage
of this fact to get the animals into good condition for market.
Mares which were previously troublesome and difficult to work
become quiet and tractable. The abdomen becomes visibly enlarged, as may be most easily seen from behind and undergoes an
alteration in shape, the flanks tending to become hollow, while
the belly sinks. These changes in the mare are noticeable after
about four months. In the meanwhile the foetus is developing in
the uterus, and by the end of the fourth month may be seen to
respond to stimuli; thus a bucket of cold water given to the mother
on an empty stomach will cause the young foal to make a sudden
twitching movement which can be seen externally on the left side
of the mare. The enlargement of the mammary glands may be seen
most easily in animals pregnant for the first time. It begins almost
immediately after conception but is not pronounced until after
two or three months in the mare or cow. In animals which have
previously been pregnant the change is not very apparent until
shortly before parturition. In the last weeks a serous fluid can be
expressed from the teats and as parturition approaches this fluid
becomes more and more opaque and milk-like. In lactating mares

and cows the milk supply diminishes and the animal 'dries off' as
a new pregnancy proceeds, there being little or no secretion from
about the seventh or eighth month in the mare or the sixth or
seventh month in the milch cow until the new supply begins in the
final stages of pregnancy. With heifers in calf for the first time
pregnancy of five months may be diagnosed by the thick honey-
like secretion in the teats replacing the thin watery fluid that was
there before. The secretions from the cervix uteri may also be
utilised for determining pregnancy, these becoming thick, glairy
and tenacious in the pregnant cow, whereas in the non-pregnant
animal they are either thin and watery or non-existent (see p. 224).

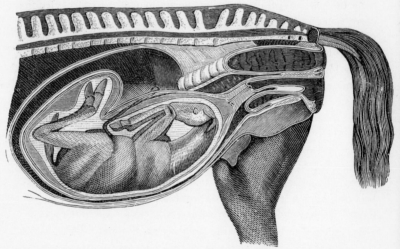

Fig. 102. Normal position of foal before parturition (after Franck, from
Fleming, Messrs Baillière, Tindall and Cox).

Parturition. During uterine life the young foal, calf or lamb
lies on its back within the uterus on the floor of the mother's
abdomen, but shortly before birth the foetus turns on its side
taking a lateral position, and then turns still further, assuming an
upright position. The foetus is then brought into a position in which
the muzzle rests upon the fore legs, these being extended in the
direction of the vaginal opening, while the hind limbs are drawn
up under its body. This method of presentation (anterior or 'head
presentation') is the most normal, but it often happens that the
hind legs appear first (posterior or 'breach presentation') or the
foetus may be presented transversely or cross-wise.

The mother, as the time for parturition draws, near becomes increasingly disturbed and restless, frequently changing her position, and the udder becomes noticeably swollen. When the actual 'pains' commence she shows evident signs of distress, and the skin becomes hot and the pulse rate rapid, but each 'pain' is succeeded by an interval of calm.

The 'pains' are caused by the contraction of the longitudinal muscles of the uterus which in this way dilate the os or mouth of the uterus. Even in the virgin the uterine muscles undergo very

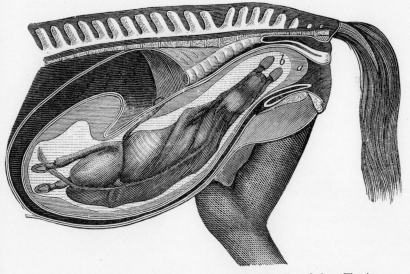

Fig. 103. Second position preparatory to parturition (after Franck, from Fleming, Messrs Baillière, Tindall and Cox).   *a*, allantois; *b*, amnion.

slight rhythmic contractions, as may be seen when the organ is withdrawn from the body and kept in salt solution at body temperature, and these contractions may be greatly increased by applying mechanical stimuli. During the anoestrum the uterine contractions are always very slight and infrequent, and it is only during pregnancy and with the approach of parturition that they become considerable. At such times, as already mentioned, the muscles of the uterus are very greatly developed.

The dilatation of the os marks the first stage of labour. In the second stage all the uterine muscles contract, as well as those of the abdominal wall and the diaphragm. These co-ordinated muscular movements expel the foetus from the uterus to the vagina, and thence to the exterior, the final propulsion from the vagina being due chiefly to the contractions of the abdominal muscles. The foetal membranes which contain fluids and serve as a sort of elastic bag round the young animal, thus protecting it from mechanical shock or jar, are the first to appear. The 'water bag' then ruptures, some of the fluid escaping, and the young animal soon afterwards makes its appearance.

The third stage of parturition consists of the expulsion of the foetal membranes which together constitute the afterbirth. This is

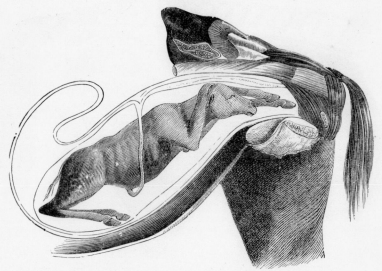

Fig. 104. Third position preparatory to parturition (after Franck, from Fleming, Messrs Baillière, Tindall and Cox).

done by further contractions of the uterine muscles accompanied by the action of the diaphragm and muscles of the abdomen. Sometimes, as not infrequently happens in the mare, the young animal is born within the intact membranes and should be liberated in order to avoid asphyxiation, but more usually a few minutes or more elapse before the placenta is detached and got rid of. Occasionally the membranes are retained in the uterus, where they are liable to become infected with bacteria and set up inflammation; if they are not discharged steps should be taken to remove them.

The duration of parturition varies in the different species. In the mare it takes from 5 to 15 minutes, in the cow about two hours, in the sheep 15 minutes for each lamb born, in the sow, bitch and cat from 10 to 30 minutes with sometimes an interval of one hour between each birth. In the Carnivora, the mother usually gnaws through the umbilical cord, but in the other animals it is torn. The afterbirth may not be got rid of until several hours after the young is born (as in the mare).

The normal process of parturition depends upon the integrity of the spinal cord which co-ordinates the various muscular movements, but, as already mentioned, the uterus undergoes rhythmical contractions independently of its nerve connections and will do so after separation from the body if maintained at the normal temperature and suspended in a suitable saline fluid. Goltz has shown

Fig. 105. Cow in act of calving (after Fleming, Messrs Baillière, Tindall and Cox).

that the bitch will give birth to pups after the complete exsection of the spinal cord in the lumbo-sacral region, and Simpson, in an experiment on the sow in which the posterior spinal cord was destroyed, showed that a litter of young pigs could be expelled by uterine action alone, excepting for the last pigling which remained in the vagina owing to the abdominal muscles not acting and there being no young ones in process of passing out from the uterus to propel the last pigling through the vaginal opening.

There is also an endocrine mechanism of parturition. The posterior lobe of the pituitary body produces a hormone (pituitrin) that has a powerful stimulating influence on the uterine muscles which are much hypertrophied at this time. There is evidence that as the corpora lutea regress, an ovarian hormone acts upon the posterior pituitary (see below, p. 258). Knaus has shown, further, that there is a hormone formed by the corpus luteum which acts

antagonistically to the posterior lobe hormone, so that as long as
functionally active corpora lutea are present in the ovaries the
uterine muscles are not greatly acted on by pituitrin but as soon
as the corpora lutea have sufficiently regressed the uterine muscles
begin to contract forcibly, and finally expel the young. These and
the other hormones concerned in the reproductive processes are
dealt with below.

Abortion or premature parturition may occur at any time during
gestation. There are two kinds, sporadic and contagious abortion.
The former may occur as a result of undue muscular exertion,
fatigue, injury, excitement or fright, or it may be caused by illness
(e.g. digestive trouble or the taking of frozen food) or by eating
ergot or other substances which act upon the uterine muscles.
Contagious abortion is due to a bacillus and is especially common
in cattle; it may be transmitted by the bull or the contagion may
be spread through contaminated litter, the bacilli probably entering through the vagina and passing into the uterus. Immunity,
at any rate for a certain period, is acquired through an attack.
Contagious abortion also occurs in mares, and occasionally in
sheep and pigs but is due usually to different organisms which are
in some degree specific for the animals attacked.

Lactation. The mammary glands, which have been already
described, commence to secrete at or shortly before parturition,
the thin colostrum which at first appears rapidly giving place to
true milk. There is, however, as mentioned above, a thick honey-
like secretion formed in the glands of the heifer at the fifth month of
pregnancy. The capacity for milk production varies widely in the
different breeds, some cows going on yielding until the approach
of a new parturition before going dry. The drawing off of milk is
itself a factor in the yield, since, as is well known, a 'quarter' will
go dry if the milk secreted is not removed by milking or sucking;
in such cases the milk constituents are reabsorbed and lactose may
often be found in the urine. The physiological factors in the growth
of the glands and the secretion of the fluid are referred to below in
dealing with the ovarian secretions.

Fecundity. The number of young produced at a litter is dependent primarily upon the number of ova discharged at ovulation
which occurs during oestrus. With the mare and cow this number
is generally one, but double and even triple births are not unknown.
With the ewe one or two young are born at a time, while triplets

are not uncommon, and four or five lambs have occasionally been produced at one time. The sow may give birth to any number up to sixteen, and occasionally more, a litter of twenty-four having been recorded. The bitch has been known to produce as many as twenty-three pups, but any number higher than twelve is very rare, an average sized litter consisting of four or five pups, while the number is often fewer.

The condition most conducive to fertility in farm animals generally is a nice improving one (not too fat and not too lean). Adiposity is a common cause of sterility, and animals unduly fattened for show or sale are frequently barren, at any rate temporarily.

The number of lambs produced may be increased by the process of 'flushing' the ewes, that is, by giving them extra feeding, cake, corn or turnips for a few weeks before tupping time, this practice not merely increasing the number of ripe follicles available for ovulation at any one time, but also having the effect of hastening forward the sexual season. After tupping is over, extra feeding is no longer of use in increasing fecundity, since the number of developing young has already been determined.*

It is now known that light may be an important factor in bringing animals into a breeding condition. Bissonette has shown that ferrets may be brought on heat and made to breed by subjecting them to artificial light (ordinary electric illumination) in the anoestrum. Baker also, as a result of prolonged experimental observations on voles, has shown that the breeding season may be extended by illumination and inhibited by darkness. The practice adopted by the poultry industry of subjecting hens to artificial illumination in order to promote egg laying may conceivably be an application of the same principle.

It is clear that, speaking generally, (in sheep at any rate) the female is a more important factor than the male, since whereas the number of ripe ova available for fertilisation is very limited, the number of spermatozoa entering the female passages is generally in excess. On the other hand, it has been shown by Williams that among stallions and bulls reduced fertility due to the degeneration of the spermatozoa as a result of bacterial injection or disease is not very uncommon.

* Flushing, by tending to bring all the ewes on heat at the same time, renders it easier for the shepherd at lambing time, since lambing is got over more quickly.

In the sow Hammond has shown that whereas a very large
number of ova may be fertilised, some of these may only undergo a
very limited degree of development. It is conceivable that some
of the ova possess an insufficient vitality from the outset, and this

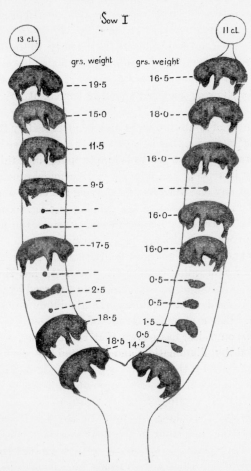

Fig. 106. Diagram of sow's uterus illustrating foetal atrophy (after Hammond).
The numbers 13 and 11 c.l. are those of the corpora lutea in the ovaries, and
show that only one ovum out of 24 shed has failed to get fertilised.

may possibly be the result of inbreeding, which is believed to tend
towards infertility. Thus Heape states that Dorset Horn ewes will
sometimes produce lambs when put to Hampshire Down rams but
will not breed when served by rams of their own variety. It is

possible that the fertilised ovum is endowed with a superior
vitality by having conjugated with a spermatozoon belonging to
a different breed. Moreover, Hammond has shown that in rabbits
in which foetal atrophy also occurs the death of the developing
young may be due to an hereditary lethal factor present in the
reproductive cells.

Fertility, like other characteristics, can be inherited, and a ram
which was one of twins and consequently of fertile stock may
transmit this capacity to female progeny. It is improbable, how-

Fig. 107. Lonk sheep aged 18 years with her last lamb. This sheep, which belonged
to Mr William Peel of Knowlemere Manor, Clitheroe, lived to be 21 after having
35 lambs, nine of which were triplets. (From Marshall.) From photograph
supplied by Lieut.-Col. W. R. Peel.

ever, in view of what has been said above, that the male parent
can often be responsible for the size of the litters produced by
the females served by him. Nevertheless fertility may be transmitted through the male in just the same way as the milking
capacity of a dairy cow may be transmitted through the male
progeny to the next generation of females.

The reproductive period in the life of the female begins at
puberty when the generative organs develop, the first batch of ova
become mature, and the first oestrous cycle commences: it ends
at the menopause or climacteric when the generative organs

become atrophic and the cycle closes. The mare begins to breed in her second year, puberty generally occurring at about 16 to 18 months. Heifers take the bull at 12 to 14 months but may experience puberty earlier. The sow may take the boar at 4 or 5 months but puberty is generally later. Ewe lambs dropped in the spring may breed in the following autumn. Bitches and cats experience puberty at 8 to 10 months, sometimes later, and occasionally earlier. The time when reproduction ceases is very variable and in practice most domestic animals die long before they reach their menopause. Mares have bred even at 30 years and ewes at 21, but such cases are very exceptional.

The Internal Ovarian Secretions. In addition to the oogenetic function, the ovaries are organs of internal secretion, and through these exercise an influence over the female metabolism comparable to that possessed by the testes in the male. In birds removal or atrophy of the ovaries tends towards the assumption of certain characters which are apparently male characters but are really those of the neutral castrated or de-sexed type. This is because in birds the neutral type is nearer to the male than to the female. Thus in oophorectomised hens there is a development of the spurs and feathering of the cock. The erectile structures about the head (comb, etc.), however, do not develop after the removal of the ovary, and the general result is a bird closely resembling the capon or castrated cock. In mammals removal of the ovaries does not lead to the development of male characters (e.g. in Herdwick sheep

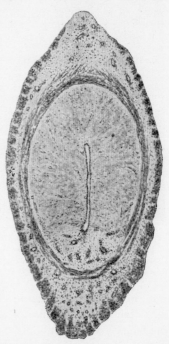

Fig. 108. Transverse section through uterus of rat, six months after ovariotomy, showing degenerative changes (from Marshall).

which are horned in the male but hornless in the female, ovariotomy or extirpation of the ovaries does not lead to horn development).

That the ovaries are responsible for the oestrous cycle is certain, for ovariotomy is followed by atrophy of the uterus and heat no longer recurs. That the ovarian influence is chemical rather than nervous is proved by the fact that successful transplantation of the ovaries to an abnormal position, such as on to the ventral wall of the body cavity or into the tissue of the kidney, is sufficient to

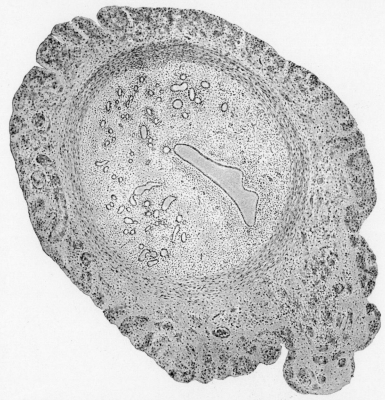

Fig. 109. Transverse section through uterus of rat six months after transplantation of ovary to ventral wall of peritoneum. The uterus is normal. (From Marshall.)

admit of the recurrence of the cycle and the normal maintenance of the uterine nutrition in spite of the ordinary nerve connections of the ovaries having been severed. The grafted ovaries are capable of producing ripe ova, and ovulation may occur, followed by the formation of typical corpora lutea.

At the prooestrous and oestrous periods, when the ovaries are in a state of enhanced activity as manifested especially by the growth and maturation of the Graafian follicles, the uterus also becomes active, undergoing growth and congestion and the other changes characteristic of heat, as already described. Furthermore, the

Fig. 110. Transplanted ovary of rat, showing corpora lutea
and small follicle (from Marshall).

mammary glands become slightly swollen. It is not, however, until a later period when the corpora lutea are formed in the ovaries that the uterine mucous membrane undergoes the pronounced hypertrophy characteristic of pregnancy or pseudo-pregnancy. The

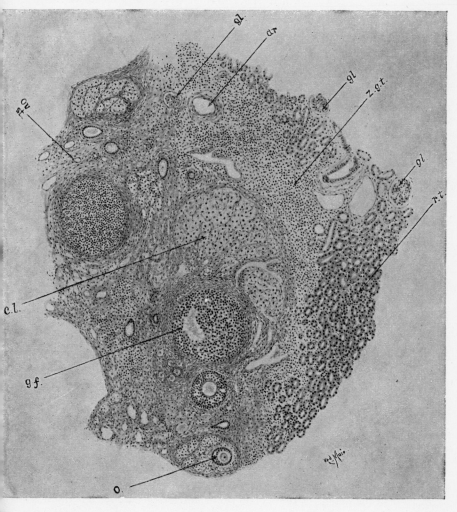

Fig. 111. Section through rat's kidney into which ovary has been transplanted. *ar.* artery; *c.l.* corpus luteum; *g.f.* Graafian follicle; *gl.* glomerulus of kidney; *o*, ovum; *ov. st.* ovarian stroma; *r.t.* renal tubule; *z.g.t.* zone between ovarian and renal tissue.

mammary glands develop during the same period. Moreover it has been established that these developmental changes, both uterine and mammary, do not occur in the absence of corpora lutea, as when ovulation had not taken place at oestrus. Experiments have proved clearly that both the uterine growth and the mammary growth are dependent upon the presence of luteal tissue in the ovaries, and under the influence of the corpora lutea the mammary glands develop to an extent sufficient to admit of milk production at and after parturition or at a corresponding period at the end of pseudo-pregnancy. In polyoestrous animals the corpora lutea, if pregnancy does not occur, usually degenerate after a short interval and before another heat period is due, since the presence of these organs in the ovaries has an inhibitory influence upon follicular development and upon the occurrence of oestrus (p. 236).

In view of these and other facts it is evident that the ovaries are organs elaborating internal secretions which change both in character and quantity during the successive phases of the oestrous cycle, and that these secretions are responsible for the various processes which recur rhythmically in the uterus, vagina, and mammary glands. During the anoestrum the ovarian secretion suffices to preserve the normal nutrition of the uterus and to prevent that organ from lapsing into the infantile condition. During the prooestrum and oestrus an ovarian hormone stimulates the uterine and mammary tissues to undergo some amount of growth.* But it is not until the corpus luteum is formed that the ovary acquires its maximal influence upon the accessory generative organs and mammary glands which then undergo the extensive anabolic changes without which the young could not obtain the nourishment which is necessary for their growth and development.

The ovarian hormone responsible for maintaining the normal uterine nutrition is probably identical with that determining the development of the female sex characters generally, but there is no direct evidence as to its production or mode of action. On the other hand, there is definite proof as to the existence of oestrous and luteal hormones. The former, which Parkes has called oestrin, has been prepared from the follicles and interstitial cells. It has

* An abnormal continuous oestrus (nymphomania) is associated with the presence of cystic follicles in the ovaries and there is a persistent sterility. If the cysts be squeezed out the nymphomanic mare or cow may often be got to breed.

also been obtained from the placenta, in which it may be stored, as well as from the liquor amnii and urine.* It has been variously called folliculin (Allen and Doisy), progynon (Butenandt), menformon (Laqueur), theelin (Veler *et al.*) and the α-hormone (Wiesner). Marrian has shown that in its most active form it has the empirical formula $C_{18}H_{22}O_2$ in which state it can be crystallised out. Its injection into anoestrous or oophorectomised animals causes all the symptoms of oestrus. With regard to the luteal hormones (pythin or progestin) Corner has shown that if injected into pregnant rabbits whose ovaries have been removed or corpora lutea destroyed, gestation may be made to continue and the young brought to full term by daily injections of the extract, whereas without such injections the death of the embryo invariably occurs.

It is now also substantiated that the anterior lobe of the pituitary produces one and probably several hormones, and if this organ is removed or its functional activity reduced below a certain level the ovaries and other sex organs do not function and sterility results.† One of these hormones is oestrogenic and if repeated grafting of the anterior lobe is effected or appropriate injections made, premature sexuality can be induced in a young female, and increased activity of the ovary with 'super-ovulation', that is, a discharge of an excessive number of ova can be induced in the adult female. Moreover, Bellerby has shown that injection of the extract will cause ovulation in the rabbit, thus indicating that this function usually occurs as a result of the activity of this hormone. A second anterior pituitary hormone, which is more problematical, is lutealising in its effect, for if injected it promotes the development and persistence of luteal tissue. The anterior lobe hormone in the male animal has a stimulating influence on the testis. The precise way in which the ovarian and anterior pituitary hormones act and react upon one another is not yet clear but it is certain that a functional correlation exists. Just as the gonads are inactive in the absence of the anterior lobe, so the latter organ is incapable of inducing sexual change in the absence of the gonads. There is evidence also that a hormone from the anterior pituitary acts directly on the mammary glands (Corner), and Asdell has shown

* Oestrin occurs in the urine during pregnancy and its presence there has been made the basis of a test for pregnancy. G. van S. and O. W. Smith have shown that its excretion in the urine is due to the action of the corpus luteum and that progestin, if injected, causes its appearance in the urine of rabbits.   † Zondek and Aschheim, Smith and Engle, *et al.*

that daily injections of extract will prevent the normal decline of milk yield in goats with advancing lactation.

Reference has already been made to pituitrin or the hormone elaborated by the posterior lobe of the pituitary and its action on uterine muscle. It has also been mentioned that the luteal hormone appears to act antagonistically to pituitrin. Sharpey-Schafer and others have shown that extracts of corpus luteum and posterior lobe of pituitary during lactation have a galactogogue influence upon the mammary glands, causing an instant and copious secretion of milk. These observations further emphasise the functional connection between these organs and the milk glands, but it is possible that the sudden injection of these extracts in considerable quantity has a somewhat different and more violent effect than the slow passage of the problematical hormones into the circulation, such as one may presume to occur in nature. Moreover it may be that this building up of the mammary tissues is a process not essentially different from that concerned in milk secretion but that the two phenomena are in reality parts of a process of the same nature throughout (that is to say, it is not necessary to regard them as representing two opposing tendencies, one anabolic and the other katabolic).*

It is known that double ovariotomy results in the hypertrophy of the pituitary gland, and it is said that double ovariotomy during lactation leads to almost indefinite continuation of milk secretion, and it seems possible that these two facts are connected. Furthermore, it is conceivable that the hypertrophied pituitary compensates for the absence of the corpus luteum, and that, unlike the latter organ, persists for a very extended period during which it exercises a stimulating influence over the mammary tissue.

Ovariotomy (oophorectomy) or spaying is practised on the sow in order to promote growth or fattening but this is only done in some parts of the country and by no means habitually. It has been fairly established, however, that when the operation is done properly the results are commercially profitable. Faulty spaying, in which ovarian tissue is left behind, has helped to discredit the practice, and this result has been unfortunate. The sows should be operated on at about seven weeks old or the same age as that at which the males are castrated. Spaying in sows also prevents the

* Apart, however, from these factors, the removal of the secretion in sucking or milking is necessary for continued lactation, and a cow whose milk is not withdrawn very soon becomes dry.

development of seedy-cut (see p. 226), since the pigment-containing tissue of the mammary glands fails to develop or only develops to a very minute extent. Hobday recommends ovariotomy for troublesome mares to render them easy to work during oestrus and has obtained some useful results. Ovariotomy is only very rarely performed on the cow but when done during lactation is said to lead to long-continued milk secretion, as just mentioned, but the evidence is by no means conclusive.

Note on the Female Organs of the Fowl. In the fowl only one ovary, the left, normally develops. It is situated at the anterior end of the kidney and is attached by a fold of peritoneum to the dorsal wall of the body cavity. In the sexually mature animal the ovary resembles a bunch of grapes with ova in all stages of growth protruding from its surface. The developing ovum increases in size through the deposition of yolk material. The mature ovum or oocyte consists of a fibrous vascularised capsule attached to the ovarian mass by a stalk or pedicle, and within this capsule is the yolk of the egg. The egg yolk is bounded by a thin membrane, the vitelline membrane, which contains yolk material and the nucleus or germinal vesicle. The capsule is differentiated into three layers, an internal layer of cubical epithelial cells called the granulosa, and two connective tissue layers called the theca folliculi interna and the theca folliculi externa. When ripe, the yolk escapes from the capsule by the rupture of the capsule along a slit-like area known as the stigma. In an ovary in active laying condition, in addition to the developing ova or follicles, discharged follicles in varying stages of regression, and atretic or degenerating undischarged follicles, can be recognised. According to Boring and Pearl, these two latter types of follicles are characterised by the presence of luteal cells derived from the theca interna. The connective tissue of the ovary also contains interstitial cells.

The oviduct, which receives the discharged yolk, extends from the ovarian region to the cloaca, into which it opens by an aperture situated on the left of the rectal opening. In the bird in laying condition, the oviduct is 18 to 20 inches long, and is supported by dorsal and ventral ligaments extending along its length. It is differentiated into 5 regions, the infundibulum, which consists of a fimbriated or funnel-shaped membranous portion adjacent to the ovary, the albumen-secreting portion, the isthmus or shell membrane-secreting portion, the shell gland or uterus, and the vagina.

CHAPTER XIX

HEREDITY AND SEX

It is now generally admitted that the chromatin material of the nucleus, both in the male and in the female generative cells, mediates in the transmission of most, if not all, of the hereditary characters.

That the chromosomes, or chromatin filaments of which the nucleus is composed, are of fundamental importance is shown by a group of well-ascertained facts. With certain exceptions their number is constant for all the body cells in the individuals of the same sex in any particular species, and when it varies it does so in multiples of a definite number, though this condition, which is then called 'polyploidy', is uncommon. In the maturation of the germ cells, both ova and spermatozoa, in all species, the number of chromosomes is reduced to one-half (or approximately one-half, since one of the special sex chromosomes may sometimes disappear) of the original number (see above, p. 205).

The fertilised ovum, as already described, contains the full complement of chromosomes. The conclusion that the characters of heredity are localised in the chromosomes was accepted by Weismann, who made it the basis of his famous theory of heredity. This theory assumes (what is now widely believed) that the conjugation of the gametes is the source of variation, and that acquired (as contrasted with innate or congenital) characters cannot be inherited.

The theory of Mendel, first formulated in the middle of the nineteenth century, and re-discovered about thirty years ago, may be said in some respects to be an extension of the theory of Weismann, and it likewise assumes that acquired characters are not transmitted, while its modern developments are susceptible of a confirmatory interpretation derived from the study of chromosome inheritance. It marks a very definite and important advance upon Weismann's theory in that it enables one to discuss variability in terms of the conjugating cells themselves, and not merely in terms of the resulting zygotes.

The original experiments of Mendel were upon hybridisation in peas, the two parent varieties initially selected differing from each other in one particular character. The hybrids produced by crossing were all similar superficially, and resembled one of the parents in the character in question, which was therefore called the *dominant* character, the other character being known as *recessive*. When the hybrids were crossed among themselves, approximately one-half of the offspring were found to be identical with their hybrid parents (dominant hybrids), one-quarter resembled one of the original varieties (the grandparent with the dominant character), while the remaining quarter were like the other pure variety (the grandparent with the recessive character). Consequently the pure dominants and the dominant hybrids resembled one another outwardly, but they differed in their capacity to transmit the characteristics in question, since the pure dominants alone invariably bred true. The recessives also always bred true. Mendel drew the conclusion that in the hybrid the gametes (both male and female) were of two kinds, which were respectively identical with the two kinds represented by the gametes of the original pure varieties. The differentiation of gametes carrying different characters is the essential principle in Mendel's theory, the existence of dominant and recessive characters, though often observable, being by no means universal.

Another example, taken from the work of Bateson and Punnett, will be sufficient to elucidate further the Mendelian conception of gametic differentiation. Breeders of blue Andalusian fowls have always recognised the practical impossibility of obtaining a pure strain of this breed. However carefully the birds are selected they invariably produce two sorts of 'wasters', some being pure black, and some white with irregular black marks or splashes. Bateson and Punnett were the first to supply the explanation. They found that, on breeding from a large number of blue Andalusian fowls, on an average half of the offspring were blue like the parents, a quarter were black, and a quarter were 'splashed-white'. They consequently drew the conclusion that the mechanism of inheritance in the Andalusian fowl is comparable to what Mendel supposed to exist in his hybrid peas. The gametes of the breed, according to this hypothesis, instead of being all similar and carrying the blue character (as one would suppose on Weismann's theory), are of two different kinds, those of the one kind being bearers of the black character, and those of the other being bearers of the splashed-white character. Such gametes, uniting by chance when the fowls mate together, give rise to three kinds of offspring, one black-white (becoming blue, actually, like the parents), one black-black, and one white-white, these appearing (on an average) in the proportion of $2 : 1 : 1$, according to the law of probability (see Fig. 112). In this particular case of Mendelian inheritance, neither of the two alternative parent characters (i.e. neither black nor splashed-white) is dominant and neither is recessive. Why black-bearing gametes uniting with white-bearing gametes should give

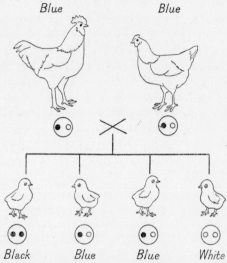

Fig. 112. Diagram illustrating mode of inheritance in the blue Andalusian fowl (C. J. Baker).

rise to blue individuals the Mendelian theory does not attempt to explain.

The determiners of the hereditary characters are called factors or *genes*. Thus in the case just described of the Andalusian fowl we speak of the gene for blackness and the gene for whiteness. The cross-bred bird (the first filial or F_1 generation), which is blue in colour, does not carry a factor for blueness but a pair of factors —those for blackness and whiteness—and these are believed to reside independently in the two separate chromosomes of a pair and to become segregated out in the process of gametic maturation, i.e. in the reduction division. The birds belonging to the second filial (or F_2 generation) will consist, as already indicated, of one-quarter carrying the factor for whiteness, one-quarter the factor for blackness, and one-half with both factors in equal number as in the F_1 generation.

Individuals which transmit characters of the same kind, and in respect of this character produce only one kind of gamete, are said to be *homozygous*, whereas those which transmit two (or more) alternative characters, and produce two (or more) gametes corresponding to them, are called *heterozygous*. Thus the blue Andalusian fowl is heterozygous for colour.

In the illustrations just given, consideration has been restricted to a single pair of genes, but actually the parental individuals generally differ in respect of a number of character-pairs, and the genes which determine these are inherited independently. Thus, if we cross Aberdeen-Angus and Hereford cattle—two breeds in which the most striking differences are that, whereas the Aberdeen is polled and black and has a face which is not specially marked, the Hereford is horned and red and has a white face—all the individuals in the F_1 generation are polled and black and white-faced (these characters being dominant); in the F_2 generation, however, there are no less than twenty-seven possibilities in the way of combinations, though actually only eight appear, as certain of the animals which have different constitutions are superficially alike. It may be stated in general that when two parents which differ in regard to more than one character-pair are crossed, the F_1 generation will exhibit dominant characters irrespective of which parent contributed them.

The Inheritance of Acquired Characters. Of the inheritance of characters acquired after the fertilisation of the ovum and during the lifetime of the individual there is still no satisfying evidence, although MacBride and many other zoologists believe in its occurrence. Darwin was disposed to admit its actuality and to regard it as a factor in the evolution of new species, and in order to explain the process he postulated the existence of carriers of heredity, which he called gemmules, and which he supposed to pass centripetally from all the cells of the body to the germ cells, where they caused permanent change.

The evidence as to the inheritance of acquired characters in its crude form is mostly or wholly negative. Thus, as a result of the de-horning of cattle, which is largely practised in America, the offspring of de-horned individuals are never born polled. The experiments of Weismann and Cope, who cut off the tails of mice for many generations, were likewise negative, the offspring never being born tailless or even deformed. The effect of circumcision with man is another case in point, children not being born without the prepuce, although the operation may have been carried out for innumerable generations.

On the other hand, there is evidence as to abnormal food or environment or special drug treatment having a general effect which may be transmitted, probably due to a lowering of vitality in the germ cells which are affected in common with the other cells of the body. Thus, with Stockard's experiments on the influence of alcohol on guinea-pigs, it was found that signs of deterioration, malformations, and deformities appeared in the offspring, and the organs most liable to be adversely affected were often the most delicate ones or those that needed very perfect adjustments, such as the eye. These results, however, have not been confirmed.

Telegony and Saturation. It is still commonly believed by many stock-breeders that a female may be permanently infected through intercourse with a male, so that the latter can impress some of his characters, not only upon his own immediate offspring, but upon subsequent offspring produced by the female as a result of union with another male. Such a phenomenon is called 'Telegony' or 'Infection'. The classic case, and one in which Darwin believed, was that of Lord Morton's Arab mare. This animal was first mated with a quagga and produced striped hybrid offspring, and subsequently on two occasions the mare was mated with an Arab stallion, and both the resulting foals had stripes on the fore-legs and back. It was supposed that the striping in these foals somehow resulted from the original mating with the quagga. It has been shown, however, that the presence of stripes is a common phenomenon among several breeds of horses, including Arabs, and that it is specially prone to occur among cross-bred horses, which in this respect may be supposed to have reverted to an ancestral condition. Moreover, numerous experiments by Ewart and others, not only with horses (the quagga experiment having been repeated with a Burchell's zebra and various breeds of mares), but also with dogs, fowls, and other animals, have uniformly failed to show any evidence of telegonic influence. Again, none of the cases in which telegony has been supposed to occur have stood the test of scientific examination. It may be pointed out, further, that were the telegony

hypothesis correct it would involve the inheritance of acquired
characters, since the only way in which the characters of a previous
sire could be transmitted to subsequent offspring would seem to be
through the body of the mother, who must be supposed to transmit
characteristics which she had acquired either from her former mate
or from their joint offspring in the uterus.

'Saturation' is the name given to the supposed process whereby
the dam becomes permanently affected by the ova of a particular
sire, so that the offspring come to resemble that sire more and more
with successive pregnancies. It is merely a description of the
cumulative effect of telegonic influence and as a statement of fact
is equally devoid of foundation.

Maternal Impressions. The popular belief that mental impressions received by the mother at the time of conception or during
pregnancy are transferred to the child as physical peculiarities is
devoid of scientific foundation. Nevertheless, it is a very persistent
one, and there are innumerable instances of its supposed occurrence,
both among man and among animals. Thus an injury or physical
impression suddenly produced by contact and accompanied by
fright is supposed to result in a birthmark on the child in the position of the injury to the mother; a woman alarmed by an idiot is
said to have given birth to a mentally defective child, or a woman
chased by a black man to have produced a child who was partly
coloured. A common way of giving effect to the belief among
breeders of animals has been to paint buildings or fences a particular colour, where stock are being bred, with a view to obtaining
that colour in the young.

Prepotency. It has long been known to stock-breeders that
certain sires have the faculty of impressing their characters (or
certain of them) upon their offspring, and when these qualities are
desirable ones, such a 'prepotent' sire is of great value as a stock-
getter. Thus a bull may beget female progeny which yield a higher
amount of milk than their dams, and so be said to be prepotent for
milk production. It has been known also that inbreeding favours
prepotency. In the light of Mendelian interpretation prepotency is
seen to be a condition belonging to animals which are homozygous
for certain dominant factors or genes, and since this condition in
general is characteristic of pure bred and inbred animals, it explains
why these are so often prepotent over crossbred or mongrel ones.

Sex. In most kinds of animals the gametes of either one sex or the other are dimorphic and have different chromosome constitutions. In mammals there are two sorts of spermatozoa but only one sort of ovum, but in birds the converse is the case, there being one sort of sperm and two sorts of ova. Further, the sex is correlated with certain special chromosomes called the X-chromosomes, which are somewhat smaller than the ordinary chromosomes. Thus, in mammals the females have two X-chromosomes in every cell and the males one X-chromosome. When the ova mature one of the X-chromosomes passes out at the reduction division, leaving the egg with one X instead of two. When the spermatozoa are formed, the final products of division are equally divided into sperms with one X-chromosome and sperms without any X-chromosome. The fertilisation of any egg (which has one X) by a spermatozoon with one X results in a female (XX). The fertilisation of any egg by a sperm without an X results in a male (X). Thus in the spermatozoa the total number of chromosomes is not always the same; there are two kinds which may be called male and female spermatozoa, the latter having one chromosome more than the former. Similarly, in the body cells of the female animal there is one chromosome more than in the body cells of the male. In birds, on the other hand, the ova vary in their sex chromosome numbers, the spermatozoa being all the same.

Since in mammals the two kinds of spermatozoa are produced in equal numbers, the males and females resulting from gametic union are likewise usually found occurring in equal numbers according to Mendelian expectation.

Sex-linkage. Some characters are sex-linked, like the orange colour of certain male cats and the tortoiseshell colour of certain females. In such cases it is believed that the factors or genes for colour are somehow actually located in the sex chromosomes.

The discovery that certain characters are sex-linked, being transmitted by a female to her male but not her female offspring, has had important commercial consequences in agriculture. It has already been pointed out that the Andalusian fowl is heterozygous, and can therefore never produce offspring all of which resemble their parents. Punnett, working with fowls, found that certain plumage and skin colour characteristics were transmitted by a hen to her sons and not to her daughters. By making suitable crosses, and taking advantage of the peculiarities of this sex-linked transmission of plumage characteristics, it becomes possible to distinguish day-old cockerels and pullets, a distinction that is not possible otherwise. The commercial importance of this fact is that it enables poultry breeders to sell guaranteed day-old pullets or cockerels, and also enables breeders to distinguish pullets from cockerels at hatching, thereby reducing the brooder accommodation needed in the case of the commercial egg farmer, who otherwise, in order to get the necessary number of pullets, would have to rear an approximately equal number of cockerels to the stage at which the sex differences begin to show themselves.

There are two characters that are of commercial importance, in that the distinction between the sexes is readily made by the poultry keeper. These are silver ground colour of plumage as opposed to gold, and barred plumage as opposed to unbarred. All breeds of poultry, except the pure white, belong to the silver class, and all breeds in which the cockerel is some form of black-red or buff or red belong to the gold class. Thus Light Sussex is an example of the silver class and Red Sussex an example of the gold class. With regard to the barring character, not all forms of barring are sex-linked. The barring known as 'cuckoo' barring that occurs in the Plymouth Rocks and Scotch Greys is sex-linked; that which occurs in Campines or Pencilled Hamburghs is not sex-linked. The mode of inheritance is as follows: The silver type of plumage or the barred plumage is transmitted equally by the cockerel to both his sons and daughters, whereas the silver or barred hen only transmits these characters to her sons. A Light Sussex cockerel mated with a Red Sussex hen will consequently give silver pullets and cockerels, whereas a Red Sussex cockerel mated with a Light Sussex hen will give silver cockerels and gold pullets. The male chicks from such a cross are creamy silver with blackish markings, whereas the pullets are all golden in colour.

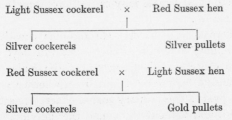

Light Sussex cockerel   ×   Red Sussex hen

Silver cockerels   Silver pullets

Red Sussex cockerel   ×   Light Sussex hen

Silver cockerels   Gold pullets

Similarly, a Plymouth Rock cockerel mated with a Black Minorca hen gives all barred offspring, whereas a Black Minorca cockerel mated with a Plymouth Rock hen gives barred cockerels and black pullets. The male chicks in this cross have black down with a characteristic white patch at the back of the head, whereas the female chicks are entirely black.

One serious disadvantage of sex-linked crosses is that the offspring from such crosses, being mongrels, cannot be bred from. This disadvantage has recently been removed by Punnett, who has evolved a breed, the Cambar, which is sex-linked within itself, i.e. the pullets and cockerels show distinct down differences as chicks. This breed was evolved from a Barred Plymouth Rock Gold Campine cross. The male chicks are pale grey in colour, striped with brown, whereas the female chicks are of a much darker brown.

Inter-sexuality and sex reversal. Notwithstanding the fact that the two sexes are ordinarily correlated with the chromosome constitution, it would appear that in some circumstances this may be overridden, and an animal may possess some or even all of the characteristics of one sex in conjunction with the chromosome constitution usually associated with the other. Moreover, there is evidence that all animals have in some degree the potentialities of both sexes and even among mammals hermaphroditism is not unknown. Thus it has been recorded among pigs and goats, and Crew has described varying degrees of inter-sexuality in horses, cattle and sheep. Moreover, sex reversal may take place, as when the ovaries atrophy and testicular tissue develops. Crew has recorded a number of such cases in fowls and other animals. Experimental sex reversal has been brought about (as by Steinach in guinea-pigs) by extirpating the gonad from an animal and then in place of the removed organ transplanting a gonad from an individual of the opposite sex. An ovary grafted into a castrated male may stimulate mammary growth and milk secretion and a testis transplanted into an oophorectomised female may cause the clitoris to develop into a penile structure.

Thus, whereas normally the chromosome constitution of an individual animal determines whether it will develop testes or ovaries, the other sexual characters of the male or female in mammals depend for the most part upon whether the gonad is a testis or an ovary. The primary sexual characters are centralised in the gonad, and without the gonad the individual tends to be neutral.

When in the case of twin cattle two embryos of originally

different sexes have shared a common chorionic circulation, the female twin is known to develop abnormally, being sterile and having some of the characters of the male. This condition is unusual but by no means rare. Lillie and also Tandler and Keller have shown that it is due to the influence of the testicular hormone of the male twin, since the testis develops somewhat ahead of the ovary in the female and exerts its effect at a slightly earlier stage. The chorionic membranes of the two foetal calves being united along with the blood vessels running in them, the hormones circulating in the blood are also common to the two animals, and thus the rudimentary sexual organs of the female are stimulated to grow, so to speak, in a male direction. The 'free-martin', as such a sterile cow born co-twin to a fertile bull is called, is an intersexual individual, having some of the characters of the bull and some of those of the cow. 'Free-martins' with a common chorionic circulation also occur among goats but are not known in other animals.

CHAPTER XX

THE RESPONSE OF THE BODY TO INJURY AND DISEASE

The Response of the Body to Injury

The living tissues of the animal body react in a very definite manner to injury. When wounding occurs, as when the skin and underlying structures are cut with a knife or any sharp surgical instrument, several well-defined phenomena occur. Bleeding first takes place from the blood vessels severed in the injury, and after a while the bleeding stops owing to the formation of blood clots. The blood clot so formed acts as a protective plaster to the tissues immediately underlying the seat of the injury. The cells immediately adjacent die as the result of the injury, and, owing to the surgical interference with the blood circulation of the area adjoining the wound, the normal nutrition of the cells ceases. Stagnation occurs in the blood vessels affected, and a process of filtration through the walls of the neighbouring capillaries occurs. The plasma so exuded causes swelling to take place at the seat of injury, and the leucocytes contained in the plasma, aided by the connective tissue cells, attack the dead tissue and the fibrin network of the blood clot, and by the aid of proteolytic enzymes gradually absorb them. Meanwhile the underlying living capillaries undergo proliferation and the blood capillaries so produced grow out into the seat of injury forming the so-called granulation tissue, the presence of which is characteristic of a partially healed wound surface. Accompanying this increased vascularisation is the formation of a fibrous tissue from cells of the connective tissue, which tissue grows out from the two cut edges of the wound and finally knits together in a compact mass. The cut edges of the epithelium also proliferate, forming a new skin which gradually covers over the fibrous mass. The final stage in the process of repair consists in the gradual contraction of the fibrous tissue, thereby causing obliteration of the blood capillaries which have grown into it, so that when repair is complete, the only sign of the injury that has been caused is the resultant white scar.

The response of the body to a simple wound injury divides itself into several distinct stages. In the first stage the coagulation of the blood causes the formation of a temporary plug or plaster which prevents further loss of body fluids and gives protection to the delicate living cells subjacent to the seat of injury; in the second stage absorption and removal of the dead and injured cellular material takes place; in the third stage fibrous tissue is formed which knits the edges of the wound together and new epithelium is produced forming a protective layer of skin over the fibrous tissue so formed.

A somewhat similar class of tissue reactions occurs following sprains and bruises. The external symptoms following a bruise are swelling of the part affected, associated with increased tenderness of the part affected and a local rise in temperature. Gradually the swelling subsides, definite colour changes take place, the part affected first becoming purple, then green and finally yellow. Eventually the tissue assumes its normal colour and appearance, and if a joint is involved, a certain stiffness may result as a permanent legacy of the injury. The swelling at the seat of injury is due to the accumulation of lymph and plasma owing to local obstruction of the normal lymph and blood circulation and increased activity of the cellular elements involved in the processes of repair, the increased tenderness is due to the increased irritability of the sensory nerve endings located at the seat of injury, and the colour changes are due to the extravasated blood cells.

The red blood corpuscles set free from the injured capillaries at the seat of injury undergo absorptive changes, in the course of which the blood pigment is set free from its constituent corpuscle and forms a reddish fluid which diffuses through the injured tissues. The haemoglobin then undergoes chemical changes in the course of which haematin or haemochromogen is set free, and the colour changes already referred to above are the outward visible sign of the changes occurring in this colour compound. The stiffness that occurs in the case of a joint is due to the formation of fibrous tissue, or in the case of the injury affecting the periosteal tissue to actual formation of bone leading to an exostosis. This regeneration of fibrous tissue or bone may be sufficiently great to interfere with the mobility of the joint, and may give rise to permanent lameness.

THE DEFENCE OF THE BODY AGAINST DISEASE

The living animal, apart from damage due to mechanical injury, is also subject to attack from other living organisms. Some organisms can only effect an entry into the body from a local injury or lesion, others have the power of effecting an entry through the normal tissues. The invasion of the living tissues of the body by a certain class of such organisms gives rise to definite pathological conditions known as disease, specific diseases being associated with the invasion of the body by definite specific pathogenic organisms. In spite of general exposure to infection by such organisms, it will be noted that certain diseases are peculiar to certain species of animals, and that in the same species certain individuals appear to possess the capacity of resisting infection from a specific disease whereas others are not so fortunate. This inherent capacity to resist a disease is known as immunity. Such immunity is said to be *natural* where the individual appears to be non-susceptible to attack, and *acquired* when the recovery from the attack of a disease in the case of a susceptible individual is followed by a period of immunity from further attacks. In acquired immunity it is obvious that the reaction of the living tissues to the onslaught of the disease has given rise in the body to a condition of resistance to attack which enables it to deal successfully with subsequent invasions of the organism in question while that period of successful resistance lasts. The immunity acquired by an individual following an attack of a disease is known as *active* immunity. If blood serum from an individual in an actively immune state is injected in the body of a susceptible individual that individual also acquires resistance to attack, and the immunity so acquired is known as *passive* immunity. The discovery that, in certain diseases, recovery from that disease was followed by a period of immunity from that disease, and the fact that this immunity could be conferred on susceptible individuals by injection of the recovered individuals' blood serum, led to a considerable amount of research into the causation and nature of such immunity. It was quickly realised that the body tissues played an important part in the causation of such immunity, and two theories of immunity were advanced, a *cellular* theory and a *humoral* theory. In the cellular theory, the body cells, and particularly the leucocytes, were said to be the active causal agents of immunity; in the humoral theory the body fluids were held to be the causal agents of immunity.

Before discussing these theories, it may be as well to study the nature of the reactions that occur as the result of attack on the living body by pathogenic organisms. Some pathogenic organisms live on the free surfaces of the living body, and exert their harmful effects by the production of substances which are absorbed by the living tissues of the host. The causal organisms of diphtheria (*Bacillus diphtheriae*) and tetanus (*Bacillus tetani*) are examples, the evil effects of their presence in the body being due to the absorption of poisons produced by them. These poisons are called *toxins* or *exotoxins*. In other diseases the harmful effects are produced by the pathogenic organisms themselves and not by products excreted by them, i.e. the toxins are intracellular (*endotoxins*) and retained within the body of the pathogenic organism itself. The causal organisms of cholera and typhoid are examples of this class. In the former case the defence of the body will be concerned chiefly with neutralising the poisonous effects of the exotoxins produced, whereas in the latter case the defence of the body will be concerned with the organisms themselves.

The Nature of the Reactions Produced. (1) *Antitoxins.* If a pure culture of tetanus bacilli be cultivated in bouillon under controlled laboratory conditions, considerable quantities of tetanus exotoxin will develop in the culture medium, and by filtration through unglazed porcelain, a bacteria-free solution of the toxin will be produced. If a quantity of this toxin be injected into a horse it will die, exhibiting all the characteristic symptoms of tetanus poisoning. If, however, a small quantity of the toxin be attenuated or weakened by heat or chemical means, the animal will successfully survive an injection, and by suitable successive injections the animal will acquire a tolerance sufficiently great to enable it to withstand injection from the pure toxin, until after some months' treatment, ounces of the toxin may be injected without causing any harm. In other words, by this treatment the animal has acquired an immunity against tetanus. If some of the blood serum of this animal is obtained, it will be found to have acquired very definite antitoxic powers. If some of this serum be mixed with a suitable quantity of tetanus toxin and the mixture be injected into a susceptible animal no harm will result, i.e. the toxin has been neutralised by some substance present in the immunised animal's serum. The same effect will follow if the serum and the toxin are injected separately into the susceptible animal. Moreover, if the serum is injected into an animal that has already been infected with the tetanus bacillus it will prevent the onset of the toxic effect of the toxins produced by the bacillus, provided the injection follows within a short period after infection. The blood serum of an animal immunised in the way described above, therefore, contains an antibody developed by the body fluids as the result of the injection of successive doses of the tetanus bacillus, and this antibody is known as *antitoxin*.

(2) *Antimicrobic sera*. Pfeiffer showed that if suitably graduated doses of a prepared culture of the causal organism of cholera were injected into the peritoneal cavity of the guinea-pig, the guinea-pig so treated gradually acquired an immunity against subsequent infection. This immunity was obviously due to the development in the peritoneal fluid of the power of destroying and dissolving the cholera organism (bacteriolysis), since peritoneal fluid drawn from such an animal readily destroyed cholera organisms mixed with it. If, however, the peritoneal fluid was heated to 50° C. before mixing with the cholera culture, this reaction no longer took place, but it could be restored immediately by adding fresh serum drawn from either an immunised or a non-immunised animal. The destruction of the cholera microbe is thus brought about by the action of two bodies, one a heat-stable one developed by the serum of an immunised animal and the other a non-heat-resistant or thermolabile body present in both normal and immunised serum. The thermolabile body is known as the 'alexin' or complement, and the heat-resistant body is known as the 'immune body', 'antibody' or 'amboceptor'.

(3) *Agglutination*. Beside the phenomenon of bacteriolysis exhibited by immunised sera, another phenomenon known as agglutination has been shown to occur. When a solution of bacteria in suspension is mixed together with its specific antiserum the bacteria often agglutinate together into clumps, and Durham and Gruber showed that this reaction was definite and distinct and could be used as a means of identifying the organism responsible for a bacterial attack. The agglutination is caused by the development in the serum of an immunised animal of relatively thermostable bodies known as agglutinins. The test is carried out by mixing in a test tube some of the serum of an animal with a

suspension of the bacteria with which it is suspected to be infected and incubating the mixture for a suitable length of time. If the animal is infected with the organism in question, the bacteria gradually form together into clumps and settle in a layer to the bottom of the test tube leaving a clear fluid above them. On the other hand, if the animal is not infected with that particular organism, the bacteria remain suspended in solution. This test has been used under the term 'Widal' reaction for the diagnosis of typhoid and paratyphoid infection, and is also used largely for the diagnosis of bacillary white diarrhoea in birds.

(4) *Precipitation.* Immunised blood serum further shows the property of causing a precipitate to form when it is mixed with a filtrate of the bacteria against which the animal is immunised. Thus if a bacterial culture solution be filtered through unglazed porcelain to remove the bacteria, and immunised serum be added, a precipitate forms. This precipitation is brought about by the formation of substances in the serum called precipitins, and, like the agglutinins, they are relatively heat stable at 50° C. but are rapidly destroyed at temperatures of 70° C. and over. A similar reaction occurs between foreign proteins and serum. Thus, if the serum of an animal be sensitised by the injection into it of a foreign protein or the serum of another animal, the serum develops precipitins, and under properly controlled conditions a precipitate will form when the animal's serum is mixed with a solution of the protein or serum against which the animal has been sensitised. This reaction can be successfully employed for the biological identification of a protein or for bloodstains, etc. Welsh and Chapman have shown that the precipitate is formed from the 'sensitised' serum and not from the protein, bacterial extract, or serum used as a sensitiser.

Theories of Immunity. The theories of immunity that have been advanced to explain the reactions noted above group themselves naturally into two classes, the *cellular* theories and the *humoral* theories. The chief exponent of the cellular theory was Metschnikoff; the chief exponent of the humoral theory was Ehrlich.

In the cellular theory as developed by Metschnikoff natural immunity against any specific disease is attributed to the phago-cytic action of the living cells of the body. This phagocytic action is possessed by the leucocytes which either engulf and digest the invading bacteria when the animal is immune, but fail to do so when the animal is susceptible, or form products which possess the power of rendering inert any toxins produced by the invading pathogenic organisms. An objection to the cellular theory was raised by Nuttall and others, who demonstrated that the blood serum itself possessed the power of dissolving bacteria, i.e. was bacteriolytic, but Metschnikoff maintained that this bacteriolytic power of the blood serum was due to products produced by the leucocytes themselves. Wright showed that in the case of phago-cytosis, the blood serum played an important part in preparing the bacteria for successful attack by the leucocytes, and he gave the term 'opsonins' to the bodies present both in normal serum and immune serum responsible for this phenomenon. It neces-sarily follows from this that neither the leucocytes nor the blood serum itself can therefore be ignored as causative agents in the development of immunity against disease.

The humoral theory has been developed chiefly by Ehrlich and his school, and Ehrlich evolved his lateral chain theory to account for the phenomena produced in immunity. Ehrlich based his theory on the consideration of the normal metabolic activity of the cell protoplasm. The normal metabolism of the cell is carried out by the protoplasm molecules, which he conceived as being formed of a stable central organic complex with less stable lateral chains of atoms attached to it. These lateral chains or 'receptors' took part in the normal cell processes of nutrition, etc. by entering into chemical union with the food substances, etc. brought to the cell. If, as the result of the introduction of a toxin to the cell, no chemical reaction took place owing to the absence of suitable receptors, the animal was said to be *naturally immune*. If, on the other hand, chemical union occurred, the normal metabolic pro-cesses of the cell would be interfered with, and cell poisoning would result. The extent of the cell poisoning so induced would depend upon the extent to which all the available receptors were used in the process. If all the receptors were used up, death of the cell would result. If, on the other hand, only a few were utilised, physiological stimulation would result, more receptors being pro-duced from the central stable complex. This stimulation would result in the production of an excess number of receptors which are thrown off from the central nucleus and form the *antitoxin*. Ehrlich also assumes the toxin molecule to consist of two parts, a stable 'haptophore' group which unites with the 'receptor' and an unstable 'toxophore' group which carries the actual poison. Toxin molecules which have lost their toxophore grouping are known as 'toxoids'. Such toxoids, although having lost the power of producing toxic affects when injected into an animal, would obviously retain the power of inducing immunity.

To explain the cases of agglutination and precipitation Ehrlich postulated a rather more elaborate receptor than that produced by the cell in the toxin-antitoxin reaction. The receptor in this case consists of a heat-stable haptophore group and a thermolabile ergophore or work-producing group. In the case of agglutination, the haptophore group links with the bacterium, thus enabling the ergophore group to bring about the agglutination. A similar explanation is applied to the precipitation phenomena.

The above theory suffices to explain the phenomena induced in the production of immunity against toxins, and further shows clearly why acquired immunity is of a temporary nature only; but it does not explain the mechanism of the action of antimicrobic sera. Ehrlich has elaborated his theory to cover these cases in the following way. The side chains set free from the central nucleus and which have been referred to in the toxin-antitoxin reactions as 'receptors' are called 'amboceptors' and consist of two groups, the cytophile group and the complementophile group. The cytophile group unites with the bacterium and the complementophile group unites with the 'complement' or 'alexin', which latter has already been shown to be present in the normal serum of the animal. The 'complement' or 'alexin' through the linkage of the 'amboceptor' or 'immune body' is enabled to exercise its dissolvant function on the bacterium. Just in the same way as the toxin molecule is regarded as being composed of two groupings, a 'haptophore' grouping and a 'toxophore' grouping, so the 'complement' is regarded as being composed of two groupings, a heat-stable 'haptophore' group by which the complement links with the amboceptor and a heat-sensitive 'zymotoxic' group by which the alexin carries out its dissolvant function. Complements which have lost their zymotoxic groupings are known as 'complementoids'.

Briefly summarising the facts already outlined in this chapter, it will be seen that the body cells and fluids react to bacterial or bacterial poison attack in such a way that immunity against the disease is acquired. The period of immunity is variable, active immunity lasting generally longer than passive immunity. To explain the nature of the immunity produced, many theories have been put forward. Both the leucocytes and the serum take part in the production of immunity against disease; according to the Metschnikoff school the leucocytes are of primary importance, according to the Ehrlich school the leucocytes play a secondary rôle only. The causal agent of immunity is the production in the body fluids of an anti-body or immune body which either neutralises the toxin produced by the causative disease organism or renders possible the destruction of the organism itself. In the latter case, a product present in normal serum plays the essential part in the destruction of the disease organism, but it can only exert its effect through the anti-body or immune body, which acts as a link between the two. In the Ehrlich theory, there are three types of immune bodies varying in complexity of structure, known as receptors of the first, second and third orders. Receptors of the first order take part in the toxin-antitoxin reactions, receptors of the second order take part in the precipitin and agglutinin reactions, and receptors of the third order take part in bacterio-lysis, haemolysis and cytolysis.

CHAPTER XXI

GROWTH

With all multicellular animals the physiological life of the individual may be said to commence with the conjugation of the ovum and the spermatozoon, and the oosperm thus formed forthwith begins to grow. As remarked by Verworn, there is an essential similarity between growth and reproduction, both processes consisting of an increase in living substance. 'The difference between that which is usually termed growth in the narrow sense and the phenomenon of reproduction consists only in the fact that in the former case the newly formed living substance remains in constant connection with the original organism and helps to increase its volume; while in the latter case a part of the substance separates itself from the original organism, either, as in most cases, being set entirely free, or, as in the increase of tissue cells, being separated merely by a partition wall and remaining in place.'

Growth, like reproduction, involves cell division. As the mass of living substance increases, the cells must multiply, for every cell has, so to speak, assigned to it a limit in size beyond which it cannot pass. Cell division goes on, though with decreasing frequency, throughout practically the whole of life; tissue formation continues, but from an early period of development onwards there is a progressive diminution in the power of growth. Increase in the number of cells is specially characteristic of the embryonic period. In the later stages of development growth occurs in great measure through cell enlargement and the deposition of intercellular substance.

The cause of division in the individual cell is still an open question. Brody suggests that just as a cell grows in an appropriate nutrient medium because it is in unstable equilibrium with such a medium, so a cell after it has reached a certain size becomes unstable in respect to its size and this instability is made good by cell division. That cells in the body are potentially capable of indefinite growth and division is shown by experiments with living tissue cultures. Thus, Carrel removed a piece of living tissue from the heart of a young chick and kept it irrigated in a nutritive fluid.

The tissue went on living indefinitely, doubling itself in bulk about every twenty-four hours.

Pincus has succeeded in keeping the fertilised ovum of the rabbit alive under tissue culture conditions (serum and blood plasma) so that it underwent segmentation and a certain degree of development. The growth of cells in the body under normal conditions does not continue owing to retarding influences which develop in the body in the progress of growth. On the other hand, there are in the living body, as we have seen already, hormonic influences (e.g. the secretions of the thyroid and anterior pituitary organs) which stimulate growth. In the domestic animals it is doubtful whether there are any 'growth cycles', and change in the rate of growth seems to depend mainly upon feeding.

Speaking generally, the rate of growth of an animal increases with its increase in size in earlier life. This phase has been called by Brody the self-accelerating phase of growth; it continues in man usually until puberty. After this period the time-rate of growth decreases with the increase in size of the body; this phase is called the self-inhibiting phase. According to Hammond, the change which may occur at puberty is correlated with a diversion of the activities of the anterior pituitary from serving as growth stimuli to producing secretions which excite the generative and sexual functions.

During the early embryonic period the cells of the body are small, simple in structure, and poorly supplied with cytoplasm. Later, there is cell enlargement accompanied by specialisation in both structure and function. Finally, such growth as takes place is due almost completely to hypertrophy alone. In the earlier phases growth is clearly predominant over senescence; in the later, when cell division is on the decline, the process of senescence is predominant. It is interesting to note that the size of the cells in an animal's body is not correlated with the size of the animal and that the cells of a mouse are hardly smaller than those of an elephant. That is to say, the dimensions of an animal are correlated with the number of the cells contained by its body rather than by the size of the cells.

The mean weight of the foal at birth according to Smith is 112 lb. During the first three months the average daily increase is 2·2 lb.; from three up to six months it is 1·3 lb.; and from six months

up to three years 0·7 lb. Smith says that many horses probably
continue to grow until they are six years old.

The calf at birth weighs about 77 lb., and the average daily
increase during the first two years is 1·5 lb. With the sheep the
increase is greater, for a young lamb in ten days can add 50 per
cent. to its original weight, and can double it at the end of the
first month, and treble it at the end of the second. In pigs, however, the increase is even more rapid, for a young pig can add
20 per cent. to its original weight by the end of the first week, and
up to the end of the first year can add an average daily increase
of 0·44 lb.

It is well known that the proportions of an animal change as it
grows up; the calf, for instance, at birth is all head and legs, while
the body is short and shallow as compared with the adult. As has
been pointed out by Hammond, those animals which pass through
the age changes quickest and to furthest extent are those which are
most valuable for meat production. The effect of putting an animal
on a poor ration during growth ('storing') is to encourage the
growth of the early developing part of the body (head, legs and
offal parts) and retard the later growing and more valuable parts
of the carcase.

The rate at which the proportions change during development
varies with the breed of animal as well as with the nutrition, and
in selecting stock for breeding it is important to take account of
the food supply available. In districts of good nutrition a large
animal is more economical for production than two small ones,
because the overhead charges in accommodation and labour are
less and because the energy required for maintenance, following as
it does surface area and not weight, is also less in total amount.
Under conditions, however, where the herbage is fibrous and
scanty, such as in dry climates or poor soils, a large animal,
because of its larger actual maintenance requirements, will have
less proportional surplus nutrition for production than a smaller
one. Thus in districts of scanty herbage cattle tend to give way to
sheep and goats. The introduction of sheep into the barren highlands of Scotland, which were formerly sparsely stocked with
cattle only, resulted in a greatly increased prosperity in these
districts. By adopting a smaller and lighter type the breeders in
the dry sandy-land provinces of Eastern Holland have maintained
the production of the black and white cattle, which would not

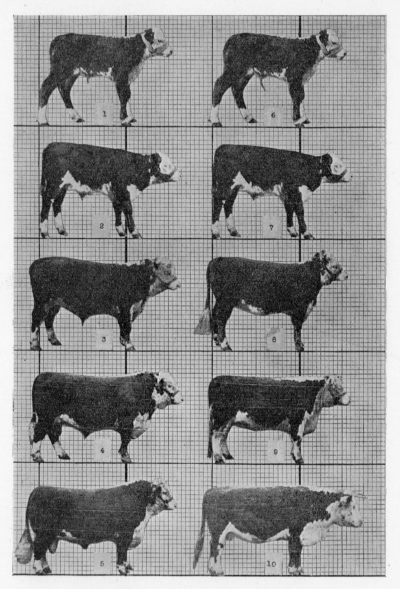

Fig. 113.   Diagram of growth changes in Hereford cattle (after Hammond).

1. Heifer, 2 days
2. Bull, 5 weeks
3. Bull, 13 months
4. Bull, 22 months
5. Bull, 5 years

6. Heifer, 2 days
7. Bull, 5 weeks
8. Heifer, 14 months
9. Heifer, 24 months
10. Cow, 5 years

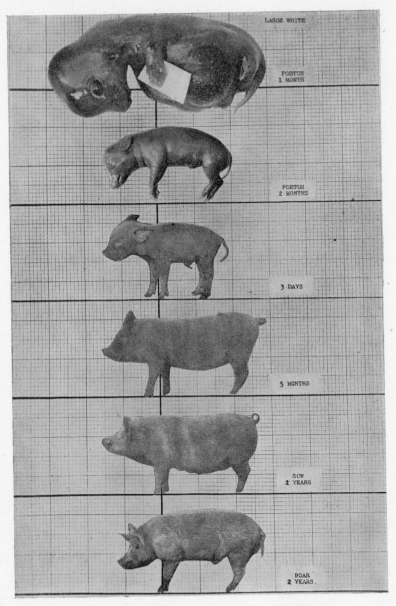

Fig. 114. Diagram of growth changes in pigs (after Hammond).

have been possible had they striven to keep the large type existing in Friesland and North Holland. In the dry south-eastern
counties of England the small dual purpose (milk and beef) Red
Poll takes the place of the larger Shorthorn of the better grass land
in the north and west. So also, by keeping the size of the animal
small, the Southdown sheep has been developed to a high degree
of excellence for mutton conformation on the scanty herbage of
dry chalk downland. All this has been pointed out by Hammond.

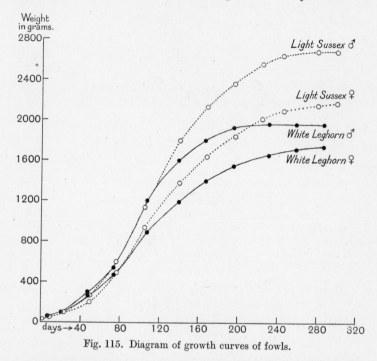

Fig. 115. Diagram of growth curves of fowls.

If the body weight of an animal during growth be plotted
against time, a curve of the type shown in the diagram will be
obtained. The curves shown represent the average live weights of
two different breeds of fowls obtained during growth experiments
carried out at Cambridge during 1924 and 1926 and are interesting
because they illustrate that not only do the mature weights of
different breeds vary, but also that there is a characteristic
difference between the adult weights of the two sexes.

By carrying out a series of analyses of the bodies of animals during growth, it is possible to trace the characteristic changes in body composition that occur. As an animal grows, the first increases that take place are due to deposition of protein and ash as skeletal growth and muscular development occurs. These are followed, as maturity approaches, by the deposition of reserve material in the form of fat. Now fat-free lean meat contains, on the average, about 77 per cent. of moisture, and adipose tissue contains only about 5 to 10 per cent. of moisture. As a result of this we find that the percentage moisture content of the body decreases as growth proceeds, and when maturity approaches fluctuates according to the condition of fatness of the animal. Thus White Leghorn chicks one week old contain 76·5 per cent. moisture; this has dropped to 74 per cent. at nine weeks, and as maturity approaches the cockerel contains approximately 70 per cent. of moisture and the pullet 66 per cent. This difference between the sexes at maturity is associated with differential fat storage, there being present in the mature pullet from 11 to 13·5 per cent. of fat, whereas the cockerel contains 2·4 to 5 per cent. of fat.

During the commercial process of fattening, the chief change that occurs in the adult animal is the deposition of fat, there being, contrary to general belief, little or no storage of protein. This fact is illustrated by the following figures based on an experiment on fattening mature Light Sussex cockerels.

	Average dead weight	Composition of carcase, per cent.		
		Moisture	Protein	Fat
Unfattened	2696 g.	69·8	18·1	6·4
Fattened	3026 g.	64·6	18·3	13·5

From the analyses of the carcases of animals at different ages, it is possible to ascertain the weekly increases in protein, fat and ash at different ages. These data, calculated on analyses of three-bird samples, are for the White Leghorn. (See page 286.)

Consideration of these figures shows that, so far as protein is concerned, maximum deposition of protein is occurring during the 10th to 20th weeks of life, and that the pullet matures, so far as body weight is concerned, rather more slowly than the cockerel. This retardation in body development is associated with onset of egg laying, which occurred in the 24th week. The fat figures illustrate quite clearly the fact that fat acts as a reserve food material,

Increase per week, in grams

Age in weeks	Protein		Fat		Ash	
	♀	♂	♀	♂	♀	♂
1–3	4·7	5·1	2·2	2·4	1·0	1·0
3–7	8·2	9·7	1·6	1·8	1·2	1·6
7–10	15·0	15·2	2·3	6·0	2·6	2·6
10–15	23·3	36·6	8·4	8·2	4·2	5·6
15–20	24·6	22·8	6·0	0·2	2·2	3·8
20–24	11·6	23·4	3·2	4·5	2·5	6·5
24–28	3·6	9·4	18·2	− 5·9	1·0	1·1
28–33	4·9	3·6	—	− 5·5	− 0·9	0·1
33–37	3·6	—	12·0	+ 8·5	2·2	1·5
37–41	—	—	2·0	− 9·2	− 0·2	− 1·9

since considerable fluctuation occurs in the storage of this material, particularly as the bird reaches maturity. It is significant that abnormal fat storage takes place in the pullet as maturity is reached, and this is doubtless correlated with egg production. With regard to ash, the maximum storage occurs in the pullet at the 10th to 15th weeks, indicating that growth and maturation of the skeleton is particularly marked at this age. From the 20th to 24th weeks, the cockerel again shows heavy deposition of ash constituents, this probably being correlated with the development of the heavy skeletal framework associated with sexual maturity. With maturity, the fluctuations in ash content of the body are noticeable, indicating that the skeleton acts as a reserve store of ash constituents in the same way as the fat deposits of the body act as a reserve energy store. An interesting fact emerged from the investigations from which the figures quoted above were obtained, namely, that although the adult cockerel was considerably heavier than the adult pullet, the pullet contained much more energy than the cockerel, owing to the relatively higher percentage of fat in the carcase.

CHAPTER XXII

THE ACCESSORY FOOD SUBSTANCES OR VITAMINS

It is a commonplace observation that if an individual is allowed a sufficiently free choice of naturally occurring foods, his appetite and instinct generally suffice to provide him with the food requirements necessary for the maintenance of normal growth and health. If, however, his choice is a restricted one, and he is forced to exist on a limited dietary, it will be found that, under certain conditions, symptoms of ill health occur, although the dietary contains sufficient protein and energy to supply his normal requirements. The diseases known as beri-beri, pellagra, rickets and scurvy were always associated with such conditions, but that these diseases were due to lack of proper nutrition and not to a pathological causative organism long remained unsuspected. Although Bachstrom in 1734 had pointed out that scurvy could be prevented by the consumption of fresh vegetables, a conclusion corroborated by Dr James Lind in 1755 in his publication *Treatise on the Scurvy*, no less than 7500 men of the Mesopotamian force lost their lives during 1916 from this disease.

The Dutch physician Eijkman in 1897 brought forward undoubted proof that beri-beri was caused through the modern methods of milling rice. The onset of beri-beri, an endemic disease among the rice-eating peoples of the Far East, had long been associated with the consumption of rice, but it was left to Eijkman to show that the disease was not due to any defect in the rice itself, such as the presence of moulds or other pathogenic organisms, but to the method of treatment used in the preparation of the rice for food. In his statistical treatment of the occurrence of this disease among the prisoners of the gaols of the Dutch East Indies, Eijkman showed that out of every 10,000 individuals on a rice dietary, only one case occurred among the prisoners eating unpolished rice, 416 cases among those on a mixed rice dietary, and 3900 cases among those on the polished rice dietary. It was evident, therefore, that the disease arose through the absence of some material present in the rice polishings removed during milling, and since these rice polishings formed but a small proportion of the total grain, it was apparent that the material required by the individual to prevent the onset of this disease was in the nature of something that was only required in minimal amounts. Now science had shown that individuals fed on foods as occurring in nature could be maintained in perfect health provided that adequate amounts of protein, fat, carbohydrates and salts were supplied, and it was naturally assumed therefore that proteins, fats, carbohydrates and mineral salts were all that was necessary to form a perfect diet. The history of scurvy and beri-beri had questioned the correctness of this assumption, and it was obvious that the proof of this assumption could only be shown by actually maintaining animals in perfect health on a diet consisting of pure proteins, fats, carbohydrates and salts. Lunin, as early as 1881, in studying the effect of salts in the food on mice, had fed mice on varying amounts of specially prepared milk, fat, cane sugar and casein. To some of the mice he gave in addition mineral salts, to some no salts, and as a control he fed some on fresh milk alone. The mice on the specially prepared diets died, whereas the controls fed on fresh milk lived. Lunin concluded from these observations that 'other substances indispensable for normal nutrition must be present in milk besides casein, lactose, fats and salts'. The proof that this was the case was supplied by the classical experiments of Sir Frederick Gowland Hopkins. Hopkins fed two lots of young rats on a synthetic diet consisting of specially purified casein, lard, sugar and salts, a diet calculated to supply the physiological requirement in respect to these substances. To one lot of these rats, 2 to 4 c.c. of fresh milk daily per individual were given in addition. The rats given the milk grew normally, the others ceased to grow after approximately 14 days. In a subsequent experiment Hopkins showed that the addition of milk to rats whose growth had ceased on the synthetic diet led to resumption of growth, whereas withdrawal of the milk from those already supplied with it on a synthetic diet led to cessation of growth. Hopkins thus proved conclusively that certain minimal amounts of 'accessory food factors' present in fresh milk were necessary in addition to an adequate protein, energy and salt supply to maintain growth, and that a dietary of proteins, fats, carbohydrates and salts was insufficient for normal nutrition. Results of a similar nature were obtained by Stepp in Germany and Osborne and Mendel in America, and it is now clearly recognised that there occur in natural foodstuffs accessory food substances which the animal cannot synthesise, that are catalytic in character, and whose presence in a foodstuff is necessary to enable the animal to carry out the metabolic processes associated with growth and normal nutrition. Such accessory food substances are known as 'vitamins', and much experimental work has since been carried out on these substances. It would make too long a story to treat the subject historically, or even to mention all the workers who have contributed in any way to our present state of knowledge on these substances. We can only attempt to express as succinctly as possible the facts that have emerged from the results of such work. Vitamins may be defined as accessory food substances essential to normal nutrition occurring in natural foods. No less than six of these substances have been demonstrated as occurring in natural food nutrients and contributing to the normal nutrition of the individual, and evidence has also been adduced for the presence of three others. They are as follows:

Vitamin A. This vitamin occurs in association with fats of animal origin and is known as 'fat-soluble A'. It is relatively heat stable but easily undergoes oxidation, being destroyed by heat under conditions in which oxidation is possible. The absence of this factor from a diet leads most characteristically to a diseased eye condition known as xerophthalmia, and to the occurrence of characteristic lesions in the mouth and gullet. In the young animal growth ceases. Eggs, liver, milk and dairy products and green vegetables are among the richest sources of vitamin A. In plants, evidence has been brought forward which indicates that it occurs in association with plant pigments, since the amount of vitamin A in a plant runs *pari passu* with its pigment content. It has since been established that the plant pigment carotene is the precursor of vitamin A, and that the animal has the power of forming vitamin A from carotene supplied in its dietary. The administration of carotene to an animal leads to the appearance in the liver fat of a proportionate amount of vitamin A, and recent work suggests that this vitamin is an alcohol derived from the partial oxidation of a fragment of the carotene molecule. The body has the capacity of storing in its own tissues a reserve of vitamin A, so the response to a diet deficient in vitamin A is relatively slow in an animal which previously has been maintained on a diet relatively rich in vitamin A. Moore has demonstrated that feeding a stall-fed cow on carrots increases the vitamin A content of the butter fat.

Vitamin B complex. Just as the complex originally known as vitamin A was first regarded as a single substance but has since been separated into vitamins A and D, so vitamin B complex, which was formerly regarded as a single individual, is now being resolved into several factors. Except for two of these factors, vitamin B_1 and B_2, the evidence available is not sufficiently complete to enable us to be dogmatic as to the nature and existence of the other vitamins present in vitamin B complex. It will suffice at this stage of our knowledge merely to record that evidence has been adduced for the presence in vitamin B complex of three other vitamins in addition to B_1 and B_2. They are

(1) the vitamin B_3 of Williams and Waterman, a thermolabile vitamin which protects against loss of weight in pigeons;

(2) the vitamin B_4 of Reader, which protects against loss of weight in rats; and

(3) the factor Y of Chick and Copping, which is essential for growth in rats, and is heat and alkali stable.

Vitamin B_1. Vitamin B_1, the antineuritic vitamin, is water soluble, moderately heat stable, and withstands desiccation. Yeast and cereal germs are rich sources of vitamin B_1, and it is also present to a lesser extent in egg yolk, fresh vegetables and fruit, and fresh meat and milk. Animals vary considerably in their demand for this vitamin, birds requiring relatively large amounts, whereas ruminants require considerably less than rats on an equivalent live weight basis. This lessened demand for B_1 is probably associated with the fact that certain bacteria normally present in the rumen have the capacity of synthesising vitamin B_1. It has been definitely proved that vitamin B_1 is developed in this manner in the rumen of the cow. Lack of this vitamin in the bird gives rise to a pathological condition known as polyneuritis, and in man to the condition known as beri-beri. Deficiency of this vitamin in man gives rise to peripheral neuritis, oedema and gastro-intestinal derangements. In the case of birds, loss of appetite followed by rapid loss of weight, fall of body temperature and development of paralytic symptoms follows absence of this vitamin in the diet. Since the body has a very limited capacity for the storage of vitamin B_1, the provision of ample supplies of this vitamin in the dietary is essential. Vitamin B_1 is essential for the nutrition of the nervous system, and it has now been isolated as a crystalline substance. A point of considerable interest in its chemical constitution is that sulphur plays a part in its constitution.

Vitamin B_2. Vitamin B_2, or the pellagra-preventing and growth-promoting vitamin, has a distribution in feeding stuffs similar to that of B_1, but the relative amounts of these two vitamins present in feeding stuffs vary. Thus meat and milk are relatively richer in B_2 than B_1, whereas cereals contain larger quantities of B_1 than B_2. Vitamin B_2 is relatively heat stable and water soluble. Rats, if fed on a vitamin B_2 deficient diet, cease to grow, lose weight, become weak and lethargic, and in the later stages of the disease diarrhoea accompanied with discharge of blood is common. Reddening of areas of the skin also occurs, with the formation of yellow crusts and loss of hair. In man, gastro-intestinal derangements including diarrhoea is a constant symptom. A skin rash develops; the skin becomes thickened, pigmented and dry, and cracks, with serous exudates forming pus-containing crusts. Hartwell has shown that there is a quantitative relationship between the amount of protein in a diet and the amount of B_2 needed to produce normal growth and health.

Vitamin C. Vitamin C, the antiscorbutic vitamin, is present in all growing plant tissues. Thus cereals and peas, which as seeds contain no vitamin C, develop considerable quantities when germinated. It is also present in citrus fruits, tomatoes, raw cabbage, pasture grass and green crops, root vegetables, onions and lettuce. It is water soluble, and is easily destroyed by heat, desiccation, or oxidation, but is relatively stable in acids. The body has relatively little capacity for storage of this vitamin, so scurvy is rapidly produced in animals susceptible to it when placed on a scorbutic-producing diet. Scurvy is characterised by soreness and bleeding of the gums, and swelling of the gums and joints. The bones also become brittle and the teeth become loose. Animals show considerable differences in their reactions to a vitamin C free diet. Guinea-pigs, monkeys and men are very sensitive, but rats, fowls and pigeons, calves and cattle, are remarkably non-susceptible. Pigeons have been successfully raised on a vitamin C free diet through several generations, and Thurston, Palmer and Eckles demonstrated that the livers of calves raised on a diet that was scorbutic-producing for guinea-pigs contained vitamin C, as did the milk of heifers raised on a similar diet from birth. The young rabbit is susceptible to scurvy, whereas the adult rabbit is not, and Portier, Randoin and Lomba have attributed this apparent resistance of the adult to the development of vitamins by bacterial action in the intestinal canal. A substance which protects against scurvy has now been isolated by Szent-Györgyi. It appears to be a highly reactive carbohydrate derivative, isomeric with glycuronic acid, and in its crystalline form corresponds with the formula $C_6H_8O_6$.

Vitamin D (Calciferol). The natural sources of the anti-rachitic vitamin D are codliver oil and animal fats and irradiated yeast and other substances of vegetable origin. Vitamin D, being fat soluble, is commonly found associated with vitamin A and as a consequence was first confused with it. Mellanby had shown that diets deficient in fats and rich in carbohydrates were rickets-producing. Hess and Pappenheimer showed that codliver oil, if subjected to continuous oxidation, lost its power of maintaining growth but retained its antirachitic power. It became obvious, therefore, that the antirachitic substance was a separate entity and it was therefore called vitamin D, vitamins B and C having been recognised and named such before it was realised that the antirachitic power was due not to vitamin A but to another substance occurring with it. In 1919 Huldschinsky demonstrated that ultra-violet light also had the power of curing or preventing rickets, and this observation was followed by the demonstration by Steenbock and Black, and independently by Hess, that certain foodstuffs, when irradiated by ultra-violet light, also acquired an antirachitic power that had, prior to irradiation, been absent. It became clear, therefore, that a precursor of vitamin D was present both in animals and certain foodstuffs and that irradiation of this precursor led to the formation of vitamin D itself. The substance acting as the precursor of vitamin D was found to be present in sterol compounds such as commercial cholesterol and phytosterol, and it was eventually identified as ergosterol. On irradiating ergosterol the vitamin D itself is formed, and it has recently been isolated as a pure crystalline substance, to which the name calciferol has been assigned. The potency of this compound can be judged by the fact that it has been estimated that 1 oz. of this substance daily would suffice to protect 1,000,000 children against rickets, and that 2 grains only would cure 400,000 rats suffering from severe rickets.

Snow and Bowden have presented evidence to show that vitamins are produced in nature from their precursors by means of
photochemical reactions brought about by the action of light.
These reactions are produced by monochromatic irradiation with
light of the correct wave length, when the pre-vitamins so treated
develop their maximum biological activity after comparatively
short exposure. Moreover, exposure to light of wave lengths
outside the effective wave length leads to rapid destruction of the
vitamin. Thus calciferol is rapidly produced from ergosterol by
exposure to light of wave length $\lambda 2967$ but is rapidly destroyed
when subjected to irradiation at wave lengths $\lambda 2650$ and $\lambda 2537$.

Physiological action of vitamin D. There are several hypotheses
put forward to explain the physiological action of vitamin D.
The onset of rickets is associated with a disturbance of the
normal calcium and phosphorus metabolism of the body, resulting
in loss of the power of depositing calcium phosphate in the
bone cartilage. Rickets will occur in an animal raised on a diet
deficient in calcium and phosphorus salts, but it has been shown
that an animal may be kept in normal condition on a lower calcium
and phosphorus containing diet if vitamin D is present than is the
case if vitamin D is absent. This effect has been shown to be due
to increased absorption of the calcium salts from the intestine, and
evidence has been brought forward to suggest that this increased
utilisation of food calcium is due either to the vitamin D maintaining the hydrogen ion concentration of the intestine at the level
most favourable for calcium phosphate absorption, or to its altering
the permeability of the intestinal epithelium for calcium phosphate, or both. Vitamin D also influences in some way the inter-
mediary metabolism of calcium and phosphorus. In a typical case
of rickets, the blood calcium and phosphorus values are abnormal,
and administration of vitamin D or production in the body of
vitamin D by irradiation or sunlight quickly restores these values
to normal. Freudenberg demonstrated that cartilage ossifies when
placed in calcium phosphate solutions, and attributes this ossification to the formation of a calcium-phosphate-cartilage complex
due to specific action on the protein of cartilage. Shipley in 1924
showed that whereas no calcification occurs if the cartilage or bone
of a rachitic rat is incubated in a rachitic rat's serum, it does take
place in normal rat's serum. Shipley consequently suggests that
the selective deposition of calcium salts is associated with the

activity of fluids surrounding the cartilage, and that lack of calcification in rickets is primarily due to insufficiency of the fluids rather than to the cartilage itself. Robison has advanced the hypothesis that calcification depends on the activity of an enzyme secreted by the osteoblasts and hypertrophic cartilage cells. This enzyme hydrolyses hexose-monophosphoric and glycero-mono-phosphoric esters with the liberation of inorganic phosphate ions, but the deposition of solid calcium phosphate will depend upon the hydrogen ion concentration of the fluids and the relative concentrations of the Ca and PO_4 ions present.

The Antisterility Vitamin Fat–soluble E. Evans, working on the relations of diet to fertility, established the existence of a dietary factor essential for normal reproduction in the rat. Evans observed that rats fed on the standard 'casein' diet of Osborne and Mendel eventually became sterile, and this observation led him to undertake a series of experiments into the cause and nature of this sterility. For this purpose he used a modified diet consisting of casein 32 parts, prepared maize starch 40 parts, lard 22 parts, cod-liver oil 2 parts, salt mixture 4 parts, with 0·4 to 0·6 g. dried yeast daily. The salt mixture was that formulated by McCollum and consisted of sodium chloride 51·0 g., magnesium sulphate crystals 159·6 g., monobasic sodium phosphate 104·1 g., monobasic calcium phosphate 162·0 g., dibasic potassium phosphate 286·2 g., ferric citrate 35·4 g. and calcium lactate 390·0 g. On this diet rats, while maintaining normal growth and bodily condition, eventually became sterile, the onset of sterility varying according to the rat's previous dietetic history. That this sterility was due to a dietary deficiency was definitely proved, since the addition of a small amount of wheat germ to the basic diet caused the rats to maintain their fertility unimpaired, whereas the rats kept on the basic diet alone became uniformly sterile. Moreover, the small amount of wheat germ required to ensure normal reproduction in the rat indicated that the substance responsible for the maintenance of fertility was of the nature of a vitamin, and, following the McCollum nomenclature, Evans called the antisterility vitamin vitamin E. The sterility due to feeding rats with an E free diet is quite definite, and shows characteristic histological and pathological changes in the affected animals. In the female rat the processes of oestrus, ovulation, fertilisation and implantation are quite normal, the sterility being due to death of the intra-uterine foetuses at about the 13th day after gestation, followed by resorption. In the male rat, the sterility is due to degeneration of the testis, there being complete or almost complete degeneration of the seminiferous epithelium. A male rat born of a normal mother and weaned at 21 days, and fed on an E free diet, will generally exhibit this sterility at about the 90th to 150th day of age, there being an initial period of fertility on the rat reaching sexual maturity.

Response to curative treatment. As would be expected from the nature of the sterility induced, the female and the male rats show a widely differing response to curative treatment. Sterile females placed on an E containing diet exhibit a quick response, and normal litters will result even if the diet is given for the first time during the earlier days of gestation. Indeed, Evans obtained normal litters in three cases out of five of female rats that were only placed on an E containing diet as late as six days after mating. In the case of the male, however, the response to curative treatment is exceedingly slow and uncertain in character. This is what would be expected, since the sterility is in the male due to testicular degeneration and recovery would depend to a large degree on the extent to which this degeneration has developed in the seminiferous tubules. Where degeneration of the seminiferous tubules is complete we should expect an absence of response to curative treatment; where, however, degeneration is only partial we should expect an eventual recovery, but even in this case the recovery of fertility would take time. This expectation is in accordance with Evans's results. Evans found it extremely difficult to obtain cures in the case of males kept on an E free diet to the stage where sterility manifested itself, but a certain number of cures were obtained. In the case of successful cures, fertility in the male manifested itself some 3 to 5 months after the rats had been placed on an E rich diet, and in one case 14 months elapsed before the cure was complete.

Proof of the existence of an antisterility vitamin in foods. Evans has shown that sterility manifests itself sooner or later in rats fed on certain simplified diets and that this sterility can be avoided by adding comparatively small amounts of certain foods to the sterility-causing basal diet. It is evident, therefore, that normal diets contain a substance or substances the presence of which is necessary for the maintenance of fertility in the sexually mature animal, and it is furthermore clear that this substance belongs to the class of accessory food factors known as vitamins. Storage of this substance occurs in the normal animal, and Evans has shown that the musculature and the fat are the two chief seats of storage in the body.

Female rats placed on an E free diet and permitted sexual intercourse invariably exhibit an initial fertility, the sterility only manifesting itself at the third pregnancy, the E vitamin already stored in the body being sufficient to allow for two normal pregnancies if the litters are not allowed to suck the mother. If two sets of identical females are placed on an E free diet, one set being allowed to breed and the other not, sterility will occur at the same time. Since in the case of the females not allowed to breed there has been no call on the antisterility vitamin to play its particular rôle, it is obvious that this vitamin must be gradually destroyed in the processes of normal metabolism, since if it were not so, a store of this vitamin would still be available for successful pregnancies at the time when the set of animals allowed to breed normally had lost that power. The amount of vitamin E required for the maintenance of fertility in the female is very small, Evans having maintained fertility in certain rats with a daily dosage of from 15 to 30 milligrams of wheat germ oil. Moreover, a single feeding of a dosage of 550 milligrams of wheat germ oil in the first day of gestation to a rat on an E free diet always results in the birth of living young. The above facts clearly demonstrate that for the maintenance of normal fertility an accessory food factor is necessary, and that this food factor need only be supplied in small amount. Evans has further demonstrated the fact that supplying this vitamin in excess of the minimal amount required does not increase the normal fertility of an animal, i.e. the birth-rate cannot be increased by feeding a female rat with excessive amounts of vitamin E.

Distribution of vitamin E in foods. Vitamin E is present, but not in a highly concentrated form, in most animal tissues, the musculature and fat form the chief seats of storage, the viscera and the testes being more deficient in this vitamin. It is present in the milk of animals and the yolk of eggs. Cod-liver oil and skim milk powder contain very little vitamin E. In plant products, vitamin E is present in varying concentrations. It is present in fresh and dried lettuce and alfalfa, in earthnuts, maize germ, wheat germ and banana. Fertility has been successfully maintained on a daily dosage of 0·25 g. wheat germ, 0·5 g. maize germ, 1 g. raw earthnut, and 27 g. banana. Polished rice, on the other hand, contains very little vitamin E. The cooking of fresh foods containing vitamin E does not impair their efficiency.

The chemical nature and behaviour of vitamin E. Very little is known as yet on the chemical nature of vitamin E. It is ether soluble and can be extracted from the foods containing it by the action of ether, petroleum ether, acetone, benzene and absolute alcohol. It is destroyed by submission to very high temperatures, but is heat stable in wheat germ and its products up to a temperature of 250° C. It is comparatively stable under specified conditions to the action of ultra-violet light, to atmospheric oxygen, to strong acids, and cold saponification with strong alkali. By successive treatment with suitable solvents and by the use of fractional distillation *in vacuo*, Evans has succeeded in obtaining from wheat germ oil an extremely active fraction, an orange red viscous oil, which if given to young sterile females as a single dose of 5–10 milligrams on the day of mating will effect complete recovery of fertility and lead to the successful birth of the litters.

CHAPTER XXIII

METABOLISM OF ORGANIC CONSTITUENTS

It has already been noted that the essential constituents of an animal's diet are proteins, carbohydrates, fats, mineral matter, vitamins, and, of course, water. The first three constituents are in a different category to the others in that they form the larger proportion of the dry matter of the whole diet, and are consequently of more importance from a quantitative aspect. They are, moreover, oxidisable substances, and on oxidation in the body yield up the latent energy they acquired when they were originally built up in the green plant from simple salts, carbon dioxide and water through the agency of light. This energy is in the form known as chemical or potential energy, and when chemical changes occur in the animal this energy may be transformed into heat which maintains the temperature of the body, or work in the form of muscular movements, or it may remain still in a potential form as proteins and fats stored in the body, or as milk or eggs. In actual fact, there are many forms of energy, but those of most importance in animal nutrition consist of heat energy, chemical energy, and kinetic energy or energy due to motion.

The sum of the chemical changes that go on in a living organism, whether plant or animal, is known as metabolism. The changes which go on in plants, resulting mainly in the production of complex substances from simple substances, are said to be anabolic, whereas the changes that go on in animals, which on the whole consist of breaking down complex substances into simple substances, are said to be katabolic. It is important to realise that although, on the whole, the changes which go on in plants are anabolic, katabolic changes are also present. Similarly, although the sum of changes which go on in animals are katabolic, both anabolic and katabolic changes occur in animals. It is interesting to note the mutual interdependence of plants and animals. The animal, since it requires foods to supply it with the potential energy so essential for its life processes, could not live unless the plant had made such substances through the agency of sunlight, and the plant in turn builds up these substances from what are, in fact, the waste products of animal life, i.e. carbon dioxide, simple salts and water.

It has been shown in former chapters that the food an animal eats is by the process of digestion converted into soluble substances, and that these substances, absorbed through the walls of the gut, enter the blood stream and in this manner are conveyed to the seat of active metabolism, the living cells. The amino-acids, glucose and fats, all readily oxidisable substances, together with mineral substances, hormones, etc., and with oxygen combined in loose chemical combination in the red corpuscles, thus reach the living cells and are available for taking part in the complex chemical and physico-chemical changes by which the activity of living cell tissues is made manifest. These changes, which have been conveniently grouped together under the general term metabolism, are very complex in character, but in animal nutrition it is convenient to discuss them under two main heads, changes in the protein compounds, and changes in the carbohydrates and fats.

Protein Metabolism. The nitrogen compounds derived from the food proteins are amino-acids, the chief functions of which are to repair the waste of the tissues which is constantly taking place in the body, to take part in the formation of the protein compounds present in glandular secretions and secretions of the endocrine glands and to provide energy. Although this latter function, the supply of energy, is important in cases where the food supply is mainly derived from protein, in animal nutrition it is not usual to supply protein for this purpose, since the energy represented by the protein fed can be more easily and more economically supplied in the form of fat and carbohydrate. The amount of protein required for tissue repair is comparatively small, and it becomes of interest to ascertain what happens to protein taken in in excess of the body's needs. If the distribution of the nitrogenous compounds of the urine of an animal on a low protein diet and a medium protein diet is studied, it will be found that there is relatively much less urea present in the urine secreted during the low protein diet, whereas the creatinine secreted is approximately the same in both cases. Folin, who studied this question, distinguished between nitrogen of exogenous origin, i.e. derived directly from food protein, and nitrogen of endogenous origin, i.e. derived from the breakdown of body tissue. The creatinine in the urine can therefore be regarded as a measure of tissue breakdown, whereas the urea in the urine is largely of food origin. Since, within a few hours after a protein meal, nearly 50 per cent. of the nitrogen in the protein appears in the urine as urea, it is legitimate to assume that a considerable proportion of the food protein is converted into urea without taking part in the formation of living tissue. That this is so is evidenced by the fact that if amino-acids are mixed with finely minced fresh body tissues ammonia is produced, and since if ammonium carbonate is perfused through the liver of an animal it is quantitatively converted into urea, the function of de-amination of the amino-acids and the formation of urea from the ammonia produced has been assigned to the liver. Under normal circumstances, therefore, the excess amino-acids not required for tissue repair become de-aminised, the nitrogenous portion being converted into urea, or in the case of the bird ammonium urate, the non-nitrogenous portion being utilised for energy requirements or any other function it may fulfil in metabolism. Knoop has shown that de-amination may occur by hydrolysis, or may be associated with oxidation or reduction. In any case, the products resulting from de-amination eventually leave the body completely oxidised in the form of CO_2 and water, except when the amino-acid forms part of an aromatic compound, in which case the linkage of the benzene nucleus protects it from final oxidation and it may be eliminated in an unoxidised form. Thus glycine, which in normal metabolism is finally broken down to urea, carbon dioxide and water, links up with any benzoic acid that may be present in the food supply and is excreted in the urine as the salt of hippuric acid thus:

$$C_6H_5 . COOH + CH_2(NH_2)COOH$$
$$= C_6H_5 . CO . (NH)CH_2 . COOH + H_2O$$

benzoic acid   glycine   hippuric acid +   water

Similarly, ornithine (di-amino valeric acid), which arises as an intermediate product in the protein metabolism of birds, is protected by any benzoic acid present in the food and appears in the urine as ornithuric acid. Besides urea and creatinine, a constant constituent of mammalian and avian urine is uric acid. This substance, which has the formula $C_5H_4N_4O_3$, is derived from nucleic acid which forms a constituent part of the nucleo-proteins present in all cell material. In the katabolism of nucleo-proteins the protein moiety first splits off from the nucleic acid, and the nucleic acid by stages breaks up into its final end products; carbohydrate, phosphoric acid, and purine and pyrimidine bases. The purine bases consist of guanine ($C_5H_5N_5O$) and adenine ($C_5H_5N_5$), the pyrimidine bases of thymine and cytosine. By means of the de-aminising ferments guanase and adenase, guanine and adenine are converted to xanthine ($C_5H_4N_4O_2$) and hypoxanthine ($C_5H_4N_4O$) respectively, and these substances are then oxidised by the ferment xanthine-oxidase to the final end product uric acid ($C_5H_4N_4O_3$). The uric acid present in normal urine therefore has a dual origin, being partly exogenous in character, i.e. derived from nucleo-proteins present in food material, and partly endogenous in character, being derived from the tissue katabolism of the body itself. In birds, a considerable proportion of the uric acid present in the urine is a synthetic product produced by the bird from ammonia and lactic acid. Although in man uric acid forms the major excretory product of purine metabolism, in the domestic animals the uric acid is further oxidised and appears in the urine as allantoin ($C_4H_6N_4O_3$), the further oxidation being brought about by a tissue enzyme called uricase. The ammonia present in the urine varies considerably in amount, and is usually associated with dietary conditions or with abnormal metabolism. If the diet contains an excess of inorganic acids, part of the ammonia produced during de-amination of the proteins is utilised to neutralise the excess acid, which then appears in the urine as the ammonium salt.

Synthesis of proteins from amino-acids. From the amino-acids resulting from the digestion of proteins the tissue proteins are formed, but the exact mechanism of the biochemical processes involved is still obscure. The extent to which the body is able to synthesise an amino-acid from other amino-acids is also little understood, although it has been definitely shown that, at all events, the body has the power of synthesising glycine from other amino-acids. On the other hand, it has been shown that the body is incapable of synthesising certain of the amino-acids which are essential for growth, since growth does not take place unless such amino-acids are present in the food supply. Thus cystine, lysine, tryptophane and either histidine or arginine must be derivable from the food protein, since in the absence of any one of these amino-acids neither growth nor maintenance of the existing body tissues is possible. Lysine has also been shown to be essential for growth, but not for maintenance. In view of the inability of the body to synthesise certain amino-acids, the value of a protein cannot be measured by its nitrogen or energy content but must be assessed according to the proportions of amino-acids it yields, or, as it is sometimes called, its biological value. Proteins in which the amino-acids are present in the proportions in which they occur in animal tissues will therefore be more valuable than those which lack one or more of the essential amino-acids, or which contain a preponderating amount of an amino-acid which enters but a slight extent into the composition of animal protein. For this reason proteins of animal origin have been regarded as more valuable than those of vegetable origin. Thus, the alcohol soluble protein of barley, hordein, contains about 40 per cent. of its weight of an amino-acid called glutamic acid, and since only approximately 10 per cent. of this acid would be required for the synthesis of tissue protein the remaining 30 per cent. would only possess the value represented by its energy content. Moreover zein, which is the alcohol-soluble protein of maize, contains no tryptophane and lysine, and gelatin, which is lacking in cystine, tyrosine and tryptophane, are both proteins which will be unable to support life, however much of them one includes in an animal's diet.

On the other hand, such proteins have a distinct biological value if they are used in conjunction with other proteins which contain the amino-acids they are themselves lacking in, and for this reason the results of attempts to measure the biological replacement values of proteins by feeding such proteins as separate entities cannot be applied to feeding practice, since under such conditions the feeding of mixed proteins is the rule rather than the exception.

Maintenance Protein Requirement of Farm Animals. Since the value of a protein depends partly on its amino-acid constitution and partly on the nature of the other proteins fed with it, it is manifestly impossible to state with extreme accuracy the protein requirements of any animal for maintenance. The method adopted for the estimation of the protein requirements of an animal is to place the animal on a protein-free maintenance diet and measure the nitrogenous excretion that occurs. The nitrogen output multiplied by the factor 6·25 represents the normal wastage of body protein (expressed as 'crude' protein) that occurs under maintenance conditions, and it is customary to multiply the result obtained by two on the assumption that the average protein in diets has a biological value of 50 per cent. Another method is to feed the animal on a diet deficient in protein and gradually to increase the protein fed in the diet until the nitrogen output in the faeces and urine exactly balances the nitrogen given in the food. From the figures of the nitrogen in the food and the nitrogen in the faeces the amount of digestible crude protein required for maintenance can be calculated. By such means it is possible to estimate with rough approximation the digestible protein requirements of the domestic animals.

In the case of energy computations for animals of different weights, it is usual to take the surface area rather than the weight as the unit, but since the protein metabolism is dependent on the active cell tissue, the protein requirements of animals are usually computed on a weight basis. From available experimental data it has been estimated that the maintenance protein requirements of the domestic animals are as follows:—

Animal	Digestible protein requirement per 1000 lb. live weight	
	Crude protein lb.	Pure protein lb.
Bullock	0·6	0·5
Cow	0·6	0·5
Sheep	0·6	0·55
Pig	0·5	0·48

Energy Metabolism. The body derives the energy required both for maintenance and productive purposes from the products of digestion. One gram of protein when burnt to carbon dioxide, nitrogen and water gives out energy to the extent of 5700 calories or 5·7 kilocalories. In the body, however, it is not entirely oxidised, but a large proportion of its oxidation products inevitably appears in the urine in the form of such compounds as urea, uric acid, ammonia, hippuric acid, etc. The waste products thus produced from 1 g. of protein amount to 1 kilocalorie, so 1 g. of digestible protein actually yields to the body 4·7 kilocalories of energy for storage as body tissue or for any other purpose. Both fats and carbohydrates, however, under normal conditions become fully oxidised, so the whole of the potential energy stored in them becomes available for productive purposes. 1 g. of digestible fat consequently yields 9·3 kilocalories and 1 g. of digestible carbohydrate 4·1 kilocalories.

The energy required by the body for vital processes is derived from the food supply, and mechanisms exist whereby the excess energy supplied in the food is stored away for future use. Thus the fats reaching the blood stream from the products of digestion are stored in the fat depôts of the body, and the carbohydrates share a similar fate. We have seen that carbohydrates reach the blood stream in the form of sugars, and since there exists a threshold limit for the amount of sugar that the blood can retain when passing through the kidneys, and since the sugar reaches the blood in comparatively excessive quantity during a carbohydrate-rich meal, it becomes of interest to ascertain the means whereby loss of sugar from the blood is prevented. The sugar absorbed from the gut during digestion passes into the blood stream and reaches the liver *via* the portal vein. This vein, as we have seen, breaks up into capillary networks in the liver and the sugar-laden blood is thus brought into intimate contact with the liver cells, which convert the sugar into animal starch or glycogen and thus remove it from the circulation. Experiments have also shown that glycogen can be formed in the liver from amino-acids. This glycogen is gradually converted into sugar again as soon as the sugar in the blood circulating through the liver has been reduced below its normal level owing to its removal by the other tissues of the body. Glycogen is found in most of the tissues of the body, and can be therefore regarded as a convenient form of reserve material for the storage of readily available energy. Since the power of storing this material in the body is strictly limited, stores of energy in a more permanent form are retained in the body as fat, and conversion of carbohydrate to fat is constantly occurring in animals on plentiful food supply. Although the conversion of sugar to fat in the animal body has been demonstrated beyond doubt, little evidence exists to support the view that fats are converted into sugars. We have seen that fats are esters consisting of fatty acids linked with glycerol. The formation of glucose from glycerol has been shown to occur in diabetic animals, but no such conversion of the fatty acids to glucose has been demonstrated. We must consequently assume that when fats are utilised as sources of energy, the oxidation of the fatty acids takes place without the preliminary formation of sugars. That such would appear to be the case is supported by the fact that feeding with fats animals whose glycogen reserves have been depleted does not lead to the re-appearance of glycogen in the liver. If fats were readily converted to sugars one would expect glycogen to appear in the liver, as is the case following carbohydrate or protein feeding under similar circumstances.

That fats can serve as sources of energy in muscular contraction is evidenced by the respiratory quotient. Under normal circumstances, the respiratory quotient of contracting muscle is unity, showing that carbohydrate is being used as the source of energy. It has been proved that the carbohydrate concerned is muscle glycogen. After severe exercise, or in the case of animals fed largely on fat, the respiratory quotient falls and approaches a value of ·7, thus indicating that fat is being used for this purpose.

From the energy point of view, the part played by proteins, fats and carbohydrates can be simply stated. The proteins, after undergoing de-amination in the liver, can be converted into glycogen, and presumably fats. Sugars are converted directly to glycogen or may be transformed to fat if fed in excess.

The requirements of the body for energy are thus adequately provided for. The main reservoir of energy is provided by storage fat, and temporary reservoirs are provided for by the glycogen stored in the tissues. During the active metabolism of the cell the stores of glycogen are used up and are restored to normal by the conversion of blood sugar to glycogen. The stores of blood sugar thus depleted are made good again by conversion of the liver glycogen into blood sugar. Under excessive energy demands, the liver glycogen reserve may be entirely used up, and in such cases the storage fat is called upon to supply the energy required.

CHAPTER XXIV

METABOLISM OF ASH CONSTITUENTS

In the destruction by heat in the laboratory of substances of plant and animal origin a varying amount of residue, called ash, is left behind. This can be demonstrated by heating on a piece of platinum foil small portions of animal fat, starch, blood, and bone. At first these materials char, giving off combustible gases and leaving a black residue of carbon, which on further heating disappears, leaving in the case of bone an abundant white ash, in the case of blood a small quantity of reddish coloured ash, and in the case of animal fat and starch no ash at all. The ash left after burning substances of animal origin consists of compounds of some or all of the eight chemical elements iron, calcium, potassium, magnesium, sodium, chlorine, sulphur and phosphorus, and these elements and their compounds are consequently referred to as ash constituents. In addition, minute quantities of iodine, fluorine, and silicon are present in ash of animal origin. Some of these compounds are present in the original substance as simple inorganic salts, while others are present in an organic form, and only become converted into the inorganic form when burnt or metabolised in the body. An analysis of any animal reveals the fact that approximately 5 per cent. of the body calculated on the fat free empty weight* consists of ash. The larger proportion of this ash is derived from the skeleton, a comparatively minor but none the less significant amount of this ash being derived from the body fluids and tissues. Thus, in a series of ten animals analysed by Lawes and Gilbert 77·8 per cent. of the ash of the entire animal and 83·0 per cent. of the ash of the carcase was contained in the skeleton, i.e. approximately four-fifths of the total ash of the body is present in the bones. The table which follows indicates the extent to which ash is present in various tissues and fluids of the body and the foods commonly used by farm animals.

The figures given below give credence to the fact already stated that by far the larger portion of the ash of the body is contained

---

* Fat free empty wt. = dead wt. of body less contents of digestive tract and fat present in the tissues.

*Ash content of various substances of plant and animal origin
calculated in percentage of dry substance*

	Average percentage
Fat-free dry animal bone	50–66
Fat-free lean meat (sheep)	5·6
Pigs' blood	4·2
Liver (ox)	5·5
Thymus (ox)	6·2

	Average percentage
Oats	3·7
Maize	1·5
Wheat	1·7
Rice	0·9
Linseed	4·0
Meadow hay	7·2
Oat straw	5·7
Wheat straw	7·1
Mangolds	6·8
Pasture grass	10·5

in the skeleton. The figures given for the commoner feeding stuffs draw attention to the fact that the larger part of the ash in plants is present in the vegetative parts, the seeds, as a general rule, being low in ash. The chief characteristic difference between ash of plant origin and ash of animal origin is that silica is comparatively high in plant ash as compared with animal ash. The knowledge of the percentage of ash present in a plant or feeding stuff is consequently of little use as a guide to its value for animals without a further knowledge of the component constituents. The nature of the differences between the ash of bones and the ash of the soft parts of the body can be further emphasised by comparing the percentage composition of the component parts of the ash. For this purpose, three analyses are given, one an analysis of the ash of lean beef, another an analysis of the ash of the muscle of a man, the third an analysis of the ash of cattle bones.

	% CaO	% MgO	% K_2O	% Na_2O	% P_2O_5	% Cl
Bone ash	51·3	1·1	0·2	1·1	37·5	0·04
Ash of lean beef	1·1	3·6	37·8	8·1	45·0	4·5
Ash from muscle of man	0·9	3·7	35·8	10·1	43·1	6·4

These analyses show quite clearly that from a quantitative standpoint calcium and phosphorus play the most important part in the formation of bone, whereas in the case of the formation of flesh calcium assumes a relatively unimportant rôle, phosphorus, potassium, chlorine and sodium being of considerable importance. Phosphorus in both cases is an important constituent, but even in this case a difference exists that is not revealed in the analyses, but which we know from other considerations. The phosphorus in the ash of bones is present mainly in the bones as calcium phosphate, whereas the phosphorus in the ash of meat is present in the meat in an organic form. It is important to realise that the analysis of the ash, taken by itself, can be very misleading, and in many cases can be quite fallacious as a guide to the principles of feeding.

The Sources and Nature of Supply of Ash Constituents to the Body. It is obvious that the ash constituents of the animal body are derived primarily from the food constituents. As the ash analyses already given reveal, plants and plant products supply the farm animal with a varying amount of ash. In the case of proteins, fats and carbohydrates, we can easily obtain some idea of the relative utilisation of these substances by carrying out a series of digestibility determinations. In the case of ash constituents, however, we are met with the difficulty that ash constituents may be absorbed by one part of the digestive tract and re-excreted lower down, after fulfilling any function for which they may be required while in active circulation in the body. Thus, in the case of iron, it has been clearly established that soluble iron compounds are easily absorbed by the digestive system, and it has furthermore been demonstrated that they are re-excreted in the large intestine. A digestibility determination would lead us to the conclusion that iron compounds were not digestible, whereas other physiological evidence has shown the reverse to be the case. The only fact of value that analysis of the feeding stuffs and combined excreta will show will be the extent of the *retention* of any ash constituent by the body at any given time. These difficulties have largely deterred research workers from investigating the physiology of ash constituents, and so we are not able to give such a clear picture of what happens to the ash constituents during digestion as we can in the case of proteins, fats and carbohydrates. Our best plan, therefore, is to consider in what form the ash constituents are presented to the animal organism and to utilise such facts as have been established to present a probable working hypothesis of the absorption and utilisation of the ash constituents of the body.

Nature of Supply of Ash Constituents. Although the analysis of the ash of plant materials gives us valuable information as to the nature of the ash constituents present, it is not very helpful in indicating the form in which these substances are combined in the plant. Indeed, owing to the chemical and physical behaviour of some of the ash constituents when subjected to heat, great care has to be exercised, and special precautions have to be observed, in the incineration of plant and animal materials if the ash is to be used for giving us knowledge of the extent to which these ash constituents are represented in the original material incinerated. Such knowledge as we possess is therefore derived from consideration of the original material itself. Thus, chlorine is mainly present in the original food materials as chlorides, sulphur to a minor extent as inorganic sulphates but chiefly linked in organic combination as a constituent part of proteins, and iodine and fluorine are chiefly present as iodides and fluorides. Phosphorus is present both in inorganic and organic form. In bone, as we have already seen, it is present chiefly as calcium phosphate, and phosphates of magnesium, sodium and potassium also occur. In the organic form, phosphorus is found in proteins and in certain classes of fatty materials and carbohydrates. The metals as a general rule are present in food materials as salts of carbonic, phosphoric, hydrochloric, sulphuric, and organic acids, and iron and magnesium are also met with in organic form. Iodine in organic combination has also been demonstrated in material of animal origin. Consequently, the ash constituents when presented to the animal in food materials are present either in the form simple inorganic salts, or chemically combined in comparatively complex organic combinations. These materials, to be of value to the animal, must be transported through the walls of the gut, and the problem therefore resolves itself into ascertaining how this is achieved during the normal process of digestion.

Digestion and Absorption of Ash Constituents Present in Food in Inorganic Form. It has been stated above that the ash constituents are present in feeding stuffs either in simple inorganic combination or in relatively complex organic form. Experiments have shown that soluble salts readily pass through the intestinal wall. It has further been demonstrated that the flow of lymph from the thoracic duct is not augmented during the absorption of salt solutions by the villi, so that it is reasonable to assume that these solutions do not pass into the lacteals of the villi but into the blood stream through the delicate endothelial walls of the capillary blood vessels of the villi. The fact that saline solutions are readily absorbed in the small intestine can be demonstrated in the following way. A loop of intestine of a living animal is ligatured in two places after emptying the loop by gentle sliding pressure of the fingers and a known quantity, say 30 c.c., of normal* sodium chloride solution is introduced. The loop is then let slip back into the abdominal cavity. If this is done and the contents of the loop are examined after a suitable interval of time, it will be found that a considerable proportion of the solution has disappeared, i.e. some of the water with its dissolved salts has passed through the walls of the loop and passed into the freely circulating blood stream. If, instead of using an isotonic solution of sodium chloride, a 3 per cent. solution is used, water first passes through the intestinal wall in a reverse direction until the salt solution is reaching a dilution approaching isotonicity when absorption of sodium chloride takes place. The first temporary effect of introducing hypertonic saline solutions into a loop of the intestine will therefore be to increase the volume of fluid present in the loop. Both these experiments would support the view that soluble salts are absorbed in accordance with the ordinary laws of diffusion, i.e. that the osmotic pressure exerted by the colloids of the blood plasma or lymph causes the absorption. The reverse movement of water from the walls of the intestine to the interior that occurs when hypertonic salt solutions are introduced is clearly due to the osmotic pressure exerted by the salts in solution, but that the subsequent absorption of the salts cannot be wholly ascribed to the ordinary laws of diffusion may be proved by the following considerations. First, if a slightly hypertonic solution of sodium chloride be introduced into a loop of the intestine absorption of sodium chloride begins at once. Secondly, if absorption occurred in accordance with the ordinary laws of diffusion, salts and other substances would be absorbed strictly in accordance with their comparative rates of diffusibility. This has been found not to be the case. Dextrose is considerably less diffusible than

* Normal in a physiological sense, not chemical, that is, a solution isotonic with the body fluids (see p. 320).

sodium chloride, yet it is absorbed just as quickly by the epithelial walls of the intestine as is sodium chloride. We are consequently forced to the conclusion that the cells of the intestinal epithelium exercise an apparent 'selective' power in the absorption of substances from the intestine, i.e. absorption is a function of the metabolism of the cells. Physical conditions aid this process in the sense that easily diffusible substances are as a general rule more readily absorbed than slightly diffusible substances, and where the intestinal contents are hypotonic transference of dissolved salts more readily occurs than when the contents are hypertonic. It is evident, therefore, that sodium chloride at least is readily absorbed by the walls of the intestine, and evidence has been given that this absorption is not governed strictly by the ordinary physical laws of diffusion but by the vital activity of the intestinal cells themselves. This being so, it becomes of interest to ascertain to what extent other soluble salts are absorbed by the intestinal epithelium. Fortunately, a very interesting and instructive series of investigations have been carried out by Wallace and Cushing, in elaboration of earlier experiments by Höber, on the relative absorbability of salt solutions from the intestine, and these workers have divided salts into four main groups, which they place as follows:

Group 1. *Salts absorbed from the intestine with great ease.* Chlorides, bromides, iodides, formates, acetates, propionates, butyrates, valerianates, caprates of sodium.

Group 2. *Salts more slowly absorbed from the intestine.* Nitrates, lactates, salicylates, pthalates, ethyl sulphate of sodium.

Group 3. *Salts absorbed with great difficulty.* Sulphates, phosphates, ferrocyanides, caprylates, malonates, succinates, malates, citrates, tartrates of sodium.

Group 4. *Salts not absorbed from the intestine.* Oxalates, fluorides of sodium.

Cushing has pointed out that the salts enumerated in Group 3 are so slightly absorbed, and retain their water of solution so strongly that they act as purgatives and laxatives. He also points out that the relative non-absorbability of the salts of the 3rd and 4th groups runs *pari passu* with the fact that their calcium salts are insoluble. In view of the importance assigned by research workers in the field of animal nutrition to the need for an adequate supply of calcium in animal dietaries this fact is of intense interest. The experimental evidence already adduced shows that the main simple ash constituents are absorbed from the gut in a water soluble form, and before proceeding to the formation of a working hypothesis, it is desirable to state our knowledge regarding the absorption of water from the alimentary canal. It has been demonstrated that the absorption of water in the stomach is nil. Furthermore, it has been shown to be impossible to render faeces watery by abnormal consumption of water, i.e. any water taken into the alimentary canal is readily absorbed by it. The regulation of excess water in the body is mainly affected by the activity of the excretory organs, the kidneys and the skin, and not by differences in absorption from the alimentary canal. It has been assumed, owing to the fact that the percentage of water in the intestinal contents in the region of the ileo-caecal valve is the same as that of the intestinal contents of the duodenum, that no water is absorbed in the small intestine, i.e. that as much water is re-excreted into the small intestine as is absorbed through its walls. This assumption is false because it overlooks the fact that the actual amount of intestinal contents passing the ileo-caecal valve is considerably less than that passing through the duodenum, so that it must be assumed that a considerable amount of water is absorbed in the small intestine. Inspection of the contents of the large intestine at different portions amply demonstrates the fact that water is readily absorbed from the large intestine, but it is important to realise that the water so absorbed is relatively small in amount compared with the total absorbed throughout the alimentary canal.

Proceeding to a working hypothesis, based on the facts already adduced, it may be stated with some degree of reliance that the normal absorption of the metallic elements present in ash of animal origin takes place in the small intestine when these elements are present as chlorides, bromides, etc., to a lesser extent when present as nitrates, salicylates, etc., and to a lesser extent still when present as sulphates and phosphates. It must be clearly emphasised, however, that the fact that metallic elements are not originally present in the food as salts of groups 1 and 2 does not necessarily involve their non-absorption in the small intestine, since interaction may occur in the alimentary canal which may lead to the formation of a salt of the class suitable for absorption. Thus if a dietary contains sodium citrate and calcium carbonate, the hydrochloric acid of the gastric juice would react with some of the calcium carbonate to form calcium chloride, and this would react with the sodium citrate to form sodium chloride and calcium citrate. The sodium, although administered in a form unsuitable for easy absorption by the small intestine, would, by the time it reached the small intestine, be in a form suitable for absorption. With regard to the non-metallic ash constituents, chlorine and iodine obviously would readily be absorbed if presented as chlorides and iodides, but, according to Cushing's experiments, phosphorus would be absorbed with difficulty if presented as a phosphate. The relative absorption of phosphates will be referred to in detail later (p. 317). Sulphur again would not be easily absorbed if given as an inorganic sulphate, but would be more readily absorbed if given in the form of an ethereal sulphate. It is not very probable, therefore, that the sulphur present in the animal body is derived to any great extent from inorganic sulphates administered with the food.

Digestion and Absorption of Ash Constituents Present in Food in Organic Form. Phosphorus and sulphur are the two elements of importance that are present in organic combination in feeding stuffs. Sulphur is present in all naturally occurring proteins and it is this form that provides the main source of supply of sulphur to the body. It has been shown earlier that proteins are converted by the action of the digestive juices into amino-acids and absorbed from the intestine as such. The sulphur is present in proteins as a constituent part of an amino-acid, cystine, and can therefore be readily absorbed in this form. It has been shown by experimental methods that the percentage absorption of sulphur from the intestine closely follows the percentage absorption of the protein, i.e. for any given protein, a series of experiments will show that the ratio of nitrogen to sulphur absorbed from the gut is the same. Owing to the difference in percentage of sulphur present in different proteins, the $N : S$ absorption ratio will obviously vary according to the nature of the protein undergoing digestion. For instance the ratio of nitrogen to sulphur in casein is $19 \cdot 7 : 1$, in egg albumin $9 \cdot 6 : 1$, and in legumin $49 \cdot 9 : 1$. This constancy of the $N : S$ absorption ratio for any given feeding stuff further supports the conclusion already arrived at that sulphur of inorganic origin is practically non-absorbed from the intestine, since, if this were not the case, the N : S absorption ratio would fluctuate according to the varying amounts of inorganic sulphates present in a feeding stuff. Thus, the addition of soluble sulphates to a feeding stuff will not alter the N : S absorption ratio of the feeding stuff, i.e. the N : S absorption ratio will be the same whether soluble sulphates be added to the feeding stuff or not. If the soluble sulphates were absorbed to any marked extent, the N : S absorption ratio would be much narrower when sulphates were added. It can therefore be assumed with confidence that sulphur can only be utilised by the organism if presented in an organic combination, and that the proteins of feeding stuffs constitute the principal supply of this element to the body.

The problem with regard to the phosphorus supply to the body is somewhat more complicated. Phosphorus exists in organic combination in many forms, and the nature of the changes undergone by these organic combinations during digestion is not very clear. In the case of proteins, phosphorus is present in two main groups, phosphoproteins and nucleoproteins. In phosphoproteins, available chemical evidence suggests that the phosphorus is probably directly combined with one of the constituents of the protein molecules; in nucleoproteins the phosphorus forms part of the nucleic acid radical. In the case of substances of a fatty nature, the phosphorus is present in a group of substances known in the literature as 'phospholipins' or 'phosphatides'. Lipins, according to Maclean, are substances of a fat-like nature yielding on hydrolysis fatty acids or derivatives of fatty acids and containing in their molecule either nitrogen, or nitrogen and phosphorus. Lecithin, a compound of glycerol, fatty acids, phosphoric acid and an organic base, is one of the best known phospholipins, and is universally distributed in animal tissues. The best known phosphoproteins are caseinogen of milk and vitellin of egg yolk. Nucleoproteins are prepared from plant and animal cell nuclei and are characterised by containing nucleic acid combined with a protein. In addition to the three sources of supply of organic phosphorus already mentioned, i.e. nucleoproteins, phosphoproteins, and phospholipins, there is also present in materials of plant origin, particularly seeds, a fourth class of compounds known as 'phytates', which are salts of 'phytic' acid. In wheat bran, 52 per cent., and in oatmeal, 54 per cent. of the phosphorus is in the form of 'phytates'.

Digestion and Absorption from the Intestine of Organic Phosphorus Compounds.

Phospholipins. As early as 1877 Bokay concluded that lecithin was acted upon by the lipase of the pancreatic juice or by intestinal ferments and subsequent workers have demonstrated that lecithins undergo digestive changes in the alimentary canal, the cleavage products resulting being cholin, fatty acids, and glycerophosphoric acid. Stassano and Billon in 1903 by microscopical methods concluded that, under certain circumstances, lecithin may be absorbed unaltered, a conclusion that was supported later by Slowtzoff, who found that appreciable quantities of lecithin administered by the mouth reach the blood unchanged, as well as in a saponified condition. Slowtzoff also showed that the cleavage of lecithin occurs in the duodenum. Marjori in 1905 demonstrated that glycerophosphoric acid when given to dogs and man was absorbed from the alimentary canal. Ehrmann and Kruspe later showed that the absorption of lecithin from the alimentary canal is considerably lowered if bile is occluded. The experimental evidence already given, together with the results of numerous other workers enables us to construct a clear story in so far as the digestion and absorption of the phospholipins is concerned. In the stomach little or no cleavage of the phospholipins occurs. In the small intestines, particularly the duodenum, the steapsin of the pancreatic juice, aided by the bile, converts a large part of the phospholipins into their respective cleavage products, the phosphorus being contained in the glycerophosphoric portion. Such lecithin as remains unattacked is absorbed unaltered, and, like the fats, reaches the central lacteals of the villi. The glycerophosphoric acid is easily absorbed by the mucous membrane of the small intestine.

Phytates. As already mentioned, considerable quantities of phosphorus are present in feeding stuffs of cereal origin in the form of salts of phytic acid. Phytic acid is inositol phosphoric acid, and the calcium magnesium compound of this acid is known as 'phytin'. Experiments on Carnivora have shown that the phosphorus of phytin is absorbed and is chiefly excreted in the urine as inorganic phosphate. Jordan, Hart and Patten showed that both trypsin and pepsin have no hydrolytic action on 'phytin' and Plimmer has shown that enzymes of the digestive tract have no action on phytin. This lack of digestive action on phytin has been shown to extend to Herbivora. On the other hand, the absorption of the phosphorus of phytin has been demonstrated in the case of Herbivora, absorption taking place from the alimentary canal. Since phytin itself is not absorbed from the digestive tract, a fact that is further supported by evidence showing that phytates are never present in animal tissues, it is necessary to seek in another direction for an explanation of the action that must occur in the digestive tract. Suzuki and Takashi found the probable solution of the difficulty when they demonstrated that bran contains in considerable quantity a zymase (phytase) which has the power of hydrolysing phytin into inositol and phosphoric acid. Inositol is a common constituent of animal tissues, and it is extremely likely therefore that phytin undergoes digestion in the digestive tract of animals through the action of phytase present in the feeding stuff fed and that assimilation occurs in the form of inositol and phosphoric acid. Since the work of Cushing and Wallace has shown that phosphates are absorbed with extreme difficulty from the intestine, it must be assumed that the absorption takes place owing to the phosphorus being released gradually in an un-ionised form and being absorbed before reaction can occur with any calcium compounds present in the intestine.

Phosphoproteins. It is interesting to note that the phosphorus present in nutritive media intended for the nutrition of the young occurs chiefly in the form of phosphoproteins. Thus in milk the phosphorus is chiefly present as caseinogen, and in eggs as ovovitellin. The phosphorus of the roes of fishes also occurs as a phosphoprotein. Plimmer and others, by artificial digestion methods, have shown that pepsin has little action on phosphoproteins, the reaction that occurs being very slow and therefore unlikely to be of any significance during ordinary digestion. Trypsin, on the other hand, quickly converts the phosphorus of caseinogen into a soluble form, nearly 100 per cent. conversion occurring in 24 hours, 65 per cent. of the soluble phosphorus being in an organic form and 35 per cent. in an inorganic form. The reaction of ovovitellin to trypsin is considerably slower than that of caseinogen, only one-third being found by Plimmer to be converted into the soluble form in 24 hours. The later results of work carried out by Rimington and Kay support Plimmer's results. Plimmer, as the result of his work, came also to the conclusion that all organic phosphorus compounds except phytin were hydrolysed by the intestinal mucosa and assimilated as inorganic phosphate and the organic radical with which the phosphorus is combined. The later work of Rimington and Kay shows that this conclusion of Plimmer needs modification. Rimington and Kay gave particular attention in their research to the soluble organic phosphorus compounds produced as the result of tryptic action as phosphoproteins and suggest the name of 'phosphopeptone' for the soluble organic phosphorus compound split off from caseinogen. In investigating the action of pepsin and trypsin on caseinogen and phosphopeptone, these authors found that no inorganic soluble phosphorus compounds were formed by the action of pepsin. In the case of trypsin, complete conversion of the organic phosphorus of caseinogen to inorganic phosphorus occurred, but the process was a comparatively slow one. Phosphopeptone was formed as an intermediate stage in the process. On the other hand, 50 per cent. of the organic phosphorus of phosphopeptone was liberated in 20 hours, the formation of soluble inorganic phosphorus being relatively more rapid. The absorption of the phosphorus of caseinogen and other phosphoproteins by the intestinal mucosa therefore probably occurs in the form of the soluble organic phosphorus compound, i.e. 'phosphopeptone', and the work of Plimmer suggests that the conversion to inorganic phosphate occurs in the intestinal mucosa itself.

Nucleoproteins. Nucleoproteins, when fed to an animal, first undergo digestive changes in the stomach. Under the influence of gastric juice, the nucleoproteins swell up and dissolve. The protein portion is changed into proteoses and peptones, and the phosphorus containing portion is precipitated as insoluble 'nuclein'. Loewe, working mainly with human subjects, found that nuclein undergoes partial digestion in the small intestine, the phosphorus resulting from such digestion not being absorbed but excreted in the faeces. The major portion of the nuclein is absorbed from the intestine.

Inorganic phosphates. The evidence with regard to the digestion and absorption of inorganic phosphates is not complete enough to render a dogmatic statement possible. Orthophosphoric acid (H_3PO_4) being a tribasic acid, forms a series of salts with metals, and in solution acts as a monobasic, dibasic or tribasic acid, according to concentration and other circumstances. Thus sodium phosphate is disodium phosphate (Na_2HPO_4) but monosodium phosphate (NaH_2PO_4) and trisodium phosphate (Na_3PO_4) are also known. Similarly three salts of calcium are known, monocalcium phosphate ($CaH_4(PO_4)_2$), dicalcium phosphate ($CaHPO_4$), and tricalcium phosphate ($Ca_3(PO_4)_2$). The various phosphates of the metals show considerable differences in their solubilities in water. Monosodium phosphate, disodium phosphate and trisodium phosphate are all soluble in water, as are the corresponding salts of potassium. Monomagnesium phosphate and dimagnesium phosphate are also soluble in water, but trimagnesium phosphate is insoluble in water. The double salt ammonium magnesium phosphate is sparingly soluble in water. Monocalcium phosphate is soluble in water, but both dicalcium phosphate and tricalcium phosphate are insoluble in water. Ferric phosphate is insoluble in water and also acetic acid. All the phosphates mentioned above as insoluble are soluble in dilute hydrochloric acid. Ferric phosphate, although insoluble in water, undergoes a gradual decomposition in water, so that during digestion in the stomach a proportion of the ferric phosphate will be converted into ferric chloride, and as such will be available as a source of iron to the body. Now Wallace and Cushing, in their experiments, found that approximately 8 c.c. of an isotonic solution of disodium or monosodium phosphate were absorbed from the intestine of the dog in half an hour, so that the soluble phosphates given above will serve as a source of supply of phosphorus to the body. With regard to the insoluble phosphates, and particularly with regard to tricalcium phosphate, it is difficult to find a chemical explanation of the experimental facts obtained in feeding this product to animals. McCollum, in experiments with growing rats in which the phosphorus was presented largely in an inorganic form, obtained evidence to show that tricalcium phosphate could be utilised by the rat as a source of phosphorus. Hart, McCollum and Fuller, in experiments with pigs, similarly showed that precipitated calcium phosphate (70 per cent. dicalcium phosphate and 30 per cent. tricalcium phosphate) could serve as a source of phosphorus to the animal body. Numerous feeding experiments have also shown that bone meal, in which the major part of the phosphorus is in the form of tricalcium phosphate, can serve as a source of phosphorus to the body. On the other hand, in cases where phosphorus is excreted in the faeces, it is very often excreted as tricalcium phosphate. In the case of Herbivora, phosphorus is largely excreted in the faeces in this form, there being comparatively little excretion of phosphates in the urine of these animals. Furthermore, the experiments of Wallace and Cushing already referred to demonstrate quite clearly that the relative absorbability of salts is in direct relationship to the relative solubilities of their calcium salts, those salts which form soluble calcium compounds being readily absorbed from the intestine, those which form comparatively insoluble calcium salts being absorbed with difficulty, if at all. We should therefore expect tricalcium phosphate not to be absorbed from the small intestine, and Zuckmayer actually found in experiments with dogs that tricalcium phosphate when introduced into the small intestine in a state of fine suspension was not absorbed. Zuckmayer's work offers a clue to the possible mechanism whereby such an insoluble product as tricalcium phosphate may be absorbed from the intestine. Zuckmayer prepared a colloidal solution of protein containing a large proportion of $Ca_3(PO_4)_2$ which he called 'tricalcol', and found that calcium phosphate when introduced into a loop of the intestine of a dog in this form was readily absorbed, an absorption of 76·01 per cent. occurring in one experiment and 66·24 per cent. in another, forming a marked contrast with the result obtained when tricalcium phosphate alone was given. These results were further confirmed by balance experiments carried out over periods of 6 and 9 days. As the result of this work Zuckmayer formulated the theory that in normal digestion tricalcium phosphate is converted into acid calcium phosphate and calcium chloride, and probably phosphoric acid also in the presence of protein cleavage products, these changes occurring during normal digestion in the stomach. As soon as the stomach contents reach the small intestine, and when the requisite alkalinity is produced by the alkali of the pancreatic juice and bile products, the dissolved calcium phosphates are again changed to tricalcium phosphate in a finely divided form which, reacting with the protein cleavage products, forms a colloidal protein calcium phosphate mixture similar to 'tricalcol' which is readily absorbable from the small intestine. This theory is a very attractive one, and would fall into line with the fact that in the large intestine tricalcium phosphate forms an excretory product and is not absorbed, since by the time the large intestine is reached the protein cleavage products produced during digestion have been completely absorbed, so that one of the requisite conditions for the absorption of tricalcium phosphate is absent.

Summary. Phosphorus in the food, whether in an organic or inorganic form, may be utilised as a source of phosphorus by the animal body. The chief sources of phosphorus supply in foods are phosphoproteins, nucleoproteins, phospholipins, phytin, and inorganic phosphates. In the case of phosphoproteins, the phosphorus is absorbed either in the form of 'phosphopeptone' or as inorganic phosphate; in the case of nucleoproteins, as 'nucleins' which resist digestive action; in the case of phospholipins partly as lecithin and partly as glycerophosphates; and in the case of phytin as salts of phosphoric acid resulting from the action during normal digestion of phytases present in the feeding stuffs. In the case of inorganic phosphates, absorption of soluble phosphates has been shown to occur, and in the case of the insoluble tricalcium phosphate Zuckmayer's theory offers a possible solution of the mechanism whereby absorption of this product can take place from the small intestine.

The Functions of Ash Constituents. The analyses given at the beginning of this chapter clearly show that ash constituents, particularly calcium and phosphorus, play a very important part in the building up of the skeletal structure of the body. In addition, as we have already seen (see p. 110), they are of extreme importance in maintaining neutrality in the body fluids, an essential condition for the efficient functioning of the cells of the body. They further enter into the chemical composition of some of the more important compounds of the soft tissues and secretions, e.g. lipoids, the amino-acids of proteins, thyroxine, and haemoglobin. Apart from these functions, their presence is essential for the occurrence in living tissues of those physico-chemical reactions which we call 'vital phenomena'.

If red blood corpuscles are placed in distilled water and examined microscopically it will be found that they rapidly change their shape, swelling out into spheroid bodies. Placed in strong salt solution they become much flattened and wrinkled. If, however, instead of placing them in a strong salt solution they are immersed in a weak salt solution of a particular strength, it will be found that they neither swell nor shrink, but retain their normal shape and appearance. Such a solution is called an isotonic salt solution or normal saline. The swelling of the corpuscle in distilled water is of course due to imbibition of water by the cell, and the wrinkling that occurs in strong salt solution is due to migration of the fluid of the corpuscle through the cell wall to the surrounding salt solution. The phenomenon of transference of a fluid through a permeable membrane owing to the presence of salt solutions of differing concentrations on either side of the membrane is known as osmosis, the transference taking place owing to the difference of osmotic pressures between the two solutions. Ash constituents fulfil an important rôle in maintaining osmotic equilibrium between the cells and the fluids surrounding them. It is obvious that if the fluids surrounding the cells exert an osmotic pressure widely different from that of the cells themselves, the fluid contents of the cells will be diluted or concentrated, thus seriously impairing the cells' functional activity. Ringer, in his investigations on the contractility of the heart of the frog, found that maintaining the osmotic pressure of the fluid used for perfusion was not sufficient, i.e. the beating of the heart quickly ceased when perfused with an isotonic solution of sodium chloride, nor would such a heart so treated respond to electrical stimuli. If, however, a small quantity of calcium chloride was added to the perfusion fluid, the spontaneous beat of the heart was soon resumed, together with response to electrical stimuli. The recovery thus obtained was not perfect, since the beats were not normal and the heart tended to remain in the contracted state. By adding still further a trace of potassium chloride, Ringer corrected this abnormality and the heart beats became normal. Ringer thus showed that in addition to the part played by ash constituents in maintaining isotonicity, both calcium and potassium were essential in maintaining the normal heart beat, potassium acting in a sense opposite to calcium. That the effects produced were due to the calcium and potassium ions and not to the chlorine ions was proved by Ringer, since the same effects were obtained by carbonates, phosphates, and sulphates of these metals. Neukirch much later demonstrated that magnesium was also important in the maintenance of the regularity of contraction of the musculature of the rabbit's intestine. Magee and Reid have shown that iodine and manganese improve the rate and magnitude of the contractions of the intestine of the rabbit, and Hooker has demonstrated that the contraction of the walls of the blood vessels of the frog is brought about by calcium, whereas potassium and sodium have a reverse effect. The work of Ringer

and others has resulted in the production of isotonic salt solutions
by means of which the excised muscles of animals may be made
to function, thereby enabling great progress to be made in our
knowledge of the physiology of muscle. The best known solutions
are:

	Ringer's solution (for frog's heart muscle)	Ringer-Locke solution (for mammalian heart)	Ringer-Tyrode solution (for rabbit intestine)
	g.	g.	g.
NaCl	0·65	0·9	0·8
KCl	0·014	0·042	0·02
CaCl	0·012	0·024	0·02
MgCl	—	—	0·01
NaHCO	0·02	0·02	0·1
NaHPO	0·001	—	0·005
Glucose	0·2	0·2	0·1

(The quantities of salts indicated above are made up to 100 c.c.
by the addition of distilled water.)

The facts already given illustrate the extreme importance of
ash constituents in the maintenance of the normal physiological
activities of tissues, and the necessity of studying the mineral
requirements of animals as well as the protein, fat, carbohydrate
and vitamin requirements in constructing dietaries for any given
purpose.

The Mineral Requirements of Farm Animals. The adequate recognition of the importance of ash constituents in the
dietary of farm animals is, so far as this country is concerned, due to
the work of Orr and his associates. Orr has drawn attention to the
many cases of disease and malnutrition in farm animals that can be
attributed to deficiency or excessive supply of ash constituents, or
to a faulty balance of the constituents present in the diet. Thus
goitre, a thyroid gland disease so prevalent among sheep in Michi-
gan, U.S.A., is associated with lack of iodine, and can be prevented
by feeding iodine salts. The disease known as 'lamziekte', which
occurs in cattle grazed in certain districts of South Africa, has
been shown by Theiler and his associates to be due to a pathogenic organism which the cattle acquire through eating parts of
diseased carcases in their attempt to correct the phosphorus
deficiency in their normal diet. Aston has further shown that a

condition of malnutrition in animals grazing in certain areas of the North Island of New Zealand is due to a deficiency of iron in the pastures. Elliot and Crichton have shown that the condition known as 'bent leg' in sheep is due to a mineral deficiency and can be prevented by feeding a suitable mineral supplement to the animals grazing in the affected districts. Excessive feeding of bran to horses will give rise to the condition called by Ingle 'bran rickets', and there is little doubt that this condition is due to the excess of phosphorus over calcium in the food intake. Elliot and Orr have obtained a condition resembling rickets in pigs by feeding a diet deficient in calcium, and have obtained normal growth in these animals by including calcium in such diets.

In addition to the actual onset of pathological conditions due to deficiency or excess of minerals, or faulty mineral balance (imbalance), a deficiency or partial deficiency of minerals in a diet otherwise adequate will seriously affect growth, meat production, or milk or egg production. Thus Kellner showed that improved growth would follow the administration of salts of calcium to calves, and Mitchell obtained increased growth rate in chickens and increased egg production in fowls fed on cereal diets by including a modicum of common salt in the dietary, a fact that has since been substantiated by Scott Robertson in Northern Ireland. Orr has further demonstrated that the normal dietary of pigs is apt to be deficient in calcium, sodium, chlorine, and in some cases iron and iodine, and that addition of salt mixtures including these elements in the diets of such animals will lead to improved growth, health, and reproductive capacity. Davidson, at Cambridge, has definitely established that deficiency of calcium in the diet of breeding sows leads to birth of weak litters with high post-natal death rate, with eventual complete sterility in the fourth generation. Addition of salt mixtures to the diet of heavy yielding milch cows has been shown to have beneficial results on the milk yield, and von Wendt has shown that the addition of salt mixtures to cows and heifers prior to lactation will increase the subsequent milk yield. Co-operative work at Aberdeen and Cambridge on the nutritive value of pastures has shown that the nutritive value of pasture grass is often associated with its mineral content, but Woodman and Evans have shown that the failure of animals to thrive on mineral deficient pastures is not due to lack of palatability or inefficient digestion of the organic constituents of the fodder.

Quantitative requirements. With regard to the quantitative mineral requirements of farm animals, it is not possible to be precise. The salts taken in the food are constantly being excreted by the kidneys and the intestinal wall, and in the case of animals provided with sweat glands, through the skin. Salts taken in excess of the physiological optimum are consequently rapidly excreted. Thus, if common salt is given, the chlorides in the urine increase in amount. If salt is withheld, the chlorides in the urine rapidly fall in amount. The extent to which a mineral substance is retained will therefore depend on the amount that is fed, and the previous nutritive history of the animal to which it is fed. The relative availability of a given ash constituent will therefore vary according to circumstances, and it is consequently not possible to assign a definite value to the availability of a given mineral constituent. Kellner, in assessing the availability of an ash constituent, assumed that for productive purposes one-third of the food ash was available for production. Orr, in his estimates, generally allowed one-half.

As we have already seen, the availability of a mineral constituent is governed by the relative ease with which it is absorbed through the walls of the intestine. The absorption and assimilation of mineral substances are also affected by other conditions than the exact form in which the minerals are given. Thus, Husband, Godden and Richards found that the presence of cod-liver oil, linseed oil, and olive oil in a cereal dietary led to an increased assimilation or retention of calcium and phosphorus. Orr, Magee and Henderson found that irradiation of pigs with the light of a carbon arc was followed by an increased calcium and phosphorus retention, due either to increased absorption from the gut or lessened re-excretion of the absorbed products. In addition, the absorption of an increased amount of one mineral, such as potassium, may involve a bigger physiological demand for another, such as sodium.

For these reasons, it is impossible to define within narrow limits the quantitative requirements of farm animals for minerals. Orr has estimated that a sow suckling pigs loses daily from her body $1\frac{1}{2}$ oz. of mineral matter, of which $\frac{1}{2}$ oz. is calcium expressed as lime. On a 50 per cent. availability basis, her daily diet should include 3 oz. of mineral matter, including 1 oz. of lime. Similarly, Orr has calculated that the diet of a cow giving 4 gallons of milk daily should include $3\frac{1}{2}$ oz. of lime, $3\frac{1}{4}$ oz. phosphoric acid and over an ounce of chlorine. He has pointed out, that so far as the calcium is concerned, a cow on good pasture would obtain the amount indicated without recourse to mineral supplements. To satisfy growth requirements, a three-month old pig requires to be supplied with $\frac{3}{4}$ oz. of lime in its dietary, and a growing calf just double this amount.

Under normal conditions, therefore, it is usual for the stock feeder to provide a mineral supplement and to allow the animals free access to such supplements. In the case of ruminants, a block of rock salt, sometimes iodised, is placed in a manger or other convenient place; in the case of pigs, a salt mixture consisting of common salt 20 parts, ground chalk 40 parts, bone meal 40 parts, potassium iodide ·04 parts, is left in a convenient hopper. In the case of fowls, a mixture of 2 parts bone meal, 1 part common salt, is mixed with every 100 parts of the mash, and the birds are in addition allowed free access to a hopper containing grit and a calcium rich substance such as ground chalk, limestone grit, or oyster shell.

CHAPTER XXV

THE ENERGY REQUIREMENT OF THE BODY

During the maintenance of vital processes food and oxygen are continually being taken in and waste products in the form of faeces, urine, carbon dioxide and water are constantly being given out. Since the law of the conservation of energy holds for physical and chemical change in the animate as well as the inanimate world, by constructing a balance sheet of the income and outgo of energy during any given period it is possible to ascertain exactly how much energy an animal requires under any given conditions and the directions in which this energy is utilised. The amount of energy available to the animal from any given foodstuff can also be obtained by this means. In an animal receiving food and kept under normal conditions the energy of the food may be utilised in several ways, for work of digestion, muscular movements, storage of fat or protein and production of heat, as well as the energy required to maintain life. In the resting and fasting animal, the body tissues themselves are called upon to supply the energy required for carrying on the vital functions such as the maintenance of the circulation, body temperature, respiration, etc. The sum of the oxidations required is called the *basal metabolism*, and represents the minimum requirement of the animal. The ascertainment of this biological fact is important, because it represents a continual charge on the food supply as long as the animal lives. Upon withholding food from an animal, the energy required for this purpose is first derived from the glycogen store of the body or from the food substances still undergoing digestion and absorption in the digestive tract. It is not until some time after the animal is deprived of food that the energy is derived from the katabolism of the tissues themselves, and measurements of basal metabolism are not therefore made until this stage is reached. The sum of the oxidations that occur at this stage, i.e. the post-absorptive state, appear as heat and are also measured by the oxygen consumed, the carbon dioxide evolved, and the urine produced. There are thus two methods of ascertaining the basal metabolism, the direct method, in which the heat evolved is directly measured by a heat calorimeter, and the indirect method, in which the oxygen consumed and the CO_2 evolved are measured and the energy represented by these gases calculated. In the direct method a calorimeter similar to that shown in Fig. 116 is used. It consists essentially of an internal metal box insulated from the exterior by thick slabs of cork and an exterior wooden lining and closed by an air-

Fig. 116.   The heat calorimeter at the Animal Nutrition Institute,
School of Agriculture, Cambridge.

tight insulated door. The experimental animal is placed inside the metal and wire cage which slides into the internal metal chamber. Soldered to the outside of the metal chamber is a coil of lead tubing through which water circulates at constant temperature and pressure. When the calorimeter is closed ventilation is affected by a suction fan partly visible at the lower rear right of the photograph and the volume of air passing through the chamber is measured by the pressure differences existing on both sides of a

metal plate containing an aperture of known area through which
the air passes. By means of wet and dry bulb thermometers
situated at the air inlet and the air outlet the humidity of the air
intake and the air outflow is measured. The temperatures of the
inlet water and the outlet water are measured both visually by a
delicate thermometer and also mechanically by means of thermo-
pile junctions which are connected to a sensitive galvanometer,
the oscillations of which are recorded on a graph paper fixed to a
drum actuated by a clock mechanism. The difference between the
temperature of the outlet water and the inlet water is thus recorded
as a double curve, a commutator serving to switch the galvanometer into circuit alternately with the inlet water thermo-junction
and the outlet water thermo-junction at half minute or minute
intervals. The heat given out by the animal during the experiment
is ascertained by adding together (1) the heat taken up by the
water circulating round the inner chamber through the lead
piping, (2) that used to heat the ventilating air, (3) the latent heat
of vaporisation represented by the difference between the water
content of the inlet and outlet air, and (4) the small amount of
heat lost through the insulated sides of the calorimeter. This last
is ascertained by a series of experiments in which a known amount
of heat is used instead of the experimental animal. The measurements are taken when the animal is in a post-absorptive condition,
and asleep.

In the indirect method, a respiration chamber is employed. Two
types are used, the closed circuit type and the open circuit type.
In the closed circuit type, a constant volume of air is used and this
is kept circulating by means of a fan through the chamber in which
the animal is kept. On the outlet side the air has to pass through
separate vessels containing sulphuric acid, calcium chloride, and
water in which are traces of sodium carbonate. The sulphuric
acid removes the moisture from the air and the calcium chloride
absorbs the CO_2 produced by the animal. The water container
restores the humidity of the air and the trace of Na_2CO_3 present
serves to neutralise any acid that may be carried over from the
sulphuric acid container. The oxygen required to replace that used
up by the animal is supplied from an oxygen cylinder, and the
amount required judged by a tension equaliser. The tension
equaliser consists of a rubber diaphragm stretched over a funnel-
shaped opening in connection with the circuit. As the oxygen is

used up the pressure within the circuit is lessened and the diaphragm is pressed in. Oxygen is then released from the cylinder
until the pressure in the circuit becomes normal. The oxygen used
during the experiment is ascertained by weighing the oxygen
cylinder before and after the experiment and the CO_2 produced is
ascertained from the increase in weight of the CO_2 absorption
apparatus. Any urine produced during the experimental period is
collected and analysed. From consideration of the oxygen utilisation, carbon dioxide, and nitrogen excretion figures, the relative
amounts of oxygen used in the combustion of protein, fat, and
carbohydrates can be ascertained and the basal metabolism in
kilocalories computed, knowing that 1 litre of O_2 used for burning
protein generates 4·60 kilocalories, for burning fat 4·686 kilocalories, and for burning carbohydrates 5·047 kilocalories.

The closed circuit type of respiration calorimeter, while convenient for ascertaining the basal metabolism of small animals, is
unsuitable for farm animals, and for these the open circuit type
is used. In this type similar methods of calculation and analysis
are used, but instead of analysing the entire gases produced, aliquot
samples representative of the total gaseous excreta are taken and
analysed. Respiration calorimeters are extremely simple in con-
struction and can be utilised also for studying animals under
varying conditions of nutrition and particularly for studying the
mutual replacement values of feeding stuffs. Where respiration
calorimeters are also designed to act as heat calorimeters their
structure becomes extremely complicated, as will be seen from
Fig. 117.

Rubner, who some 40 years ago measured the basal metabolism
of adult dogs varying in weight from 2 lb. to 100 lb., found that
although the heat given out by small animals was much greater
than that given out by larger animals per unit of weight, the heat
evolution was a constant if calculated on the surface area. This
fact, which is known as Rubner's surface law, is generally accepted
by physiologists although they do not think nowadays that there
is any causal relation between the surface area of an animal and
the amount of its basal metabolism. Calorimetric determinations
have shown that the basal metabolism of man is 39·7 kilocalories
per square metre of surface per hour, that of woman about 10 per
cent. less, while that of adult pigs is just over 40 kilocalories per
square metre per hour.

In computing rations, the basal metabolism is an important figure. For any adult animal, it can be approximately estimated by multiplying 40 kilocalories by the surface area measured in square metres. This gives the basal metabolism per hour, whence by multiplying by twenty-four the basal metabolism per day may be ascertained. The ascertainment of the surface area of an animal by direct measurement is by no means simple. On the assumption that the density of all animals is approximately the same, it

Fig. 117. The respiration calorimeter at the Institute of Animal Nutrition of the Pennsylvania State College (by courtesy of the Director, E. B. Forbes).

follows that the volume is proportional to the weight. Since volume is three-dimensional in character, and area is two-dimensional in character, the square of the cube root of volume is proportional to the surface area. Furthermore, since the weight of an animal is proportional to the volume, the square of the cube root of the weight of the body of an animal is proportional to the surface area. This may be written in the form of an equation $S = KW^{\frac{2}{3}}$, where S = area of surface, W = live weight, and K is a constant depending upon the shape of the animal and the units of area and weight employed. If the weight is measured in grams and the area in square centimetres, K for most farm animals is approximately 9. If expressed in kilograms and square metres $K = \dfrac{9}{10,000}$ and if in lbs. and square metres $K = \dfrac{5\cdot3}{100}$.

Using the appropriate factors for K, it is possible to compute the surface of an animal from the live weight in grams, kilograms or lbs. The annexed figure illustrates this relationship in a curve, by the

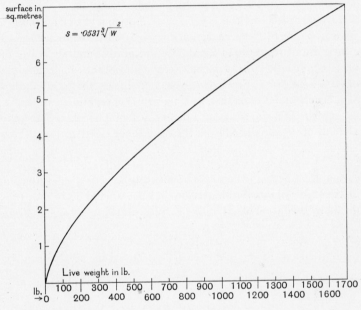

Fig. 118. Relationship between live weight and surface area of farm animals.

aid of which it is possible to read off the surface area of any animal, given the live weight.

Thus the surface area of an animal weighing 1000 lbs. is 5·31 sq. metres and its basal metabolism is $5\cdot31 \times 40 \times 24$ kilocalories per day $= 5197\cdot6$ kilocalories. Deighton has recently stressed the fact that surface formulae based on weight are much less accurate than the experimenter is led to expect; largely, no doubt, owing to variation in body form. For pigs, Deighton has evolved a new method of calculation which is partly photographical and partly mathematical. This method is intended for use in cases where an accuracy of $\pm$ 2 per cent. is required. Two photographs are taken, one of the top and one of the side of the animal. These are used as a basis for calculating the *surface* of the *edge* of an elementary slice of the pig at any point, taken at right angles to the line of the greatest length. By appropriate mathematical treatment of the data so obtained, the true area of body of the pig is calculated, and to this is added the areas of the ears, legs and tail obtained by direct measurements.

It is possible to ascertain the sources from which the energy is derived which serves to supply the basal metabolism, if the nitrogenous excretion and the oxygen consumption and CO_2 output are measured. The nitrogen excretion in grams multiplied by 6·25 gives a measure of the protein katabolised in grams, and since 1 g. of protein gives rise to 4·7 kilocalories, the kilocalories due to protein oxidation can be ascertained and deducted from the total katabolism. The amount of oxygen used for protein oxidation can then be calculated from the equation 1 litre $O_2 = 4·60$ kilocalories, and the amount of CO_2 produced from the respiratory quotient for protein oxidaton, i.e. $\dfrac{CO_2}{O_2} = 0·8$. Deducting these volumes of oxygen and carbon dioxide from the totals obtained from actual measurement in the respiration calorimeter, the oxygen used and the CO_2 produced by oxidation of fat and of carbohydrate are obtained. From the respiratory quotient $\dfrac{CO_2}{O_2}$ the relative amounts of oxygen used for oxidation of fat and carbohydrate respectively can be calculated, since $\dfrac{CO_2}{O_2}$ for fat = 0·7 and $\dfrac{CO_2}{O_2}$ for carbohydrate = 1. From the oxygen figures thus obtained the relative amounts of fat and carbohydrate katabolised can be calculated.

The basal metabolism thus found represents the sum of the oxidations occurring when the animal is asleep and starving. In normal life, a considerable amount of extra energy is used up in the work of digestion and in muscular movement. Even standing motionless involves a considerable amount of muscular effort, and it has been found that this may increase the basal metabolism by as much as 30 per cent.

The basal metabolism figure therefore fails to give us the information we require, that is, the amount of food energy required to maintain the animal in energy equilibrium under normal conditions, i.e. maintenance requirement. The extra expenditure of energy involved in food intake and digestion could be represented as a charge on the food energy itself, in which case it would be possible to regard the basal metabolism as representing maintenance requirement, but since the energy charge for muscular movements obviously varies with the individual and the conditions of food intake, i.e. whether out to pasture or in stall, there can be no direct correlation between the basal metabolism and the *economic maintenance requirement*. Armsby attempted to reach a solution of the problem by stating the maintenance requirement in terms of *net energy*. In this system, the *gross energy* of a food represented the energy as measured by a bomb calorimeter, i.e. the energy set free by complete oxidation of the food. The *metabolisable* energy represented the difference between the total gross energy of the food and the gross energy of the liquid, solid and gaseous excreta, i.e. that part of the energy of the food that is available for the production of work, tissue, body fluids, etc. The metabolisable energy of a food less the extra expenditure of energy involved by its ingestion is known as the *net energy* of the food. Armsby ascertained the net energies of foods by feeding an animal in his calorimeter on varying quantities of food under sub-maintenance conditions, i.e. quantities of food less than sufficient to support daily life. The extent to which the food reduced the call of the animal on its own tissues was thus ascertained and was called the *net energy* of that food. The table which follows illustrates from an experiment by Armsby and Fries the method of calculation.

Net energy value of Timothy hay (*estimated on a steer*)

	Dry matter of hay eaten	Meta-bolisable energy kilocalories	Heat produced	Gain of energy
Period 4	10·21	9444	9812	− 268
Period 3	6·17	5768	8064	− 2296
Difference	4·04	3676	1748	2028
Difference per lb. of hay		935	433	502

Under this method of computation the extra expenditure of energy incidental to food ingestion is automatically allowed for, so that the basal metabolism expressed in kilocalories of net energy actually represents the true maintenance requirement of the animal, but does not represent the economic maintenance requirement. Wood attempted to measure the extra demands on food energy involved by muscular movement and exercise of farm animals under normal conditions of farm practice by pedometer methods, with a view to correlating Armsby's maintenance requirement to the *economic* maintenance requirement, but the difficulties of the task proved eventually insuperable and the attempt was abandoned. Moreover, since the energy of muscular movement is dependent on body weight rather than surface area, it is not feasible to correlate the economic maintenance requirement with the basal metabolism. From the standpoint of scientific feeding standards, therefore, attempts have recently been made to ascertain the *economic maintenance requirement* directly by experiments carried out under field conditions instead of attempting to reach it by means of basal metabolism + energy allowances for movement, etc.

The method, as developed by Wood, consists in keeping a number of animals under field conditions, with the exception that the animals are individually fed with a ration just above the maintenance point, and are weighed also at frequent intervals.

Then if

R = the ration eaten by an animal in lb. starch equivalent,*
m = the maintenance requirement per day per square metre,
c = the weight of starch equivalent required to make 1 lb. live weight gain,
g = gain in lb. live weight per day,
and A = the surface area of the animal,

Then $R = Am + gc$.

R is known, A can be read off the curve on p. 331 and g is known from the frequent weighings. It thus becomes possible to write an equation for each animal, the unknowns being m and c. By the method of simultaneous equations it then becomes possible to ascertain m. In an experiment carried out by this method with thirty-two sheep Wood found that m was 1·1 lb. starch equivalent per square metre per day, which corresponds to 49 kilocalories per square metre per hour. The excess, 9 kilocalories above the

---

* For definition of starch equivalent see p. 336.

basal metabolism of 40 for the sheep, represents the energy in standing and normal movement.

Although Rubner's surface law has been found to be applicable to the basal metabolism of adult animals of different weights and species, it by no means follows that this law will hold true for the growing animal. It has been assumed in the case of growing sheep and cattle that the basal metabolism per square metre of surface is a constant throughout life and no experimental evidence has been adduced to indicate that the contrary may possibly be the case. In the pig, however, Deighton's work with the Cambridge calorimeter has indicated considerable differences in the basal metabolism per square metre of surface at different ages. At birth and in the adult pig the basal metabolism per sq. metre is 43 kilocalories, at weaning time it is 56 kilocalories and at 4 months has reached the maximum of 72 kilocalories.

Metabolisable and Net Energy. An important consideration with regard to the utilisation of energy of feeding stuffs is the extent to which metabolisable energy is available for maintenance purposes. For many years in the case of man and carnivores the isodynamic theory that nutrients were of value in strict accordance with their metabolisable energy content was held to be true, but Rubner himself, who had originally propounded the isodynamic theory, found that this was no longer true if the experiments were conducted above the critical temperature, i.e. the environmental temperature surrounding the animal at which neither heat radiation from the body nor heat absorption takes place. In this case the administration of protein to a fasting animal increases the total heat evolution. A proportion of the metabolisable energy therefore appears as heat and the effect of nutrients in raising the heat production above the fasting level is known as *specific dynamic action*. The work of Lusk and his associates has traced this action in the case of proteins to the specific stimulus to cell metabolism caused by certain amino-acids, particularly glycine and alanine. In the case of carbohydrates and fats, the specific dynamic effect, which is much less pronounced than in the case of proteins, is explained as being due to a mass action effect, i.e. the effect of a greater supply of non-nitrogenous material to the cells. Below the critical temperature, where radiation losses will occur, thus raising the basal metabolism of the animal, the thermic energy represented by the difference between the metabolisable

energy and the net energy will be available for making good this
heat loss. It is important therefore to consider, particularly in
cases where the animal is kept in a temperature much below the
body temperature, the type of food used for maintenance. The net
energy indicated by the basal metabolism should be supplied by
fodders in which there is a considerable margin between the net
energy and the metabolisable energy.

The net energy values of all the ordinary feeding stuffs have
been found. Kellner called them starch equivalents, i.e. he expressed as lb. of pure starch the net energy that 100 lb. of the
feeding stuff in question would give. Armsby expressed them in
terms of the number of kilocalories of net energy yielded to the
body of an animal by the digestion and absorption of 1 lb. of the
feeding stuff. Since the actual number of kilocalories is usually
large he adopted a larger unit, the therm, 1 therm being equal to
1000 kilocalories.

Kellner's starch equivalent system has not found much favour
among pure scientists owing to its apparent indefiniteness. Kellner
deliberately adopted the starch equivalent rather than the kilocalorie or therm, because he realised that the fat-producing
capacity of an animal varied from individual to individual, and
was also affected by the previous nutritional history of the animal
in question. He was interested therefore in finding a method of
expressing the relative replacement values of feeding stuffs rather
than their absolute values, leaving to a later stage of his investigations the expression of starch equivalent in terms of energy
stated as fat, milk, work, etc. For this reason, the English
school of workers in animal nutrition have adopted the starch
equivalent system rather than Armsby's net energy conception.
By expressing an animal's requirements for any given purpose in
terms of starch equivalent the same values will hold for whatever
purpose the feeding stuff in question is used. On the other hand,
expressing the value of the feeding stuff in terms of net energy
inevitably leads to different values according to the purpose for
which the food is used. Thus, while cattle, sheep and horses extract the same proportion of net calories from a given feeding
stuff for fat production, the cow extracts relatively more for milk
production, and the pig extracts still more for live weight increase.

By Armsby's system, therefore, a feeding stuff will require to be
given three values for net energy according to whether it is being

used for fattening bullocks or milk production or pork production. On the other hand, according to Wood, the same starch equivalent value will serve for all three classes, 1 lb. starch equivalent for increased live weight in the ruminant being equivalent to 1071 kilocalories, for milk production 1350 kilocalories, and for increased weight in the pig 1500 kilocalories. In fattening, there is little doubt that this conversion of starch equivalent to net calories is correct, but Hansson, working on the Scandinavian food unit system, found that foods have a higher value for milk production than is indicated by the starch equivalent system, protein having a higher value for milk production than for fattening. Richardsen has shown that if Kellner's starch equivalents for feeding stuffs for milk are calculated using the following factors: pure digestible protein 1·41, amides 0·47, digestible carbohydrates and fibre 1·0, fat 1·91–2·41, the figures obtained agree with the values obtained by Hansson by the food unit system. The starch equivalent system is therefore subject in this case to the same defects as the Armsby system, and in the starch equivalent system two values will have to be assigned to every feeding stuff according to whether it is intended for milk production or fat production.

CHAPTER XXVI

FEEDING STANDARDS

The introduction of feeding standards for cattle coincides with the introduction of stall feeding conditions. Under pastoral conditions, cattle were fed in the meadows during the spring and summer months, and after a short time on the stubbles were wintered on straw and hay. During the latter half of the eighteenth century the practice of feeding cattle in stalls had developed, and with this development there gradually grew up a demand for a more exact knowledge of the rational feeding of farm animals. The variety of foods available for stock feeding had increased and the farmer particularly wished to obtain a better knowledge of the replacement values of such feeding stuffs. The scientists endeavoured to satisfy that demand. Regarded historically, the expression of the nutritive requirements of feeding stuffs for cattle developed in four distinct stages.

In the first, the mutual replacement values of foods were assessed by chemical considerations and expressed in terms of 'hay'. This constituted the 'hay value system', with which Thaer, Boussingault, and Emil von Wolff are associated.

In the second stage, the food requirements of animals were assessed on the chemical composition of the crude nutrients, a development due to H. Grouven of Salzmunde.

In the third stage, the food requirements of animals were expressed in terms of digestible nutrients.

In the fourth stage, the food requirements of animals were expressed in terms of 'starch equivalent' and net energy, and digestible protein.

In 1809 Thaer, who had founded an agricultural school at Mechlin, set himself the problem of establishing a table of equivalents which would indicate the relative feeding values of the feeding stuffs then in common use in farm practice. Thaer used hay as a basis for comparison, and by the help of his chemical colleague, Einhof, tables of equivalents were established. Einhof, by treating the different feeding stuffs with warm water, dilute acids and alkalies, obtained a figure for each feeding stuff indicating the extent to which these feeding stuffs were rendered soluble by chemical treatments, and it was assumed that the part thus rendered soluble represented the nutritive portion of the feeding stuff in question. A table of hay equivalents was constructed in which every feeding stuff was given a hay value which represented the number of pounds of the feeding stuff in question that contained the same amount of soluble nutrients as 100 lb. of good pasture hay. This method of expressing the nutritive value of feeding stuffs was obviously an unsound one, since, apart from the defects of the method of estimating, the standard used, hay, was notoriously a very variable product, and it was further obviously unsound to compare a concentrated feeding stuff such as linseed cake with a forage material such as hay. In spite of the defects of this system, it was immediately adopted throughout Central Europe, and held sway until the development of physiological knowledge on the nutrition of animals rendered possible the demonstration of the defects of the system.

In 1836 Boussingault, impressed by the researches of Magendie, Macaire and Marcet on the rôle played by nitrogen in the nutrition of animals, drew up a table of hay equivalents based on the nitrogen content, which table he tested in part by two experiments, one on a cow and the other on a horse. The next decade witnessed considerable developments in the knowledge of the nutrition of animals. Liebig in 1842 distinguished between two main groups of substances of food value, a nitrogenous group which included fibrin, albumin, flesh and blood, and a non-nitrogenous group which included fats, starch, gums, sugars, pectins, etc. Claude Bernard, in his historic researches on the glycogenic function of the liver, had demonstrated the value of the non-nitrogenous food substances in animal physiology and the work of Lawes and Gilbert at Rothamsted had indicated the extent to which both nitrogenous and non-nitrogenous substances entered into the normal composition of the bodies of farm animals. Henneberg and Stohmann, armed with the new knowledge on the physiology of nutrition, by a carefully controlled set of feeding experiments on sheep and oxen, clearly demonstrated that Thaer's system of hay equivalents had no real value. Emil von Wolff, the Director of the Royal Agricultural College of Hohenheim, who had attempted to modernise the Thaer system by taking into account both the woody fibre of the feeding stuff and the nitrogenous substances as well as the soluble substances given by Thaer, was led to abandon the attempt when Henneberg's results were made public. Wolff made the first attempt to express in terms of digestible protein, carbohydrates and fats, the nutritive requirements of stock. These requirements were arrived at by him as the result of an exhaustive survey of all pre-existing records of feeding trials, and they are of particular interest to us because they became available to the English farmers by the appearance in 1895 of an English translation of the sixth edition of Wolff's book.

The standard of albuminoids given was based on the false assumption that protein was the chief source of body and milk fat, an idea that had been founded partly on the observation made by Baur, that phosphorus poisoning led to fatty degeneration of the tissues of the body, and partly on the common observation of the formation of waxy material in dead bodies.

Grouven in 1859 also proposed a definite feeding standard, as opposed to the hay value system. He took as a basis the total quantities of protein, fat and carbohydrates as measured by chemical analysis, i.e. his standards were based on the crude nutrients of feeding stuffs.

These standards did not distinguish between the maintenance requirements and the production requirements, and were strongly criticised by Julius Kühn on these grounds. It is to Kühn we owe recognition for showing that a portion of the food fed to an animal is used for maintenance and a portion for production. Kühn pointed out that the quantity of dry substance that could be fed to a dairy cow could vary from 20 to 33·5 lb. or even more in some cases, and emphasised strongly the practical importance of keeping the total daily ration of a dairy cow within these limits. Kühn furthermore insisted on the necessity of distinguishing between the digestible albuminoid and amide compounds in estimating the protein requirements of dairy cows. In the feeding system Kühn developed, he advocated fixing first the ration that should be given to a dairy cow that represented the minimum requirements per 1000 lb. of live weight, 'that is, the quantity which covers the needs of the cows which are dry or nearly dry, and which while producing little or no milk are usually more or less advanced with calf'. This ration he called the *basal ration*, the digestible albuminoids required varying from 1·5 to

1·8 lb. according to whether the cows were of high or low productive capacity. Having fixed the basal ration, foods were then fed in strict accordance with milk yield. It is important to note that Kühn's standards were intended, not to obtain the maximum yield of milk possible, but the maximum *economic* yield, taking into account the state of the market with regard to the relative prices of concentrated feeding stuffs and dairy products. Thus Kühn quotes an experiment carried out at Möckern, in which the addition of 1 lb. of rape cake to a ration then in practical use for dairy cows, increased the milk yield by 1·5 lb., the addition of a second lb. increased it 1 lb., the addition of a third lb. increased it 0·5 lb., whereas the addition of a fourth lb. had no effect whatever. Kühn points out that with the price of dairy products low and the cost of rape cake high, the addition of the third lb. of cake, although it increased the milk yield by 0·5 lb. would have been unsound in practice, as the cost of the rape cake would have been greater than the sum received for the 0·5 lb. of milk produced.

The work of Henneberg and Stohmann, E. von Wolff, Heiden, and Winke had established digestibility values of the commoner feeding stuffs for horses, cattle, sheep and swine, and, chiefly by carefully controlled feeding experiments, feeding standards for cattle were established. Not satisfied with the exactitude of such methods, Henneberg and Stohmann began to attack the problem by means of respiration experiments, but the experiments initiated by Henneberg were not completed at the time of his death. Meanwhile Gustav Kühn at Möckern had initiated the series of experiments by calorimetric methods on oxen upon which the modern feeding standards are based, a series of investigations that were brought to a brilliant conclusion by his successor O. Kellner. Kellner, by actual experimental trials, controlled by respiration calorimetry experiments, established the following facts:

1 kg. digestible pure protein yields			234	g. fat in the animal	
1 kg.	,,	starch	,,	248	,,	,,
1 kg.	,,	fibre	,,	248	,,	,,
1 kg.	,,	sugar	,,	188	,,	,,
1 kg.	,,	dry fat	,,	474–598	,,	,,

The variability of the fat formation was associated with the origin of the food fat, food fat from roots giving a low value, food fat from oil cakes and feeding stuffs of animal origin giving a high value. Taking starch as a basis, the 'production values' of the nutrients of feeding stuffs were expressed as follows:

	Kellner (fat-production values)	Richardsen (1926) (milk-production values)
Digestible N-free extract	1·00	1·00
Digestible fibre	1·00	1·00
Digestible pure protein	0·94	1·41
Digestible fat: in roots and coarse fodders ...	1·91	1·91
in grains and cereal by-products	2·12	2·12
in oil seeds and oil cakes ...	2·41	2·41

Using these factors for the digestible nutrients of an oil cake such as palm kernel cake, Kellner found that the deposition of fat expected by theory agreed very well with practice. Thus, in an actual experiment, 1 kg. of palm kernel cake, which according to theory should yield 179 g. of body fat, gave 183 g. of body fat. On the other hand, with forage and some other feeding stuffs the result obtained in actual practice did not agree with theory. Thus 1 kg. wheat straw chaff according to theory should yield 99·8 g. body fat, whereas in actual trial it only yielded 24·8 g. body fat. In the case of coarse fodders, Kellner found that this discrepancy was associated with the crude fibre content of the feeding stuff and a satisfactory method of reconciling the results of theory and practice was evolved. In the case of concentrated feeding stuffs, Kellner correlated practice with theory by the use of a 'value number' or *wertigkeit*. In America, Armsby and Fries, who independently attacked the problem by methods similar to those used by Kellner, adopted 'net energy' as a standard instead of starch, and in Scandinavia Fjord and Hansson adopted a 'food unit' consisting of 1 kg. of barley.

The development of feeding standards in Scandinavia followed purely practical methods of experimentation. Fjord in 1872 initiated the systematic co-operative dairying experiments upon the results of which the Scandinavian feeding standards are based. These investigations began originally in creameries and private dairies distributed throughout Denmark and were directed originally towards solving problems met with in the cheese, butter and cream industry. They had as their main object the ascertainment of the comparative values of feeding stuffs for milk production, and were carried out on various estates distributed throughout Denmark. At the initiation of each

experiment, the Director of the Research Station in consultation
with the estate owners and others interested, settled the
plan of experiment and the control of the experiments on the
farms was exercised by officers specially detailed for this purpose
from the Research Station. Two types of experimentation were
employed, 'group-feeding' experiments and 'period' experiments.
In the group-feeding experiments, three or four lots of cows
were used; in the period experiments one group only of cows
was used. In the group-feeding experiments 30 or 40 cows were
selected from the herd, which in some cases numbered 200. These
cows were divided into groups of ten, as near alike as possible so
far as age, live weight, time from calving, milk and milk-fat production was concerned, this selection being attained by means of
a preliminary feeding period during which the cows were fed on
a uniform ration and studied individually with regard to their
production. The success in securing uniformity may be gauged from
the following data for three lots of cows in an experiment carried
out at Bregentved in 1891.

	Lot A	Lot B	Lot C
Average daily milk yield (lb.)	27·0	26·9	27·0
Average daily fat yield (lb.)	0·856	0·855	0·854
Average live weight (lb.)	861·0	865·0	873·0
Average age of cows (years)	8·9	8·7	8·7
Average days from calving	83·0	81·0	83·0

The grouping having been successfully secured, the experiment
proper followed, generally about ten days after the final grouping
took place, during which period the change over from the preliminary uniform ration to the experimental rations took place.
The experimental period proper was followed by a post experimental period in which the cows under test reverted to the original
ration. An example will explain the method.

Object of experiment. To test the comparative values of sunflower cake, soya meal and soya cake for milk production.

Farm. Sabyholm. Three groups of six cows. Pre-experimental
period, three weeks; experimental period, four weeks; post experimental period, two weeks. Feeding during pre- and post-experi-
mental periods: basal ration + 2 kg. sunflower cake. Feeding
during experimental period: Lot 1, basal ration + 2 kg. sunflower
cake; Lot 2, basal ration + 2 kg. soya meal; Lot 3, basal ration
+ 2 kg. soya cake.

The following data were obtained:

| | Milk produced per head per day (kg.) | | | Milk production compared with control |
	Pre-experimental period	Experimental period	Difference	
Group I: Sunflower cake group (2 kg.)	14·45	14·02	− 0·43	0·00
Group II: Soya meal group (2 kg.)	14·43	14·66	+ 0·23	+ 0·66
Group III: Soya cake group (2 kg.)	14·44	14·70	+ 0·26	+ 0·69

On the basis that one food unit produces 3 kg. average milk and that 0·91 kg. sunflower cake equals one food unit, 0·66 kg. milk equals 0·20 kg. sunflower cake and 0·69 kg. milk equals 0·21 kg. sunflower cake.

Two kg. of soya meal are thus equivalent to 2·20 kg. sunflower cake, and 2 kg. soya cake are thus equivalent to 2·21 kg. sunflower cake.

In the period group experiments only one group of cows was used. The experiment was divided into three periods as before, of at least three weeks each, the first week of each period being regarded as the transition period, during which change of rations takes place. The control ration was fed during the first and third periods, during the second period the food under test was exchanged for the food used in the control ration. Comparison between the foods was then made on the average milk production of period 2 and the average milk production of periods 1 and 3.

This system of evaluating foods on a unit basis, initiated by Fjord in Denmark and carried on by his collaborator F. Friis and others after his death, was quickly adopted by the other Scandinavian countries. The later developments of this system are associated with Nils Hansson. In Denmark the 'food unit' taken for comparative purposes was 0·5 kg. mixed grain (half oats, half barley), whereas in Sweden 1 kg. of barley was used as the unit. In 1915 the Danish, Norwegian and Swedish control unions met at Copenhagen and agreed to adopt 1 kg. barley as the standard unit.

It will be noted that three different systems are at present in use for expressing the energy requirements of animals, the Scandinavian system, in which 1 kg. of barley is used as the 'food unit' the 'starch equivalent' system as used in Germany and England

in which 1 lb. of starch forms the unit, and the American system
in which the 'therm' forms the unit. These systems can be converted from one to the other by using the following factors:

$$1 \text{ therm (1000 kilocalories)} = \frac{100}{1 \cdot 071} \text{ lb. starch equivalent,}$$

1 food unit $= 0 \cdot 72$ kg. starch equivalent.

It is important to note that of these three systems, two, namely
the 'food unit' and the 'starch equivalent' systems are comparative systems, whereby the relative values of feeding stuffs are
equated for any productive purpose. On the other hand, the 'net
energy' system is absolute in character, and attempts to state the
actual amounts of productive energy produced when a given
amount of feeding stuff is fed. As the result of this absolutism,
difficulties have been experienced in the application of the net
energy conception to feeding practice, and a tendency to revert to
the older conception of digestible nutrients is now finding favour
in the United States. This difficulty has really arisen through the
inability of the pure scientist to realise that our knowledge of
feeding farm animals can never be exact in a scientific sense, at
any rate so far as the quantitative relationships of food supply
to animal production are concerned.

In England the chief developments in the application of feeding
standards to farming practice have been due to Wood and his
associates at the Cambridge Animal Nutrition Institute. Wood,
who was a farmer as well as a scientist, recognised the necessity of
maintaining a proper balance between science and practice in all
investigations relating to feeding standards, and the success of his
efforts to establish feeding standards suitable for English feeding
practice is due to the way in which he 'married' laboratory methods
with feeding trials carried out on the actual farm. In 1919
appeared *The Composition and Nutritive Value of Feeding Stuffs*
by Wood and Halnan, in which appeared Wood's first attempt to
supply feeding standards suitable for English conditions. At the
request of the Ministry of Agriculture and Fisheries, the subject
matter of this book was merged in 1920 into a bulletin, *Rations for
Livestock*, which has since served as the medium whereby Wood
presented to farmers the practical outcome of the research work
undertaken by the Institute. In the later editions of this bulletin,
the data on the composition and nutritive values of wheat
offals, pasture grass, sugar beet and sugar beet by-products,

and silage have been revised in the light of the investigations carried out by Woodman and his associates on these feeding stuffs. Wood, in computing feeding standards, distinguished between maintenance requirement and production requirement, and took into consideration the 'appetite' of the animal, i.e. the bulk capacity of the daily ration as measured in terms of dry matter. This conception is by no means novel; we have already seen that J. Kühn in 1887 had originated this method of expressing the daily rations of an animal. What was novel, however, and a distinct advance, was the initiation of the formula (see p. 334) whereby the computation of the daily requirements of an animal under various conditions of production, could be ascertained with comparative accuracy. The method used by Wood consisted in ascertaining the composition of the live weight increase of animals by slaughter and chemical analysis methods, and equating this with the food required to produce such live weight under actual commercial conditions. It is necessary to emphasise that this method of computation of the requirements of animals is only possible when it is supplemented by the more accurate data that calorimetry investigations under laboratory conditions can give.

The main results obtained by Wood are given in the tables below.*

COMPUTATION OF RATIONS

(1) *Fattening cattle (stall conditions)*.

Live weight of animal	Appetite in dry matter per day	Maintenance ration per day starch equivalent	Protein equivalent† per day
cwt.	lb.	lb.	lb.
5	14½	4	1¼
6	17	4½	1¼
7	19	5	1½
8	20½	5½	1½
9	22	6	1½
10	23½	6½	1½
11	25	7	1½
12	26½	7½	1½
13	28	7¾	1½
14	29½	8¼	1½
15	31	8½	1½
16	32½	8¾	1½

* For method of using the tables *Rations for Livestock*, as revised by Woodman, should be consulted.

† For explanation of protein equivalent see page 349.

Production requirement (fattening cattle)

Age of animal	Condition	Food required per lb. live weight increase lb. starch equivalent
Under 2 years	Store	2
	Fresh	2¼
About 2 years	Store	2¼
	Fresh	2½
Over 2 years	Store	2½
	Fresh	2¾
	Half fat	3
	Fat	4

(2) *Cattle on grass.*

For cattle on grass, Wood adds to the maintenance requirements given above, 3 lb. starch equivalent per day for poor pastures, 2 lb. per day for average pastures, and 1 lb. for good fattening pastures, per head. This extra amount of starch equivalent is the amount computed to be used by the animal in searching for food.

(3) *Sheep.*

Live weight	Appetite in dry matter per week	Maintenance requirement starch equivalent	Per week protein equivalent	Protein requirement for growth and fattening per week
lb.	lb.	lb.	lb.	lb.
20	8	3	·08	¾
30	11	4	·12	1
40	13	4¾	·16	1
50	15	5¼	·20	1¼
60	17	6¼	·24	1½
70	19	7	·28	1½
80	21	7¾	·32	1¾
90	22½	8¼	·35	1¾
100	24	9	·38	1¾
110	25½	9½	·42	1¾
120	27	10	·46	1¾
130	28½	10½	·50	1¾
140	30	11	·54	1¾
150	31½	11½	·58	1¾
160	33	12	·62	1¾
170	34	12½	·66	1¾
180	35	13	·70	1¾
190	36	13½	·74	1¾
200	37	14	·78	1¾

Production requirement per lb. live weight increase

Live weight	Food requirement starch equivalent
lb.	lb.
20–30	1
40–50	$1\frac{1}{4}$
60–80	$1\frac{1}{2}$
90	$1\frac{3}{4}$
100	2
110	$2\frac{1}{4}$
120	$2\frac{1}{2}$
130	$2\frac{3}{4}$
140	3
150	$3\frac{1}{2}$
160	$3\frac{3}{4}$
170	4
180–200	$4\frac{1}{4}$

Wood also computed that ewes suckling lambs require 3 lb. of starch equivalent containing 1 lb. of digestible protein for every gallon of milk they produce. A ewe suckling lamb produces $2\frac{1}{4}$ to $3\frac{1}{2}$ gallons of milk per week.

(4) *Pigs.*

In the case of pigs, the usual maintenance requirement as ascertained in the calorimeter is much less than the actual, since there is a considerable demand for muscular movement owing to the restless activity of the growing pig. Owing to the comparative simplicity of the diet Wood expressed the food requirements of the pig in terms of meal, assuming that the average pig meal mixture contains 67 to 70 per cent. of starch equivalent.

Live weight	Appetite per day	Maintenance per day	Digestible protein per day	Requirement per lb. live weight increase
lb.	lb. meal	lb. meal	lb.	lb. meal
50	2·0	1·5	·3	0·7
100	4·0	2·9	·5	1·0
150	5·9	3·3	·6	1·5
200	6·9	3·6	·6	2·0
250	7·0	3·8	·7	3·0
300	8·0	4·1	·7	3·5

(5) *Dairy cows.*

Halnan, as the result of a critical survey of the research work carried out all over the world on the requirements of the dairy cow, put forward the tables which follow as a suitable standard for dairy cow feeding.

Maintenance requirements

Breed	Average live weight	Starch equivalent	Protein equivalent
	lb.	lb.	lb.
Dexter	650	3·8	·39
Jersey	800	4·3	·48
Kerry	850	4·5	·51
Guernsey	950	4·8	·57
Ayrshire	1000	5·0	·60
Red Poll	1100	5·3	·65
Devon ⎫ Welsh Black ⎬ Blue Albion ⎭	1150	5·5	·68
British Friesian ⎱ Dairy Shorthorn ⎰	1250	5·8	·74
Longhorn ⎱ Lincoln Red ⎰	1300	6·0	·77
South Devon	1450	6·4	·86

Production requirements per gallon of milk of varying fat percentages

Fat content of milk (per cent.)	Protein equivalent	Starch equivalent
	lb.	lb.
2·5	·48	1·9
3·0	·50	2·1
3·5	·54	2·3
4·0	·57	2·5
4·5	·62	2·7
5·0	·66	2·9
5·5	·69	3·1
6·0	·73	3·3
6·5	·76	3·4
7·0	·80	3·6

Protein equivalent =

$$\frac{\text{Digestible Pure Protein} + \text{Digestible Crude Protein}}{2}.$$

In calculating the maintenance ration, the fat production starch equivalent values are used; in calculating the milk production requirements the starch equivalent values for milk production are used.

Composition and nutritive value of feeding stuffs for cattle, sheep and horses

Food	Weight per bushel*	Average composition per cent.									Digestible true protein	Protein equivalent	Starch equivalent	Starch equivalent for milk production
		Dry matter	Protein	Oil	Soluble carbs.	Fibre	Ash	CaO	P₂O₅	Chlorine				
	lb.													
1. ROOTS														
Carrots	40	13·0	1·2	0·2	9·3	1·4	0·9	·09	·11	·04	0·4	0·6	8·8	9·1
Kohl-rabi	—	12·7	2·0	0·1	8·2	1·4	1·0	·15	·14	·06	0·3	0·5	8·3	8·5
Mangolds	45	13·2	1·2	0·1	10·2	0·8	0·9	·04	·09	·08	0·1	0·4	6·8	7·0
Parsnips	45	15·0	1·3	0·3	11·3	1·2	0·9	·08	·15	·03	0·6	0·8	11	11·4
Potatoes	56	23·8	2·1	0·1	19·7	0·9	1·0	·03	·14	·03	0·1	0·6	18	18·3
Sugar beet	—	23·4	1·1	0·1	20·4	1·1	0·7	·05	·10	—	0·3	0·6	15	15·3
Swedes	45	11·5	1·3	0·2	8·1	1·2	0·7	·05	·09	·02	0·3	0·7	7·3	7·6
Turnips	42	8·5	1·0	0·2	5·7	0·9	0·7	·09	·10	·04	0·2	0·4	4·4	4·6
2. GREEN FOODS														
Cabbage (drumhead)	—	11·0	1·5	0·4	5·9	2·0	1·2	·20	·15	·10	0·7	0·9	6·6	7·0
Cabbage (open leaved)	—	15·3	2·5	0·7	8·1	2·4	1·6	·20	·15	·10	1·2	1·5	9·5	10·2
Kale (narrow stem)	—	14·3	2·4	0·2	6·4	3·8	1·5	·20	·15	—	0·9	1·3	8·8	9·4
Kale (thousandhead)	—	14·8	2·5	0·3	8·7	1·7	1·6	·20	·15	—	0·9	1·3	8·9	9·5
Lucerne	—	24·0	4·5	0·8	9·6	6·8	2·3	·90	·20	·42	1·7	2·4	9·1	10·2
Pasture grass (extensive grazing)	—	20·0	3·5	0·8	9·7	4·0	2·0	·25	·19	·42	1·7	2·1	11·2	12·2
Pasture grass (close grazing)	16	20·0	5·3	1·1	8·9	2·6	2·1	·25	·19	·42	3·8	4·1	14·7	16·6
Silage, vetch and oats (green fruity)	—	27·3	3·4	1·2	12·5	8·0	2·2	·26	·14	·09	1·1	1·6	12·8	13·6
Silage, sunflower	—	18·9	2·3	1·0	9·3	3·9	2·4	—	—	—	0·9	1·5	7·0	7·7
Sugar-beet tops and leaves	—	19·5	2·4	0·4	8·3	3·0	5·4	1·5	1·0	—	1·1	1·3	9·5	10·1
Vetches	64	17·5	3·2	0·5	7·2	5·1	1·5	·50	·15	·04	1·4	1·8	7·5	8·3
3. HAY														
Clover	—	83·5	13·5	2·9	37·1	24·0	6·0	1·20	·45	·06	5·5	7·0	38	42
Lucerne	—	83·5	14·2	2·6	29·2	29·5	8·0	2·52	·65	—	6·2	7·9	29	33
Meadow, poor	5	85·7	7·5	1·5	38·2	33·5	5·0	1·00	·40	—	2·5	2·9	22	24
Meadow, medium		85·7	9·7	2·5	41·0	26·3	6·2	1·00	·40	—	3·8	4·6	37	40
Meadow, very good		84·0	13·5	3·0	40·5	19·3	7·7	1·00	·40	—	6·5	7·8	48	52
Seeds	—	86·0	12·0	2·8	37·4	27·5	6·3	2·00	·60	—	3·6	4·9	29	32

4. Straws													
Barley	—	86·0	3·3	1·8	42·4	33·9	4·6	0·50	·20	·35	0·6	0·7	23	23
Bean	—	86·0	4·5	0·8	33·0	43·1	4·6	1·20	·29	—	1·3	1·7	23	24
Oat	5	86·0	2·9	1·9	42·4	33·9	4·9	·29	·23	·28	0·8	0·9	20	21
Pea	—	86·0	9·2	1·6	36·0	33·4	5·8	1·59	·35	—	3·4	3·8	19	21
Wheat	—	86·0	2·1	1·3	40·7	36·6	5·3	·37	·22	·17	—	0·1	13	13
5. Grains and Seeds													
Barley	55	85·1	8·6	1·5	67·9	4·5	2·6	·05	·77	·02	5·9	6·2	71	74
Beans	64	85·7	25·4	1·5	48·5	7·1	3·2	·16	1·21	·05	19·0	20·0	66	75
Buckwheat...	50	85·9	11·3	2·6	54·8	14·4	2·8	·12	1·33	·04	7·5	8·0	53	57
Butterbeans (haricot)	52	89·2	23·6	1·1	56·4	3·7	4·4	—	—	—	15·0	15·0	68	75
Dari...	60	88·9	9·6	3·8	71·2	1·9	2·4	—	—	—	6·7	7·2	74	77
Gram	60	89·0	23·4	1·1	54·3	5·1	5·1	—	—	—	15·0	15·0	71	78
Lentils	62	86·0	25·5	1·9	52·2	3·4	3·0	·15	1·00	·05	19·0	20·0	70	79
Linseed	52	92·8	24·2	36·5	22·9	5·5	3·8	·30	1·40	·86	18·0	19·0	119	128
Locust beans, pods	—	85·0	5·8	1·3	69·0	6·4	2·5	·54	·19	·11	3·2	3·6	71	73
Maize	60	87·0	9·9	4·4	69·2	2·2	1·3	·01	·63	·0001	6·6	6·8	81	84
Millet	60	87·5	10·6	3·9	61·1	8·1	3·8	·02	·75	·02	7·4	7·7	59	65
Oats...	42	86·7	10·3	4·8	58·2	10·3	3·1	·12	·78	·05	7·2	7·6	60	64
Peas...	64	86·0	22·5	1·6	53·7	5·4	2·8	·12	·90	·04	17·0	18·0	69	77
Rye	54	86·6	11·5	1·7	69·5	1·9	2·0	·07	·94	·02	8·7	9·1	72	76
Soya beans...	—	90·0	33·2	17·5	30·5	4·1	4·7	·20	1·20	·01	26·0	28·0	79	92
Vetch seed	—	86·7	26·0	1·7	49·8	6·0	3·2	—	—	—	20·0	21·0	70	80
Wheat	62	86·6	12·1	1·9	69·0	1·9	1·7	·06	·93	·06	9·0	9·6	72	76
6. Oil Cakes and Meals													
Coconut cake	39	88·6	20·7	9·9	41·4	11·2	5·4	·50	1·50	—	16·0	16·0	79	86
Cotton cake, Bombay	40	87·7	20·2	4·8	35·2	21·7	5·8	·30	2·50	—	15·0	15·0	40	47
Cotton cake, Egyptian	40	87·9	23·0	5·5	32·4	21·2	5·8	·45	1·80	·03	17·0	17·0	42	50
Cotton cake, dec.	45	90·2	40·2	9·9	25·9	7·6	6·6	·34	2·78	·03	33·0	34·0	71	87
Cotton seed meal	50	91·3	42·1	10·9	24·9	7·4	6·0	·34	2·78	·03	35·0	35·0	74	90
Ground nut cake, dec.	46	89·7	46·8	7·5	23·2	6·4	5·8	·68	1·55	·014	41·0	41·0	73	92
Ground nut cake, undec.... ...	40	89·7	30·2	9·1	21·8	22·9	5·7	—	—	—	27·0	27·0	57	70
Ground nut meal, undec. ext. ...	40	92·4	31·8	1·9	29·1	25·3	4·3	·10	·97	—	28·0	29·0	44	58
Linseed cake	44	88·8	29·5	9·5	35·5	9·1	5·2	·52	1·79	·05	24·0	25·0	74	86
Palm kernel cake and meal ...	36	89·0	18·8	7·7	45·3	13·4	3·8	·30	1·10	—	16·0	17·0	75	83
Palm kernel meal, ext.	30	90·0	19·0	2·0	49·0	16·0	4·0	·30	1·20	—	16·0	17·0	71	79
Sesame cake	39	90·7	44·5	11·9	20·9	4·5	8·9	—	—	—	38·0	39·0	73	91
Soya bean cake	45	85·5	42·4	7·0	25·8	5·0	5·3	·30	2·20	—	34·0	36·0	69	86
Soya bean meal, ext.	50	88·7	44·7	1·5	31·9	5·1	5·5	·30	2·30	·007	36·0	38·0	64	82
Sunflower cake, undec.	39	92·9	19·1	7·4	28·9	30·0	7·5	·54	2·15	—	16·0	16·0	50	57
Sunflower meal, ext.	30	92·9	19·1	2·0	32·3	32·0	7·5	·54	2·15	—	16·0	16·0	42	49

* For sliced, fingered or pulped roots deduct 5 lb. Figures for hay and straws are for chaff, and for oil cakes, broken.

Composition and nutritive value of feeding stuffs for cattle, sheep and horses (cont.)

Food	Weight per bushel	Average composition per cent.									Digestible true protein	Protein equivalent	Starch equivalent	Starch equivalent for milk production
		Dry matter	Protein	Oil	Soluble carbs.	Fibre	Ash	CaO	P₂O₅	Chlorine				
7. MANUFACTURED AND BY-PRODUCTS														
Barley-brewers' grains, wet	40	29·7	7·0	2·4	13·1	5·9	1·3	·10	·40	·03	4·8	5·0	17	19
Barley-brewers' grains, dried	20	90·2	19·1	6·6	44·5	16·4	3·5	·30	1·20	·06	13·0	13·0	49	55
Barley-distillers' grains, wet	40	26·2	8·4	3·0	10·4	3·6	0·8	·10	·40	—	5·8	6·0	16	19
Barley-distillers' grains, dried	20	92·0	27·7	11·6	40·8	10·1	1·8	·40	1·50	·36	19·0	19·0	57	66
Barley-malt culms	17	90·0	24·4	2·0	42·4	14·0	7·2	·19	1·82	·60	12·0	16·0	43	50
Fish meal ...	48	87·0	55·6	4·4	2·1	—	24·9	10·5	6·30	—	46·0	48·0	53	77
Hominy, chop. ...	—	89·9	10·6	8·0	64·3	4·4	2·6	—	—	—	6·1	6·5	78	81
Maize, flaked ...	20	88·0	10·3	1·9	74·4	0·6	0·8	·01	·63	·0001	7·4	8·6	83	87
Maize, germ meal (dry process)	—	89·3	13·0	13·5	55·1	4·1	3·6	·10	·85	—	10·0	10·0	85	90
Maize, germ meal (wet process)	—	90·0	21·0	11·5	48·5	6·5	2·5	·10	·85	—	14·0	16·0	78	85
Maize, gluten feed ...	42	89·6	23·5	3·4	56·7	3·5	2·5	·10	·70	·04	18·0	19·0	76	85
Meat meal ...	44	89·2	72·2	13·2	—	—	3·8	·40	·70	·001	64·0	65·0	91	122
Middlings, fine ...	44	86·7	17·0	4·2	60·8	2·3	2·4	·07	1·50	—	11·0	12·0	69	75
Middlings, coarse ...	32	86·0	15·8	4·9	56·8	4·9	3·6	·10	2·60	—	9·9	11·0	58	63
Rice meal or bran...	40	91·1	12·9	13·7	49·5	6·4	8·6	·10	2·60	—	6·6	7·0	72	75
Sugar-beet slices, dry	20	88·8	8·1	0·6	58·5	17·6	4·0	·90	·24	·04	3·6	3·8	51	53
Treacle or molasses	—	74·2	3·1	—	64·7	—	6·4	·31	·05	·32	0·0	2·7	51	52
Wheat bran ...	16	87·0	15·1	3·8	52·8	9·5	5·8	·16	2·63	·09	9·3	10·0	42	47
Yeast, dried ...	53	95·7	48·5	0·5	35·5	0·5	10·7	·30	5·00	·03	40·0	41·0	67	76
8. MILK PRODUCTS														
Dried whole milk ...	—	95·8	25·5	26·5	37·4	0·0	6·4	1·85	2·03	1·21	24·0	24·0	117	128
Dried separated milk	—	89·8	32·8	0·3	48·8	0·0	7·9	1·66	2·17	1·20	29·6	29·6	75	89
Dried buttermilk ...	—	90·0	42·3	11·2	24·3	0·0	12·2	2·70	3·30	1·97	39·9	39·9	82	101
Semi-solid buttermilk	—	29·6	13·9	3·7	8·0	0·0	4·0	—	—	—	13·1	13·1	27	33
Dried whey ...	—	92·8	13·6	3·0	68·4	0·0	7·8	1·29	1·90	1·71	11·7	11·7	81	86
Condensed whey ...	—	57·6	8·7	1·3	36·2	0·0	6·2	0·80	1·18	1·06	7·8	7·8	45	49

(6) *Poultry.*

The tables given below were computed by Halnan and are intended for use in computing rations for egg production. Owing to the material differences in digestibility between fowls and other livestock, the usual tables of digestibility cannot be used.

Growth and maintenance requirements of pullets and cockerels per head per day

Weight of bird	Digestible protein	Starch equivalent
lb.	g.	g.
3	6·5	51·7
4	7·4	58·1
5	8·3	64·1
6	9·2	69·7
7	10·1	75·0
8	11·0	80·0

Production requirements per 2 oz. egg

Digestible protein	Starch equivalent
g.	g.
15·0	40·0

The Dietetic Effects of Feeding Stuffs

Apart from the value of feeding stuffs for the supply of proteins, energy, mineral salts and vitamins, other considerations have to be taken into account in constructing dietaries for farm animals.

After grain or hay is harvested, ripening or fermentative changes occur, and these changes must be allowed to be completed before the grain or hay can be considered safe for stock feeding. Similarly mangolds when first harvested contain considerable quantities of nitrates, which during the ripening that occurs in the clamp disappear. It is for this reason that mangolds are not fed to animals until some time has elapsed from harvesting.

Another important point is the extent to which feeding stuffs tend to form dough-like masses when moistened with water. This is particularly important in the case of ruminants and horses, mixtures which tend to cling together into solid lumps being unsuitable for feeding to this class of animals. Such feeding

Composition and nutritive value of feeding stuffs for poultry.

	Chemical composition per cent.						Proportion per unit of weight		Bulkiness c.c. per ounce	
	Dry matter	Crude protein	Oil	Soluble carbs.	Fibre	Ash	Digestible Protein	Starch equivalent	Dry	Wet
Alfalfa meal	89·3	14·6	1·8	33·5	31·0	8·4	·092	·211	75	—
Barley and meal	85·1	8·6	1·5	67·9	4·5	2·6	·060	·636	{Whole 43 / Meal 58}	—
Beans and meal	85·7	25·4	1·5	48·5	7·1	3·2	·203	·641	{Cracked 46 / Meal 48}	—
Biscuit meal	90·6	13·9	0·7	74·6	0·3	1·1	·125	·840	70	·98
Blood meal	86·0	81·0	0·8	1·5	—	2·7	·714	·694	33	—
Buckwheat	85·9	11·3	2·6	54·8	14·4	2·8	·069	·582	{Whole 50 / Meal 45}	—
Buttermilk (dried)	90·0	42·3	11·2	24·3	—	12·2	·345	·724	45	
Cabbage	11·0	1·5	0·4	5·9	2·0	1·2	·011	·061	—	
Coconut cakemeal	88·7	19·5	6·7	42·5	13·6	6·4	·142	·641	60	
Cottonseed meal	91·3	42·1	10·9	24·9	7·4	6·0	·345	·683	47	
Dari	88·9	9·6	3·8	71·2	1·9	2·4	·064	·782	{Whole 40 / Meal 50}	
Earthnut cake meal	89·7	46·8	7·5	23·2	6·4	5·8	·376	·684	46	
Fish meal	87·0	55·6	4·4	2·1	—	24·9	·504	·571	43	
Groats	92·0	16·4	5·9	66·0	1·9	1·8	·122	·838	{Whole 40 / Meal 75}	
Hempseed (crushed)	91·1	18·2	32·6	21·1	15·0	4·2	·137	·809	40	
Insects (dried)	85·2	57·6	10·5	—	13·1	4·0	·397	·573	—	
Linseed (crushed)	92·8	24·2	36·5	22·9	5·5	3·8	·209	·943	41	
Linseed meal	88·2	35·7	3·1	33·9	9·0	6·5	·308	·598	46	
Maize and meal	87·0	9·9	4·4	69·2	2·2	1·3	·079	·759	{Whole 41 / Meal 49}	
Maize, flaked	89·0	9·8	4·3	72·5	1·5	0·9	·088	·853	{Flake 130 / Meal 49}	

Feedstuff								Form		
Maize gluten feed	89·6	23·5	3·4	56·7	3·5	2·5	·200	·743		57	—
Maize gluten meal	90·9	35·5	4·7	47·5	2·1	1·1	·306	·815		—	—
Meat meal	89·2	72·2	13·2	—	—	3·8	·557	·790		45	—
Meat and bone meal	90·8	50·5	10·0	5·0	2·2	23·1	·390	·592		45	—
Millet, bulrush	89·2	12·9	4·7	67·7	1·6	2·3	·117	·784	{Whole / Meal}	37 / 52	—
Milk, fresh	12·8	3·4	3·9	4·8	—	0·7	·032	·162		—	—
Milk (dried whole)	95·8	25·5	26·5	37·4	—	6·4	·240	1·17		48	—
Milk (dried skim)	89·8	32·8	0·3	48·8	—	7·9	·296	·747		48	—
Pasture grass	20·0	5·3	1·1	8·9	2·6	2·1	·045	·136	{Dry, fine gnd}	100	—
Oats and S.G.O.	86·7	10·3	4·8	58·2	10·3	3·1	·068	·567	{Oats S.G.O. Whole / Meal}	53 / 74	—
Peas and meal	86·0	22·5	1·6	53·7	5·4	2·8	·179	·656		36	—
Palm kernel cake meal	89·0	18·8	7·7	45·3	13·4	3·8	·132	·611		55	—
Potatoes	23·8	2·1	0·1	19·7	0·9	0·7	·010	·176		52	—
Rice, whole	89·8	7·8	2·0	66·7	8·8	4·5	·058	·646		48	—
Rice, hulled	87·8	9·1	2·0	74·5	1·1	1·1	·077	·842		35	—
Rice, polished	87·6	8·7	0·4	77·4	0·4	0·7	·069	·826		35	—
Rice meal	91·1	12·9	13·7	49·5	6·4	8·6	·104	·839		45	—
Rye	86·6	11·5	1·7	69·5	1·9	2·0	·080	·676		52	—
Soya bean meal (ext.)	88·7	44·7	1·5	31·9	5·1	5·5	·372	·634		112	—
Sunflower seed cake	90·8	36·4	11·0	22·9	14·0	6·5	·290	·605		42	—
Sugar-beet pulp, molassed	93·9	10·0	0·6	64·3	13·6	5·4	·044	·204		39	250
Wheat (strong vars.)	87·9	13·0	2·2	69·6	1·6	1·5	·114	·750	{Meal / Whole Meal}	50	95
Wheat (weak vars.)	88·5	9·5	2·0	73·8	1·7	1·5	·084	·750	{Whole Meal}	40	—
Wheat bran	87·0	15·1	3·8	52·8	9·5	5·8	·091	·336	{Meal	47	140
Wheat middlings (fine)	86·8	8·4	2·3	72·7	1·6	1·8	·064	·748	Whole Meal	185	50
Wheat middlings (coarse)	87·0	16·4	4·4	56·4	6·1	3·7	·131	·561	Whole Meal}	52	70
Whey, dried	92·8	13·6	3·0	68·4	—	7·8	·122	·846		79	—
Yeast, dried	95·7	48·5	0·5	35·5	0·5	10·7	·444	·750		42	—

mixtures, when fed to stock, form balls in the digestive tract, with the result that the digestive juices cannot work efficiently and flatulence and digestive disturbances occur. Such considerations are less important in the case of animals with comparatively simple stomachs such as pigs and poultry.

From the energy standpoint, too, an important consideration arises that is often overlooked, that is, the relative extent to which the fats and carbohydrates contribute respectively to the total energy required. In the utilisation of carbohydrates, a considerable amount of added water is required by the animal, and the energy becomes available to the animal comparatively quickly after the ingestion of a meal. In the utilisation of fat, on the other hand, the energy becomes available much more slowly, and, in addition, little or no added water is required. Where animals therefore require to be supplied with considerable daily amounts of energy, such as animals in heavy production or in heavy work, care should be taken to ensure that a proportion of the energy required is supplied in the form of fat. In the case of man fats generally form about 25 per cent. of the total energy of the diet. Kellner states that in the case of ruminants digestive disturbances result when the daily amount of digestible fat in the ration exceeds $1\frac{3}{4}$ to 2 lb. per 1000 lb. live weight, and that only exceptionally should the ration contain more than 1 lb. digestive fat per 1000 lb. live weight. Pigs, on the other hand, and young animals may be allowed double this quantity.

The laxative or constipative effect of a food also needs consideration, and the stock owner always keeps a careful watch on his animals so as to correct any adverse effect a ration may have. Thus Bombay cotton cake, which is constipative in character, is commonly fed to cattle on grass in the early spring to counteract the laxative effect of the young grass, whereas in autumn, when the cattle are grazing on coarse herbage, linseed cake is fed to have the reverse effect.

The effect of a food on the resultant product is also extremely important. Thus, in butter production, care should be taken to include carrots, cabbage, green food and swedes in order that the butter may be of a golden yellow colour. The relative hardness of the butter fat is also affected by the nature of the foods fed. Thus cotton cake, peas and beans, vetches, clover and dry fodder crops if fed in quantity tend to produce a butter harder than normal, whereas maize, bran, linseed cake and oatmeal have the reverse effect.

In the production of meat, too, the nature of the food fed has a marked effect on the character of the carcase fat produced. In the case of cattle and sheep, the natural body fat produced tends to be hard in character, whereas in the case of pigs a soft fat is normally produced. Cattle or sheep intended for the butcher should consequently be fed on foods which tend to produce a soft fat, such as linseed cake, sunflower cake, earthnut cake, rape cake, and maize. Pigs intended for pork or bacon, should, on the other hand, be fed on barley meal, sharps, bran, milk products and foods poor in oil; and the foods noted above as suitable for meat production in cattle and sheep should be avoided. It is especially desirable to avoid the inclusion of fish meal rich in oil or in excess of 10 per cent. of the concentrates of the ration if taint is to be avoided.

In the case of egg production, the colour of the yolk of the egg has been shown to be entirely due to colour compounds of a xanthophyll nature present in the food. Green foods and yellow maize should always, therefore, form an important part of the dietary of egg-producing fowls, and care should be taken to avoid the inclusion of foods known to produce a bad yolk colour. Thus shepherd's purse and penny cress give rise to yolks of olive or olive green colour, and cottonseed meal gives rise to yolks which on cold storage develop an undesirable dark colour. Acorns also give rise to badly coloured yolks. On the other hand, in the case of yellow-legged breeds intended for table, the use of foods considered desirable from the egg colour standpoint should be avoided, since these foods tend to colour the fat of the carcase and render it undesirable from the selling point of view.

INDEX

362 INDEX

Histones, 24
Hock joint, 169
Homoiothermal animals, 140
Homozygous individuals, 263
Hoof of ruminants and pigs, 184
Hordein, 24
Hormones, 190, 216
Horn of horse's foot, 180
Horse, foot or hoof of, 177
  postures and movements of, 170
Humoral theory of immunity, 272,
  275
Hybridisation, 260
Hybrids, 261
Hydra, 5
Hydrochloric acid, 25, 60
Hydroxyproline, 29
Hypertonic salt solutions, 310
Hypogaeic acid, 37
Hypoglossal nerves, 152

Ileo-caecal valve, 83
Ileum, 66
Immunity, cellular theory of, 272, 275
  humoral theory of, 272, 275
Incus, 159
Indican, 131, 133
Infundibulum, 198, 259
Inhibition, 154
Injury, response of body to, 270
Inorganic phosphates, 317
Inositol, 316
Insemination, artificial, 213
Inspiration, 113
Insulin, 193
Internal ovarian secretions, 252
  respiration, 115
  secretion, 11, 191
  testicular secretion, 214
Internus metacarpi flexor, 165
Intersexuality, 268
Interstitial cells, 204
Intestine, small, 66
Intestines, large, 72
Inulin, 39, 40, 43
Invertase, 42, 72, 85
Involuntary muscles, 9, 20
Iris, 157
Irradiation, 324
Islets of Langerhans, 71, 141
Isotonic salt solutions, 310, 320

Jaundice, 70, 132
Jejunum, 66
Joints, 169

Keratin, 24

Keratogenous membrane of horse's
  foot, 177, 178
Kicking of horse, 172
Kidneys, 9, 124
Knee (or wrist), 170

Lachrymal glands, 147, 157
Lactase, 72, 85
Lactation, 222, 248
Lactic acid, 60, 163
Laevulose, 39
Laminae of horse's foot, 177, 181
Laminitis, 181
'Lamziekte', 322
Langerhans, islets of, 71, 192
Larynx, 111, 189
Lateral cartilage, 178, 189
Lauric acid, 37
Lecithin, 92, 314
Lens, 157
Leucine, 26
Leucocytes, 7, 98, 275
Lever, 167
Lieberkühn's crypts, 68, 72
Lignine, 94
Linamarin, 45
Linoleic acid, 36, 37
Lipase, 85
Lipins, 314
Lips, 47
Liquor folliculi, 219
Littré, glands of, 208
Live weight of farm animals, 331
Liver, 11, 68
Locomotion, 163
Loop of Henle, 125
Lumen, 83
Lungs, 7, 111
Luteal hormones, 257
  tissue, 257
Lying down of horse, 171
Lymph, 6, 103
Lymphatic vessels, 77
Lymphocytes, 18, 201
Lymphoid tissue, 18
Lysine, 26

Maintenance requirements of farm
  animals, 333
Malleus, 159
Malpighian capsules, 125
  corpuscles, 201
Maltase, 72, 85
Maltose, 39, 42, 85
Mammary glands, 222, 254, 256, 257,
  258
Mastication, 47, 49, 82

CAMBRIDGE: PRINTED BY WALTER LEWIS, M.A., AT THE UNIVERSITY PRESS